# HYPNOSIS AND RELATED STATES

*Austen Riggs Center Monograph*
*Number Two*

*By the same authors:*

HYPNOTHERAPY (1947)

# Hypnosis *and* Related States

*Psychoanalytic Studies in Regression*

*by* MERTON M. GILL, M.D.
*and* MARGARET BRENMAN, Ph.D.

INTERNATIONAL UNIVERSITIES PRESS, INC.
*New York*

Manufactured in the United States of America
by Hallmark Press, New York

# CONTENTS

## PART II

# ACKNOWLEDGMENTS

An attempt to make specific acknowledgment to the many people who participated in the collection of data on which this book is based would take pages. It would include many of the Menninger Foundation staff between 1943 and 1948, as well as many of the advanced psychiatric residents in the Menninger Foundation School of Psychiatry. We have included their names in the text. If any has been omitted it is sheer inadvertence. We are indebted to all of them and in particular, to Dr. Karl A. Menninger who made this work possible from the outset. Besides Dr. Menninger, four men— then senior members of the Menninger staff—provided us with the aid of several meetings, have managed to discuss in regular supervision of our research cases; they were Drs. Robert P. Knight, Jan Frank, Ernst Lewy, and Alfred Gross.

During these early years of generous spiritual and financial backing from the Menninger Foundation, we were considerably helped also by the Josiah Macy, Jr. Foundation, and by the tactful and wise counsel of its medical director, Dr. Frank Fremont-Smith. The New York and Hofheimer Foundations added grants for clinical work.

During the years 1947-1952, our major sources of support were the Austen Riggs Center and the United States Public Health Service. It is difficult to express adequately our deep indebtedness to Dr. Robert P. Knight, who, as Chief of Staff of the Menninger Foundation and later as Medical Director of the Austen Riggs Center, contributed not only his clinical acumen in the supervision of cases but also direct collaboration in numerous aspects of the research itself. He has co-authored several of our published papers; in addition, he has provided consistent administrative patience under sometimes trying conditions.

The Riggs Center made a grant to Dr. Gill in 1956-57 to free some of his time for work on the book, and the Kaiser Foundation of Oakland, California, gave him some assistance in the last phase of writing.

To David Rapaport we owe a great debt. Those who have been fortunate enough to have his critical attention to their work will know how important this has been to us. From the inception of the "hypnosis research project" to its completion now, he has discussed our work with us every step of the way.

To our former librarian, Claude Picard Bisnoff, we give thanks for her aid with references.

Miss Suzette H. Annin has played an important part in the writing of this volume. Her careful preparation of the many drafts of our manuscript has been only incidental to her help in organizing research data, in rewriting our frequently clumsy sentences, in catching unclarities and inconsistencies, and in keeping a keen and gifted eye on the total organization of this book as it slowly developed; her ideas and suggested formulations on specific content have been invaluable. We are deeply grateful to her.

The Authors

# INTRODUCTION

When we first decided to present a summary of our experiences with hypnosis it seemed to us a sufficiently complex and long-term project. However, as we proceeded with this initially circumscribed job, it became increasingly clear that the task was necessarily even more complex than we had thought. It gradually seemed to us that the difficulties we had encountered both in conducting the study and in conceptualizing our observations demanded our adding, to our own specialized narrative, considerations of broader significance. We increasingly felt the necessity to work out a comprehensive theoretical framework within which to place our data and have abandoned our original intention of presenting a simple account of our own investigations. We have tried, rather, to present in condensed form a fair sampling of our actual experiences over a period of roughly ten years—and more important, the sense these experiences seem to make when placed alongside of data from other bordering areas—in a contemporary theoretical context.

We have taken it for granted that our reader is reasonably familiar both with the standard literature on hypnosis and with the basic theoretical premises of psychoanalysis. However, we have tried to present a sufficient sampling of our actual observations so that the material might be evaluated by others who hold a theoretical viewpoint different from the psychoanalytic.

Because some of what we have observed and thought has been published by us in scattered journals, we have omitted details of our studies available elsewhere to the specialized reader. However, most of what we present in this volume we have never published in any form before.

In this introductory section, we will present first a narrative account of our explorations and then the framework which we have tried to work out for these data. It is in the nature of "telling a story"—even a research story—that one cannot avoid giving it a continuity and a kind of straight-line coherence that did not exist so sharply in fact. It is difficult, if not impossible, to give an account of all the many detours, dead ends, contradictions, confusions, and otherwise seemingly wasted hours. Suffice it to say that our study had no fewer of all of these than any other research, and more than many. We have tried to present some of our dead ends and detours, and have only indicated others.

At the outset, the prime aim of our research was essentially practical: the effort to find out whether, and in what circumstances, hypnosis could be used as a device to shorten the duration of psychotherapy. Inasmuch as we started on these investigations at the very outset of our careers as psychotherapists,[1] our efforts were colored by that peculiar mixture of boldness and defensiveness which so often characterizes the work of the novice. Our first joint paper, published in 1943, reflected this attitude. Entitled "The Treatment of a Case of Anxiety Hysteria by an Hypnotic Technique Employing Psychoanalytic Principles" (101), this paper presented a case of a civilian patient who, in a relatively short time, showed significant improvement via the use of a technique which combined hypnosis with "psychoanalytic principles."

Although, in retrospect, we are aware of how little this therapy approximated analytic work as it is usually understood, we did make an observation in this patient which later proved one of our most important springboards for the further exploration of what happens to the functioning of

---

[1] One of us (M. Brenman) was then a research associate, the other (M. M. Gill) a psychiatric resident at the Menninger Clinic.

the ego in hypnosis, namely the fact of the constant fluctuation between a highly archaic, even primitive form of functioning and the maintenance of normal ego function. We did not begin to pursue this issue systematically, however, until two years later.

In the meantime, we devoted ourselves mainly to the further exploration of the use of hypnosis to abbreviate psychotherapy, most especially in the psychiatric casualties of war, at that time a problem of the highest practical importance. We worked simultaneously with war veterans[2] and with civilian patients in a variety of ways which we will detail in the body of this book.

As we continued with our therapeutic investigations we were inevitably brought face to face with the fact that many of the patients with whom we wanted to try hypnosis were simply not hypnotizable; we began to chafe at the number of profitless hours we were spending trying to induce hypnosis in patients who remained impervious to all our attempts. It was the effort to cut down on what seemed then a prodigal waste of time that led to two major, and essentially practical, explorations.

First came the attempt to establish a screening procedure; in this we were successful: all patients being evaluated at the Menninger Clinic took part in a group hypnosis "test." One or the other of us—and later advanced residents whom we had trained—conducted a weekly session in which a group of from three to ten new patients participated. Only those who showed a positive response were worked with individually, unless we had some special reason to work investigatively with a patient who showed a poor response.

Secondly came the exploration of ways and means to increase hypnotizability; in this, we were largely unsuccessful. We varied many things: male or female hypnotist, relative

2 This work was made possible by the active help of Drs. Karl Menninger and John Greist, at the installation earlier an army hospital called Winter General Hospital, and later Winter Veterans Hospital, in Topeka, Kansas.

experience with hypnosis, the manner of approach to the patient, the physical setting, the amount of immediate motivation, and others. None of these appeared to make any significant difference. If a patient started out as a poor hypnotic subject, he *usually* stayed that way. We will discuss some interesting exceptions later on.

Now we began on a quite different tack, namely, the use of drugs in the effort to deepen hypnosis. When our first try with sodium pentothal transformed an indifferent subject into a good one, we made thirty new attempts. All of them failed. Our single exploration of the use of scopolamine and chloral produced a transient psychotic episode, an experience disturbing enough to discourage further work along this line. Work with sodium amytal yielded nothing much either.[3]

As it became increasingly evident that a person's hypnotizability was, by and large, a relatively stable matter, we began to inquire seriously and more systematically into what might be the essential differences between a good and a poor hypnotic subject. Although we emerged from this long and laborious series of investigations with data of some interest, we were unable to pin down in any definitive way (that could allow for *individual* prediction) the critical differences between people who responded well and those who responded poorly.

At first, proceeding on the impression that there were more good subjects among normal people than among patients, we formed the general hypothesis that hypnotizability varies inversely with the degree of maladjustment. We compared then a group of normals with an extremely "sick" group and another less deeply disturbed. The initial results here were quite clear: the normals yielded the highest proportion of good hypnotic subjects, the "less sick" group the next highest, and the "sicker" group the least. The attempt to break down psychiatric syndromes within the patient group showed that

[3] This investigation was carried out by Dr. Harry Rand at Winter Veterans Hospital.

although the hysterics were (like most patients), on the whole, not hypnotizable, 40 per cent of them were. This per cent was the highest of any single psychiatric syndrome and only somewhat less than in the normal population. The occasional schizophrenic who proved to be an excellent subject made it difficult for us to take much comfort from the fact that our hypothesis regarding the inverse relationship of hypnotizability and maladjustment had proved to be *generally* correct.[4]

We then proceeded to *qualitative* studies of good and poor subjects—using batteries of psychological tests, autobiographies, clinical interviews, and free-association interviews. Here we amassed the proverbial "closets-full" of data, again with some provocative and interesting results, but nothing conclusive. Probably our most suggestive data have come from the analysis of the meaning of hypnosis to patients in long-term therapy. Here again our conclusions are surrounded by reservations.

In retrospect, it appears to us that these studies of hypnotizability acted as a kind of bridge between our initially practical interest in finding suitable patients for a therapeutic short cut and what became the core of our later interest, namely, the nature of the hypnotic process and its relation to allied states. The therapeutic situation continued to be our major source of data, though not our exclusive one.

The main reason we felt it necessary to explore avenues outside of therapy issued directly from the overwhelming complexities inherent in the treatment situation. The effort, for example, to sort out the normal vicissitudes of a developing transference from those *specific* to hypnosis proved extremely difficult. Moreover, granted the success of this undertaking, what guarantee had we that it was indeed this constellation of purely *psychological* factors that accounted for the development of the hypnotic state?

4 Details of this study were reported in 1949 by Dr. Gerald Ehrenreich (52), who had carried it out under our direction.

As we were struggling with these issues, the provocative work of Kubie and Margolin appeared in print (145). Theirs was the first really systematic attempt to integrate physiological and psychological factors in a theory of hypnosis. Thus it was that concurrent with our collecting data from clinical sources, we began to pursue other approaches.

One of the first of these was via the encephalogram. With the active assistance of Drs. Henry Luster and Morton Bassan, we commenced this work at Winter Veterans Hospital. The results, at first, were startling. In hypnotic regression to a period of childhood, we began to obtain high frequencies; on the induction of hypnosis (contrary to the consensus of the literature), we obtained curves very similar to physiological sleep! But our excitement soon gave way to disappointment: we shortly discovered that these revolutionary findings had been the result of a faulty apparatus. As soon as we had it repaired, our results were consistently negative.

Now, for a time, we backtracked from the pursuit of such gross physiological changes as the key to the nature of hypnosis and, with the collaboration of Dr. Roy Schafer,[5] set up a small pilot study of an area which we regarded as lying possibly somewhere between physiology and psychology: ego functions like attention, concentration, speed of association. Our aim was the comparison of such functions in normal and hypnotic states. Our results here were again negative. We thought perhaps we were using insufficiently sensitive instruments for this comparison. It was at about this time that we heard of Dr. Ward Halstead's battery of tests which could distinguish between normal subjects and fliers suffering from (permanent or transient) organic damage as a result of cerebral anoxia—when the usual battery of psychological tests could *not* make this distinction. The use of these tests was then our next move. Again, the results were negative.

---

[5] Dr. Schafer was then on the staff of the Psychology Department at the Menninger Clinic; he is currently chief of the Clinical Psychological Service at Yale University.

We reconsidered then our plan to obtain physiological measurements in and out of hypnosis and concluded that we needed the collaboration of experts. We were able to make arrangements with Drs. Chester Darrow and Charles Henry, then at the Institute for Juvenile Research in Chicago. After numerous group-hypnosis sessions, we selected sixteen top-notch hypnotic subjects and nine who were totally refractory. Each of these twenty-five subjects was then seen individually to confirm the level of their hypnotizability and to get some data on their personalities. All twenty-five were then studied with simultaneous recording of EEG, blood pressure, EKG, eye movement, and psychogalvanic reflex. After this exhaustive run-through which took an entire day for each, we again interviewed the subject for his account of his experience during the tests.

Except for two abstracts (44, 45), the results of this work (43, 46) have never been published, the reason for this being that our two collaborators differed significantly in their evaluation of the data. We, ourselves, could have no view of the matter. We report some of the general results of this long detour in Chapter 6, "Hypnosis, Sleep, Somnambulism, and Dream." This proved to be our last expedition aimed at establishing the physiological differences between normal and hypnotic states.

Luckily, we had distributed our research eggs in several baskets. An experimental study conducted under our supervision by Drs. William Finzer, David Hilger, and Louis Kaywin was set up, designed to explore further the findings of Farber and Fisher (60) who had reported the capacity of a person in hypnosis to translate the dreams of other people. Although we were unable to confirm this result, we did find something which tied in neatly with the kinds of considerations developing in the growing body of data from our clinical work, namely, the fact that the person in hypnosis appeared to have significantly readier access to *his own* unconscious conflicts than he did in the normal state. We will report this investigation in some detail in our chapter dealing with hypnosis and psychotherapy.

Concurrent with all of this, we had continued our observations of the induction process and of the established hypnotic state in long-term analytically oriented therapy. It was actually from this clinical work that our most usable data emerged.

Looking back over our unpublished research reports, we find that even during the period when a therapeutic short cut was our major aim, we were trying to understand or at least to describe the hypnotic state. As we went along, we found ourselves separating our data into two major categories: in the first, we were amassing records of phenomena which showed in hypnosis a wide variety of changes in self-awareness, bodily experience, emotional expression, motility, and the nature of thinking. In 1946, we presented a paper at the American Orthopsychiatric meeting, written in collaboration with Dr. Frederick J. Hacker,[6] entitled "Some General Characteristics of the Productions of Patients in Hypnosis." Although, in our text, we had tentatively put forth the hypothesis that all of these changes seemed to reflect a significant *alteration of ego-functioning* in hypnosis, we did not put this in the title until our discussant, Dr. Leo Bartemeier, suggested that we ought to do so. This paper was later published in the *Bulletin of the Menninger Clinic* under the title "Alterations in the State of the Ego in Hypnosis" (27).

In the second category we found ourselves collecting observations which appeared to reflect the significance of the personal—mainly unconscious—relationship between the hypnotic subject and the hypnotist: we labeled these our "transference" data. Under this heading we collected a series of observations of different kinds. For example, we noticed the fact that patients frequently reported *spontaneous* changes in their subjective experience of the depth of hyp-

---

[6] Dr. Hacker was then a resident at the Menninger Clinic; at present he heads the Hacker Clinic in Los Angeles, California.

nosis; these might occur several times in the course of an hour. In addition, we gathered numerous reports from patients as well as nonpatients of the occurrence of spontaneous hypnotic states when not in the presence of the hypnotist. The effort to pin down the psychological setting in which these events occurred occupied us for a long time.

We also pursued the unconscious meaning of hypnosis in a variety of ways: we accumulated data from analytically trained hypnotists with regard to their own insights into the meaning of hypnosis; we tried to analyze systematically in several long-term therapeutic cases the unconscious significance of hypnosis; we attempted to systematize our observations of a spontaneous regression in hypnosis (100). We will discuss later the details of all of these data. For now, we mean only to focus on the fact that for many years we found ourselves accumulating two apparently independent bodies of data from our observations of the hypnotic state, but were unable to discern any theoretical bridge between them. The observations of "altered ego function" and of "transference phenomena" seemed to us to be in quite separate realms of discourse. It was only in the preparation of this volume that we worked out a theoretical approach which may encompass both sets of data. In part, the development of this framework emerged as an outcome of our effort to sort out the similarities and differences between hypnosis and allied states, our data on the latter being largely restricted to reports in the literature. We found that reports on such diverse phenomena as, e.g., "brain-washing," presleep states, trance dancing in Bali, and the so-called "isolation" experiments frequently included observations which were in important ways very close to ours of hypnosis—though not identical.

Gradually, from a survey of all of these data together with an exploration of recent developments in ego psychology, we emerged with the basic theoretical premise of this book: *Hypnosis is a particular kind of regressive process which may be initiated either by sensorimotor-ideational deprivation or by the stimulation of an archaic relationship to the hypnotist.* Here, then, was the link between our two sets of data. It appears to us that when the regressive process has been set into motion by *either one* of these two kinds of factors, phenomena characteristic of the other kind begin to emerge. Thus, for example, a prisoner in isolation deprived of his usual means of maintaining his hold on external reality may develop an intense, irrational set of feelings toward his jailor. Conversely, a psychoanalytic patient, in whom an ancient set of yearnings has just been released, may begin to develop bizarre bodily sensations. In hypnosis, as we will see, the attack is usually twofold and therefore more difficult to separate: the hypnotist attempts to initiate the regressive process by simultaneously stimulating intense infantile impulses and by systematic techniques of sensorimotor and ideational deprivation. When we began to consider our material in this way, we found that we were now free of the dilemma which had plagued us throughout this work: do we place the sensorimotor manipulations of the hypnotist—and the resultant changes in ego function—at the center of a theory of hypnosis, or do we give the prime theoretical importance to the revival of an archaic human relationship, i.e., "transference"? It now became clear that we do neither. Instead, the central position is occupied by the notion that the ego can become unseated, as it were, by one or the other of the two major attacks described, and that both sets of phenomena we had observed stemmed from this fact, whatever had initiated the loss of command usually held by the ego in a normal state.

In the series of related states where a regressive process is involved, each state requires its own "something more" than the unseating of the ego to achieve its own characteristic form. We would say therefore that whereas the "brown study," the presleep state, or the creative burst are like hypnosis in that they all include some form of regression, that which distinguishes one of them from another lies in the particular organization of each. We try to delineate some of these in Part II.

Before we close this introduction with a summary of contents, we will stop briefly to comment on the relationship of the view of hypnosis which we offer to the history of theories of hypnosis. The sharp conflict which has long existed between academic psychologists and psychoanalysts with regard to a theory of hypnosis represents, in our opinion, a minor skirmish in the struggle to lay claim to a systematization of the entire range of psychological function. The history of successively held theories of hypnosis reflects directly the prevailing attempts to establish a *general* framework within which to conceptualize all psychic activity.

On the simplest and most schematic level: sharp controversies have developed between those who are trying to build a general science of psychology based on some form of learning theory and those who base their theoretical formulations on some variety of psychoanalytic theory. In recent years, there have been attempts to build bridges from each side; the work of Tolman, Hilgard, Dollard, and Mowrer, for example, represents such an attempt from the side of the learning theorists. On the other side stands the work of Hartmann, Kris, Loewenstein, and Rapaport.

There can be no question that the abyss which used to separate the academic psychologist from the psychoanalyst is narrowing. There was a time when there was little or no overlap even in the content of the problems judged worthy of discussion. This is no longer true. Problems of unconscious motivation in human relationships, for instance, are no longer the concern of the psychoanalyst alone; nor are "sensorimotor" problems the private province of the learning theorists.

On both sides theoreticians are beginning to see as a proper area of inquiry problems which they have hitherto neglected, or even disdained. Such neglect or disdain is inevitable when the theory has no place for a variety of empirical observations. Thus as long as psychoanalysis, for example, remained a theory which revolved almost exclusively around "instincts and their vicissitudes," it was impossible to construct a *psychoanalytic* theory of hypnosis, or of anything else for that matter, that would transcend these limits. We are taking advantage in this book of the fact that times have changed, and we present a theory of hypnosis which pays heed to the changes.

Specifically: before the expansion of ego psychology, the implicit assumption in psychoanalytic theory-building was that all human development is a *direct* outgrowth of "instinctual drives." Functions like perception or motility were by and large never mentioned.[7] Early, the search for repressed memories was the focus. Later, problems of instinctual conflict—in one form or another—became the central point of theory. Even the growing interest in the defense mechanisms did not substantially alter matters. It was thus not until Hartmann's discussion in 1939 (114) of the apparatuses of the ego and their primary autonomy that room was made in psychoanalytic theory for the kind of consideration which had long been central for the "sensorimotor" theorists in the field of hypnosis. Kris's (135, 136) concept of regression in the service of the ego provided us with a point of departure for our view of hypnosis as such a regression, and we will suggest that the central structural feature of such a regression is a subsystem in the ego. Hartmann's (114) emphasis on adaptation and his concept of the relative autonomy of the ego from the id have been unified and broadened by Rapaport (189) into a general theory of the autonomy of the ego which he describes as relatively autonomous both from id and environment. We will propose a theory of hypnosis which leans heavily on the thesis of a diminution of these two relative autonomies. And lastly, we found Hart-

[7] It is of incidental interest that Freud himself in his major theoretical statement, Chapter VII of *The Interpretation of Dreams* (76), did not omit a consideration of these problems.

mann's (114) concepts of automatization and de-automatization of the apparatuses essential to our understanding of the distinction between hypnotic induction and the established hypnotic state.

Our definition of hypnosis is an attempt to integrate the ego-psychological concepts just outlined with the usual view of hypnosis as transference: *The hypnotic state is an induced psychological regression, issuing, in the setting of a particular regressed relationship between two people, in a relatively stable state which includes a subsystem of the ego with various degrees of control of the ego apparatuses.*

Obviously this definition is a highly condensed statement, each part of which requires considerable elaboration, a task we undertake in Chapter 5, devoted to the metapsychological theory of hypnosis.

We are aware that such shorthand references to the theoretical underpinnings of our definition do not make clear its implications. We cannot do that here. We mention them only to indicate the kinds of theoretical advances in our *general* science of psychology which have made it possible to bring together in a single theory of hypnosis considerations which for many years have been regarded as separate from, or even in conflict with, each other.

Having given a history of the theoretical development of this book, we should add a historical description in more practical terms. The history of multiple-authored works is frequently complex, as is the case with this one. A few words about it will help to explain some degree of unevenness of style and overlap of content.

The work which finally resulted in the book took place in three stages. First, the great bulk of the research data was gathered by both of us over a period of about seven years (1943-1950). During this time we worked together, first at the Menninger Clinic and then at the Austen Riggs Center, and published a number of joint papers. During the next five years, by which time we were working in widely separated places, we only sporadically attacked the task of writing up our data, our attention being mainly devoted to other work and interests. During these years the advances in our general clinical and theoretical insights resulted in our rethinking (and several times rewriting) our understanding of the data we had collected. Some of the shortcomings of this book in terms of data result from the fact that they were collected while our clinical and theoretical sophistication and understanding were much less than they are now. In the past three years, we have worked fairly steadily on the manuscript and, with the aid of several meetings, have managed to discuss in considerable detail the total structure of the book and to come to reasonable agreement about the conclusions presented.

Chapters 1 and 2 are a discussion of the phenomena of the process of hypnotic induction, the established hypnotic state, and the posthypnotic period. Chapters 3 and 4 are a critical discussion of the current psychoanalytic views of hypnosis with excursions both into the psychoanalytic interpretation of related phenomena and occasionally into certain important data gathered elsewhere than in the psychoanalytic situation. This is by no means an exhaustive survey. We have not attempted a general survey of the literature on hypnosis but rather have chosen to deal with that work which seems to us most directly relevant to our own observations and theoretical formulations. Chapter 5 is our effort to present in detail our theory of hypnosis in metapsychological terms. Part II includes our discussions of several related states: sleep and dream, fugue, traumatic neurosis, brain-washing, and trance in Bali. The last two involve considerations of a more "social" character and afford us an opportunity to link some of our ideas with the important theoretical advances made by Erik H. Erikson. Part III concludes this volume with a presentation of a variety of clinical accounts selected from our explorations of the use of hypnosis in psychotherapy.

*Part I*

# 1

# THE INDUCTION OF HYPNOSIS

## What the Hypnotist Does

It is hard to approach with a fresh eye the structure of that strange situation in which one person is said to hypnotize another: it is hard on two quite separate counts which are paradoxical. On the one hand, everyone is familiar with the standard setting for inducing hypnosis, taking for granted the procedure as one of our known psychological techniques; on the other hand, hypnotic procedures are, with certain notable exceptions, usually set apart from our less dramatic and more everyday doings by our placing them outside of the continuity of human relationships, and considering them as happenings not to be understood with the help of those general concepts that have been developed to make sense of more usual relations between people. Most frequently, textbook discussions of hypnotic induction usually occur under the heading of "miscellaneous curiosae" of abnormal psychology.

We shall describe in this section various techniques for inducing hypnosis and in subsequent discussions suggest how they do indeed constitute one extreme of continua, some everyday and familiar, others more strange. We are deferring for the moment the exploration of the unconscious dovetailing fantasies of hypnotist and subject which, though undoubtedly present in some unconscious form from the start of any attempted hypnosis, are usually not sufficiently manifest during the induction to provide usable data. For this

3

kind of material, we rely heavily on our findings from patients studied intensively during long-term therapy.

First, a brief word on the question of how most of us normally maintain our sense of reality and our being "in touch" with our physical and psychological environment.[1] From our earliest days we have been steadily confronted with a set of varied and constantly changing stimuli, ranging, for example, from a beam of sunlight to a change in voice inflection. With varying degrees of efficiency and alertness, we have learned to become attuned to this barrage of clues as to "what's going on," to select from them what is momentarily relevant, and to interpret and use them, sometimes in thought, sometimes in action. This sustained mass of stimuli coming from the outer world and variously patterned by us makes it possible to maintain some picture of outer reality and to direct, gear, and brake our impulses accordingly; in the absence of such stimulation, we fall asleep, retreat into our private daydreams, or drop into one of the many variants of either of these. We quickly learn to make some of the necessary appraisals of these impingements from the outer world with a high degree of automaticity, eventually becoming unaware of them; others remain forever matters for conscious weighing and deliberate judgment. If, in essence, this maintenance of steady two-way communication with the multifarious stimuli outside us *is* part of the scaffolding on which our sense of reality normally rests, we must ask now what happens if this steady stream is in some way grossly interfered with, as of course it is by all hypnotists during the period of hypnotic induction.

The hypnotist's first effort to introduce such gross inter-

---

[1] In this presentation of the general *phenomena* of hypnosis, we will on the whole avoid theoretical discussion. However, in order to give some initial form and order to these phenomena, we will occasionally interpolate a nontechnical and necessarily simplified note of this kind. If this is not done we run the risk of presenting a handbook on hypnotic technique together with a simple cataloguing of the standard responses of hypnotic subjects. This is not our intent.

ference usually involves the attempt to deprive the subject of the normal plethora of stimuli to which he is accustomed. If we darken a room and ask a person to attend exclusively to a light, a spot, a revolving mirror, his own breath sounds, our eyes, the sound of counting or whatever—we are in effect asking him to abdicate for the moment his familiar ways of keeping in touch with his environment, and implicitly asking him, moreover, to trust us as his intermediary in dealing with the outside world. He may or may not be willing or able in his deepest layers to go along with such an abdication even temporarily; we shall discuss this later. It is thus no accident that all standard techniques of hypnotic induction do indeed involve in one form or another the request to the subject that *he allow extensive limits to be placed on his sensory intake.* Not only is he asked to limit strictly what he may look at, but also what he may listen to: the hypnotist usually chooses an extremely quiet place to work and often tells the subject directly to exclude, as much as he possibly can, all outside noises. It has been demonstrated that this effort to deprive the subject of the normal flow of sensory intake may sometimes be facilitated by catching the subject at a moment when his attunement to sustained clues from the outside has already been weakened by other factors—such as sleepiness, abstracted reverie, drug and alcohol states.

We shall see in a later section a number of human situations not designated as "hypnosis" or sleep, culled from divers sources, where sensory intake is similarly blocked or interfered with. These range from experiments in physical immobilization and isolation to "brain-washing." Even if one disregards the most dramatic examples from this body of literature, two general (and again for the present purpose, simplified) impressions do emerge: first, that if over a sufficiently long period of time, sustained access to the usual sensory clues for maintaining a normal sense of reality is blocked, there occurs a general oversensitization to both inner and outer stimuli with a peculiar heightening of vulnerability to both; and secondly, that where such blocks to and from the *external world* are maintained, there occur mighty outbursts from the *internal world* in one form or another. We shall elaborate this latter point when we have concluded our account of "what the hypnotist does" and come to "what the subject does."

Concurrent with the hypnotist's effort to impoverish the subject's inflow of sensory stimuli is his attempt further to cut down normal guideposts by *strictly limiting the subject's bodily activity*, first by asking for his voluntary cooperation ("You will please relax as much as you can . . . sit quietly in the chair . . . let go of all of your muscles," etc.) and later by capitalizing on whatever muscular immobilization begins to appear as a result of the induction process itself. Finally, still with the intent to impoverish and to deprive, the hypnotist makes it very difficult for the subject to have much to think about. He does not usually engage in any two-way conversation during the induction period—except occasionally to check the pace of progress. He carefully limits his own utterances in such a way as to provide very little food for thought, as it were. The well-known monotonous "hypnotic patter" of hypnotists is precisely this.

As though the systematic effort to cut down normal sensory stimulation, movement, and thought were not sufficient to gain a foothold with the potential subject, the hypnotist proceeds now in more active ways to provide stimulation *of a particular and narrow kind*, circumscribed in its content, and geared still to detaching the subject from his normal moorings both in the outside and inside worlds. He may start with mild suggestions for sensory experience which a person not yet in hypnosis might reasonably have at this point ("You are feeling the room get warmer, the chair very comfortable," etc.), but he usually focuses on what we have come to feel is the second standard ingredient for most hypnotic induction procedures, once the general deprivation of sensory, motor, and ideational functions has been brought about: namely, the *attempt to alter the quality of the bodily awareness* of the subject. This may be an encouragement of a diffuse awareness of the whole body, or of separate limbs or organs; or conversely, an attempt to withdraw such awareness, generalized or selective. We say "encouragement" rather than "suggestion" because of the evidence that some alterations of bodily awareness usually begin to appear spontaneously in our good subjects during induction even prior to specific instruction.

The active effort by the hypnotist to alter in some way the quality of body awareness during hypnotic induction, as well as his observation of spontaneous changes in such awareness, characterize the work of all hypnotists, from the practical vaudeville entertainer to the most theoretically sophisticated investigator. The specific direction or quality of the change suggested varies from hypnotist to hypnotist and often from subject to subject. With some, bodily relaxation is routinely suggested; with others, rigidity of limbs and torso; and yet another avenue to the ultimate "capture" of the motor apparatus is the attempt to divest the subject of his sense of voluntariness in moving parts of his body: e.g., "Your little finger is moving by itself; your head is drooping without your actually doing it," etc.

It is certainly no accident that this focus on bodily experience as a part of hypnotic induction technique should have, on empirical grounds, found a place in most standard procedures. We must ask why is this so? We reserve for a later discussion an answer to this question in systematic theoretical terms. For the present purpose, it will suffice to interpolate a simple extension of our original proposition: if it is indeed true that the maintenance of a normal sense of reality depends in part on the maintenance of a steady flow of clues from the *outer* environment which are being constantly organized by the person, must it not also be true that such organization of clues is simultaneously being worked on by using sensations from *within* the person? It is as if the hypnotist is trying to interfere thus not only with the normal stimuli from *outside* the body—the limitation or distortion of sensory intake—but also with the normal stimuli from *within* the body. He is at the same time trying to interfere with the subject's normal efforts to keep in touch with reality by his own body *movements*.

It is as if that part of the induction effort which centers on the alteration of bodily awareness has as one of its aims the psychological dynamiting of one of the most important sources of the sense of "I-ness": namely, the taken-for-granted feeling that a large portion of motility is voluntary, however automatic certain parts of it have become. It seems paradoxical that on the one hand the hypnotist may try to shake the subject from his familiar moorings by suggesting a *lack* of awareness of his body, and on the other by suggesting a hyperawareness of his body, or more often of separate limbs. In either case, where this effort is successful, the hypnotist has succeeded in the primary aim of radically altering the subject's fixed points with relation to his familiar bodily feelings. This argument is perhaps most clearly served by discussing the procedure which involves a hyperawareness of separate limbs. The hypnotist may say, for example, "Now you will notice that, *without your doing anything about it,* your hand will move up toward your face." He does not say, "*You* will move your hand toward your face." It would appear that the hypnotist is suggesting a kind of "dissociation"[2] such as that which occurs spontaneously in a conversion hysteria where the patient stares at a paralyzed arm as though it did not belong to him. In this attempt to produce an artificial "dissociation," the hypnotist is trying, usually intuitively, to accomplish several ends: first, to shift the subject's attention from outside to inside (except for his concentrated attention to the hypnotist); secondly, to divest the subject of the automaticity with which he performs casual arm move-

2 We do not use the term "dissociation" here in Janet's sense—but only descriptively.

ments *by focusing his attention on the movement itself*; and simultaneously—with overtones of the uncanny—to show him that already he has abdicated some of his "voluntariness" and sense of personal responsibility. If his own hand can move "by itself," being given direction only by the hypnotist, what other realms of such abdication of personal responsibility might he now be led to?

Yet another means sometimes used to interfere with the normal functioning of attention is the deliberate attempt to break up the human propensity to give *coherence* of pattern to incoming stimuli; in the so-called "confusional techniques" so adroitly employed by Milton Erickson, for example, the subject may be deliberately misled by subtle misinformations regarding his orientations in time and space, often until he is obviously floundering for some anchorage point. That this technique may frequently misfire is illustrated by the following report from a subject, a nonpatient, given after the first effort to induce hypnosis; it is interesting to see how she "rights" the hypnotist's mistakes by producing her own simple image of a pulley.

I think it was during the suggestion of the raising of the right hand from the lap that I became aware of a sense of irritation with Dr. X for talking so much. He kept introducing new figures of speech, with almost no pause, and I had the feeling of being rushed from one topic into another, with insufficient time to concentrate on each. Mentally I felt slowed up, as one sometimes does physically in a dream when each step seems to take ages to accomplish. I also remember that I didn't like whatever manner of suggestion Dr. X was using about the raising of the hand, and I finally stopped listening to him altogether, and imagined that a pulley was raising my hand from my lap, wrist first. It was then that I felt a lightening and finally a raising of the hand. I also had a sense of confusion about his directions about my eyelids feeling like curtains or like heavy sacks of flour. I kept wishing that he would just say something monotonous in a low tone with long pauses and give me time to keep up with him.

We come now to that aspect of the hypnotist's strategy which is actively aimed at *breaking into the normal adjustment of the subject's human relationships*—the aim being to convert him, however temporarily, into a person whose major overt characteristic is his willingness, indeed his eagerness, to see, hear, think, and do what he is told to by the hypnotist. From the moment the subject enters the room, if he has had any forewarning at all, the tacit assumption on both sides is that the hypnotist will do everything in his power—and it is usually clear from his manner that he regards his power as considerable—to *take over* in large measure the functions normally held by the subject's senses, his body, and by his initiating and judging intellect. The specific means used to implement this second part of the two-pronged strategy of hypnotic induction will vary according to the talent and the temperament of the hypnotist. He may invest heavily in creating an atmosphere of rational or irrational "magic."[3]

During the course of the steps of any successful hypnotic induction process, the hypnotist progressively persuades the subject that he is gradually losing control of himself and that this control is being responsibly taken over by the hypnotist.

Usually implied, though sometimes explicitly stated, is the "promise" to the subject that if he will permit the hypnotist to bring about the deprivations and losses of power we have discussed, he will be rewarded by an unprecedented kind of experience; the precise nature of this experience is usually left ambiguous. Sometimes the implication is that new worlds will be opened to him, providing an emotional adventure of

[3] By "rational magic" we refer to those techniques which appear on the surface to scorn the unscientific and the occult, but which substitute oblique and sometimes pedantic references to "unplumbed depths of the mind," "frontiers of neurophysiological function," "powers of concentration and attention," etc., in an effort to impress the potential hypnotic subject with what vast and mysterious forces are closing in on him. By "irrational magic" we mean of course the efforts routinely made in the early history of hypnosis (the *baquet*, the atmosphere of a séance, the claims of supernatural power in the hypnotist, etc.).

a sort he has never known. This is quite apart from any intended therapeutic use of the hypnotic state. The hypnotic
subject in any research usually has an air of expectation, if
not eagerness, that goes far beyond a simple intellectual curiosity—an air which reflects the atmosphere created by the
hypnotist. The unspoken communication on a surface level
might be: "Abdicate your usual powers; put yourself in my
hands and I will open some of your inner doors so that you
may have a glimpse of what lies beyond them." On a deeper
level, we have come to believe the appeal is to that universal
infantile core which longs for such a wholesale abdication.
There is from the beginning a kind of unconscious emotional
barter; we shall discuss its many-layered and complex character
later on.

Although, for purposes of our presentation, we have largely
separated those efforts of the hypnotist aimed at sensory,
motor, and ideational deprivation from his efforts to establish
a (mainly unconscious) human bond with the subject,[4] it
must be clear that what we have called the hypnotist's "two-
pronged strategy" exists from the very beginning as an in-
divisible unit, behaviorally speaking. Everything he does—
whether it be darkening the room, asking the subject to fix
his gaze, to immobilize himself, etc.—carries simultaneously
*in this context* the implication that a "special" kind of human
relationship is gradually developing. Even without the deliberately created atmosphere of power and "magic," we
know now from other kinds of observation, to be presented
later, that the hypnotist is *setting the stage* for the emergence
of usually repressed, ancient impulses and longings—simply
by his techniques of deprivation. But having so set the stage,
the concurrent active "wooing" by the hypnotist of the subject is the other half of the attempt not only to shake him
loose from his usual balance, but to bring about a new one
in his general ego-functioning and in his human interplay.

---

[4] We are deliberately deferring the discussion of the nature of this bond
in "transference" terms until later.

## What the Subject Does

From the very beginning of the induction period, the subject—providing he is responding at all—begins to give evidence that in various ways his normal equilibrium *is* being shaken. The difficulties in the way of eliciting clear-cut data on this initial process are obvious: if, as we have said, the hypnotist is bending his efforts to disrupting normal moorings and normal human communication, he cannot continually interrupt the process by asking for formulated introspections. Accordingly, our data on the phenomena of induction are limited to what we can directly observe in the behavior of the subject, his spontaneous comments, and his replies to occasional inquiries from the hypnotist. We make a point of this difficulty because it is our impression that while there is a definite continuity between the phenomena of induction and those of the established hypnotic state, there are probably also important differences, differences which we think make sense in theoretical terms. We will discuss these in a subsequent section. It is a fact known to all workers in this field that as a subject becomes more experienced, the time necessary for induction diminishes radically; corollary to this is the disappearance of the typical "induction phenomena."

Because of the problems inherent in gathering data during induction, the distinctions we draw between the induction period and the established state cannot be as fully substantiated empirically as we would like.

Given these limitations we offer the impression from long observation that, while almost all of the changes in function now to be described as "phenomena of induction" persist in some form into the established state, they are significantly more fluid and unstable here than in the hypnotic state itself. Also, we see some of them largely dropping out of sight in the established state *unless this state is being used as an auxiliary to psychotherapy*. We will elaborate this point later on.

Because of the fluidity and the difficulty of establishing precisely that moment at which "induction" ends and "state" begins, there is a certain necessary overlap and therefore some arbitrariness in our division of phenomena.

Nonetheless we offer the following as most characteristic of the subject's reactions during the *induction period*:

## CHANGES IN BODY EXPERIENCE

The most striking of the spontaneous changes in self-awareness are those in *body experience*. Although not universal in hypnotic subjects, they are encountered with sufficient frequency to be called characteristic of this phase. This should not come as any surprise if one assumes that the ego is in its origin primarily a body ego,[5] and that, as we have seen, the hypnotist's manipulations are designed to disrupt the smooth functioning of this ego.

The range of the quality of experience is wide. We shall commence with the reported experiences of *changes in size*. In the complete absence of any hypnotic instructions to this effect, a subject may report an experience of a radical alteration in the size of his whole body or of a portion of it. He may say, "My legs have stretched out so long they feel as if they are 'way over by the door now," or "My arms are like great swollen objects on the arms of the chair," or "My head is like a huge balloon," or again, "I feel like a sprawling giant, with my legs hanging over the edge of the couch."

Probably the most common changes reported are the swelling of the head, mouth, and arms. Sometimes the lips feel so swollen that the subject finds it hard to enunciate. We have speculated that the high frequency of these particular bodily experiences is related to the "regressive" nature of the hypnotic process, and that the hypnotic experiences are complex resultants of an infantile experience of the body inter-

[5] See p. 108 ff.

acting with all of the intricacies of subsequent development (212). We do not believe that the hypnotic experience is a simple reinstatement of an archaic body image. If this were the case, it would be hard to understand why in some subjects the report is of "hugeness" and "swelling," usually of the hands and mouth, whereas in others the experience is of "shrinking to the size of a doll, or a baby—with tiny hands, tiny feet, short legs and a small body." The recurring emphasis on hand and mouth may well be a modified echo of that early period when the focus of interest was in fact in these areas. In some cases, the swelling of the mouth and the consequent speech difficulty, we have speculated, seem to represent on the one hand highly primitive oral conflicts—related perhaps to nursing—and on the other hand later developments having to do with the need to defend against "biting hostility" in a more general sense.

As an area for further investigation, the relationships between these "oral problems," hypnosis, and sleep have seemed to us particularly intriguing, especially in view of Lewin's (151) studies of the "oral triad" where the wish to eat and to be eaten is linked with the wish to sleep and with states of elation.[6]

Another frequent kind of spontaneous change is in the experience of *equilibrium*. Generalized sensations of giddiness or dizziness are not at all uncommon. Frequently quite specific images of changed equilibrium are reported: "I feel as if I were rocking back and forth," or "It is as if the chair were sliding away from under me and I am about to fall," or again, "It is as if my body had lost its moorings and were floating up near the ceiling," or yet another variation, "It is as though I were sinking endlessly down into space." The report of a descent of some kind during induction is extremely common. Some have said, "I'm going down, down deeper now," or "I'm

---

[6] Edith Jacobson (unpublished paper) has observed a patient with a near-psychotic depression who passed rapidly into a transient elation when she was hypnotized.

going deep into a well." It seems to us now that these images of descent may issue—in some part—from a sense of generalized withdrawal of attention or interest from the external surroundings (with the exception of the hypnotist), and that in fact the withdrawal itself is related to the heightened focus on internal events. A regular concomitant of this turning of attention inward is what might be described as a lowered sense of outer reality, variously expressed by our subjects and patients: "Everything in the room seems covered by a veil," or "It all seems shadowy and dreamlike." Such verbalizations are indistinguishable from the subjective reports of patients not in hypnosis in whom derealization is a presenting pathological symptom.

Closely related to these experiences of equilibrium change are the experiences of an alteration of the *position* of the body in space, when in fact the subject has remained motionless: "I feel as if my head were hanging 'way back as if I were looking at the ceiling," or "It is as though my arms are sticking out straight in front of me."

Not infrequently potential hypnotic subjects have reported that everything seemed to progress smoothly until these equilibrium changes began; at the moment when it seemed as if they might be in danger of "losing my balance" or of "getting that light, dizzy feeling," a panic set in, putting a prompt end to the effort to hypnotize them.

Schilder (207) has pointed out the relationship between a sense of emotional security and the willingness (if not the eagerness) to abdicate body equilibrium temporarily. He comments that secure children love to be thrown, caught, or lifted high into the air. It has occurred to us that the fluidity of the sense of equilibrium may be a reawakening of archaic feelings —"at the mercy of the adult"—as well as a reflection of the more generalized loss of moorings, and that our subjects who had to disrupt the hypnosis are those who do not trust that the hypnotist will keep them from falling, as it were, and so have to reinstate with a certain desperation the control over their own ego orientations in time and space. It would seem that those who experience these strange losses in normal equilibrium sense, and nevertheless let it go on, have a certain kind of trust that the hypnotist will not allow anything catastrophic to happen.

Interestingly enough, the symptom of psychogenic dizziness apart from hypnosis has been observed frequently in patients who feel in a more general and deeply emotional sense that they are losing their "bearings" or their "moorings." In fact, Bauer and Schilder (12) declared that "Psychogenic dizziness is an expression of the irreconcilability of two spheres of psychic experience." It is likely that such reported losses of equilibrium occur more often during the *induction* phase of hypnosis than in the established state because of that loss of psychological equilibrium associated with the *transition* from the normal state of the ego to the hypnotic.

We turn now to still another form of spontaneous change in bodily experience, namely, a subjective experience of the *loss of the body or of its parts*. Subjects going into hypnosis frequently report either isolated instances of the "disappearance" of an arm, a foot, a leg, or a smooth and progressive loss of awareness of the entire body. The comment, "I have a funny feeling as if I were disembodied" is, though by no means universal in hypnotic subjects, sufficiently frequent that any active hypnotist must recognize it as a familiar description. A common report is that the subject remains aware of his body only at the pressure points—his heels on the floor, his buttocks on the chair, his wrists on the arms of the chair. Of similar character is the report of one subject: "There is no connection between my thighs and my ankles . . ." Related to these partial and wholesale losses of bodily awareness is the not uncommon phenomenon—not restricted to the induction phase—of the carrying out of complex bodily movements without any awareness of having done so.

Often parallel with these changes are peculiar changes in tactile and temperature sensation: "I feel prickly (or numb)," or "I am suddenly terribly cold (or hot)." Similarly, alterations in distance receptors are not unusual. The most frequent in our experience involves the subject's own voice or that of the hypnotist. One excellent subject reported that she felt her own voice to be coming from behind her instead of from inside her self. Many have the feeling that the hypnotist is very close, "as though you were talking right into my ear"; others report hearing the hypnotist's voice going "further and further away" and they must strain to hear it.

Our observations with regard to the visual sense are scanty, inasmuch as we rarely continued the attempt to induce hypnosis with the subject's eyes remaining open. Even here, however, both on those occasions where hypnosis was successfully induced with eyes open or where a subject was asked to open his eyes while remaining in hypnosis, the alteration in visual function was similar: usually a report that "Things seem unreal" or "covered by a haze" or "dreamlike," again precisely the kinds of description given by patients not in hypnosis who are afflicted with the symptom of derealization.

To be sure, all of these changes of bodily awareness are usually encouraged by the hypnotist in most standard techniques of hypnosis. Nevertheless, we have seen them occur sufficiently often in the absence of specific suggestion that we do not believe this phenomenon to be simply the result of the commands of the hypnotist.

In these changes in body image and sensation, we see again a continuity with certain other altered states of ego-functioning. Anyone who has ever "watched" himself fall asleep is familiar with some of these signs of lost moorings; these occur similarly in alcoholic or drug intoxication, or even in extreme fatigue. We hear the same kind of report of body-image change in patients who are in a state of depersonalization; and interestingly enough, though less frequently, precisely this variety of occurrence is reported at various times during the course of a psychoanalysis.

We have been speaking in all of the foregoing of changes

in body image and feeling which do not appear to have an important personal or individual symbolic meaning, but have rather a more universal character that appears to be relatively independent of differentiated unconscious content; they occur in hypnotic subjects of widely differing temperament and experience. It is rare, although it does happen, that during the induction period a subject reports what appears to be a personal symbolic change in body image. For example, "I feel as if my hand is curled up, palm upward . . . like a beggar asking for pennies." We will discuss this second variety of body-image change when we come to the hypnotic state. More typically, the kind of alteration we have been discussing occurs primarily during induction, dropping out in the established hypnotic state or giving way to sporadic reports of changes which appear to be more specific to the individual and a highly condensed statement of some important area of conflict.

We have speculated that the more general and frequently recurring body-image changes have a sameness from person to person because the induction process itself revives in part a "state of mind" or more strictly a variety of ego-functioning, which is so ancient as to precede the era in which the subject was able to organize external stimuli and to move parts of his body automatically. Moreover, it may well be that this difference issues from the fact that the synthetic function of the ego is more available in the established state.

In one piece of systematic observation which we carried out, we were able to see rather sharply how a subject may struggle with the hypnotist's attempts to break down this established automaticity. A young woman who had been hypnotized some time before, and who, in the interim, had had some psychotherapy, was now to be tested for her hypnotizability. The context was such that consciously, at least, she wanted to prove that she was no longer hypnotizable. During a routine induction, she was challenged by the hypnotist, who told her she could not open her eyes, that "they are stuck, glued tight," and completely outside of her control. She conceded that perhaps she could open her eyes by deciding to move the muscles of her eyelids, and that she would feel "silly" and helpless in trying to open her eyes "when I have a funny feeling there're no eyes there." However, after a few moments' pause, and with obvious difficulty, she raised her right hand to her face and opened the eyelids with her fingers, having anticipated "it will be like handling someone else's eyelids." The opened lid now revealed an unfocused eye, and she reported a significantly greater tactile awareness in the finger that opened the eye than in the lid itself.

In this situation of conflict, the peculiar change in the subject's inner sense of "I-ness," no doubt related to her sense of voluntary motor control, became sharply apparent in her inventive and somewhat eerie resolution of the problem of how to be simultaneously in hypnosis and yet not in hypnosis. This communicated uncanny feeling was indeed comparable to the objective way a hysteric looks at and handles a paralyzed limb. Our subject might have said, "You still have my eyelid muscles captive, but *I* control my hands and arms."

This episode sharpened for us the meaning of much of the hypnotist's effort which is directed toward the conquest, as it were, of the entire motor apparatus.

## Change in Quality of Affect

Eruptions of intense feeling during the induction period have long been familiar to workers in hypnosis; these may occur spontaneously or be produced with an astonishing ease by the hypnotist. Repeatedly in our experience over the last ten years, we have witnessed such spontaneous outbursts in the initial induction session, ranging from the relatively minor explosions of uncontrollable weeping to the enacting of waking nightmares on a level of symbolism and with a quantity of feeling very similar to that known to us only in dream life, poetry, or fairy tales. Current hypnotic literature is replete with material of this kind. However, this literature by and large does not make clear whether the emotional outburst usually occurs during the induction period or during the established hypnotic state. Perhaps the reason for this omission is the same one that delayed us for a long time in seeing that there might be an important difference in the dynamics of induction and of the established state: namely, that most of such recorded material comes from research situations which are simultaneously therapeutic. During the course of our own investigations it was possible for us to gather relevant data on this point: we saw a group of excellent hypnotic subjects (nonpatients) during induction whom we were screening for a study of the physiological and electroencephalographic concomitants of the hypnotic state. *During the induction period, intense emotional outbursts, though not universal, were extremely common. Thereafter, during the established hypnotic state when the subject was being studied physiologically in a variety of ways we will later describe, there were no such outbursts.* We had the same experience with our subjects screened for a neutral study of cognition in hypnosis.[7] The following is a condensed account of a running record of an initial hypnotizability interview with a medical student, not a patient of either of us then or subsequently. He was being seen simply to establish whether or not he was a sufficiently good hypnotic subject to serve in the physiological studies. During a group hypnosis, conducted as an initial screening device, he had been rated as "Fair."

Interview begun at 4:05, standard induction procedure by M.B. with ocular fixation on fountain pen and slow counting. Astonishingly fast response. By 4:06, copious tearing of eyes. They close by

[7] It might be argued that even in these neutral situations, the subjects were aware of the fact that both investigators were therapists and might have unconsciously hoped to develop the experiments into personal therapy. However, the fact that such outbursts are common in parlor and fraternity demonstrations by amateur hypnotists (often to the dismay of the entertainer) suggests that it is not the hope of personal therapy that accounts for the emotional explosions.

count of 5. Begins to hyperventilate. Asked to try as hard as can to open eyes, but will find them stuck. Eyelids flutter, eyeballs turn up, whites showing. Nods head that had tried as hard as could *to* open them, but was unable. Voice weak and drugged. Now on hand-clasp, hyperventilation extreme. Challenged to unclasp. Mouth opens, moaning as in acute distress, writhes and continues to moan in strange cross between intense pain and orgastic climax. Says suddenly, "My hands—my hands—are buzzing." Shakes them violently—eyes fly open—overbreathing hard. Tosses head, flushes scarlet, moans. Paniclike outburst. Says, "My head—my head is buzzing." Holds hands straight out, shaking them as if they were burning. (I feel slightly alarmed, reassure him, tell him to relax, and that he will gradually come out of hypnosis.) After several minutes, seems more relaxed, only to start all over again wringing hands and shuddering. Now starts to sob uncontrollably, and is obviously coming out of hypnosis. (I continue to reassure him and to take active steps to return him to normal state.)

The intensity of feeling in this boy was sufficiently extreme, even for our good hypnotic subjects, to necessitate now an unusually long posthypnotic session, the aim of which was double: therapeutic, in the sense of helping him to put the lid back on this Pandora's box, and investigative, to establish how atypical such feeling and behavior were for him—in short, to inquire into whether this eruption was a function of the induction process or symptomatic of a developed pathology.

At first on emerging from the hypnosis he spontaneously began to talk in a peculiarly impulsive and excited manner. He said, "When you started to bring me out, I had a feeling of despair without really feeling it."

From the research record, it is clear that the investigator began this posthypnotic interview with questions which were on the surface fairly neutral, but which were designed to establish the quality of this boy's current emotional adjustment. Later, the inquiry becomes somewhat more specific with regard to a possible history of maladjustment. Again, we present a condensation of the actual record:

"(Been under any special strain in school of late?) Well, yes— grades are *pretty* good, between a B and C average, but not satis- fied with my study habits. Should really do better than that—in fact have considered going to see Dr. E., school psychiatrist, to see if could give any advice re studying more efficiently. (Discusses his medical school standing, nature of curriculum, now quite calm, matter-of-fact.) (What is your favorite subject?) Physics, I think—or maybe biology and medicine. But lately I've been bored, when have to do a long job. I got bored in the Navy too, as a petty officer. (Any emotional upsets in Navy?) No—none, just kind of bored. (How did you become interested in studying medicine?) Recalls reading Jack London's *The Sea Wolf* in high school. Maybe I got interested in problems of life after death. (Fusses with tie, moves arms now.) Seems to me I got interested in medicine to study ways of preserving life. Sometimes I think lying in a warm bed when it's freezing outside: 'Life versus death, just a few degrees of difference.' Lately I read Schroedinger's *What Is Life*. Made a big impression. Got to thinking about problems of aging. (Does this preoccupy you?) No—not that I know of. (Anxious or nervous about anything lately?) No, I don't think so. In fact I've been quite happy; have a new girl, getting along very well with her. Wouldn't say I'm any more under strain than average medical student. (Consider self in general an emo- tional person?) Not much, sometimes I have a short outburst of anger. (When last cry?) Sometimes in movies—never otherwise. Last time I really cried was when my uncle died about ten years ago. (Why do you think you cried so hard just before?) I really have no idea; it puzzled me. (Any thoughts at all about this exper- ience?) Well, I went under easily, I thought. I had a premonition something would happen—I don't know. I'd go in and slide back and go in and slide back. After I was partially under, I *knew* something would happen—didn't like it. (Did you then want to break it off?) Well, no, I just thought I'd let it take its course, but I got scared when you tried to stop it and at first it just didn't. I was afraid to come out of hypnosis lest it continue anyway. (Do you feel entirely your normal self now?) Oh yes, completely—

but I've never experienced anything like that before. I wasn't exactly cold—just like shock all over."

The inquiry now extended briefly into his history: he had never considered himself neurotic, had never gone to see a psychiatrist, and had always considered himself fairly well adjusted. Finally he was asked again whether he had had any emotional upsets lately; he replied, "This is not an upset, it's an incident," and went on to relate that his roommate had approached him homosexually, that he had felt indifferent, had submitted to fellatio out of curiosity, and had then advised his roommate to see a psychiatrist, feeling sorry for him. He was, on the surface, undisturbed in telling this, clinically objective about his roommate, and entirely calm in his manner.

After a few minutes more of neutral conversation, with the investigator watching for residual signs of anxiety, this interview was brought to an end, the subject being told he could contact the investigator should any questions arise.

We concluded from this session that, despite his history of surface adjustment and his strong denials of anything currently amiss, this young medical student was probably struggling to maintain his defensive intellectualizing against the onslaught of some unknown, intense, as yet quite unconscious conflict. From the point of view of our research, the significance of his extraordinarily violent explosion of feeling lay in the fact that it was without parallel in his normal state. From this we must conclude that something in the induction process had permitted or even brought about what amounted to an inundation of feeling normally defended against by his functioning ego. It is, however, of great interest to note that, despite this flood of painful affect, the subject held on to some defensive aspect of his ego function: first, he reported he felt despair *without really feeling it*, and secondly, that he had no notion of the meaning of the despair. Approximately eight months later we heard that this young man had decided to consult Dr. E., the school psychiatrist.

We saw a striking instance of a successfully carried-out defensive effort *against* the onslaught of such diffuse and violent affect in the case of a young ex-soldier who came to a veterans' hospital to seek therapy for stuttering, but who was not yet at this time in treatment. He, himself, asked whether hypnosis might be of help. Inasmuch as the stuttering was so extreme during this initial interview that it was almost impossible to elicit even minimal information from him, his therapist, a resident[8] who had become interested in our research, decided to try it. His hope was to relax the patient sufficiently to allow for a little more verbal exchange than had hitherto been possible. The following is taken from the case record:

He proved to be an excellent subject and promptly went into hypnosis, responding satisfactorily to the usual challenges. When the patient was unable either to open his eyes or to move his extremities, the therapist suggested that he go "into a still deeper sleep." As this suggestion was made the patient's face became contorted, his right hand went to his right side, and his body began to twist to the left. He was still in hypnosis, became pale, clammy looking, broke out into a sweat, and finally went into actual collapse, although his pulse was good. That he was still in hypnosis was evidenced by the fact that he could answer questions and respond to direct suggestions, e.g., when he was told he would immediately "feel better." It was decided that he should be brought out of hypnosis at once and so it was suggested that at the count of 7, he would "awaken," feel refreshed, and be his normal self. This was done; the patient now looked about him saying he didn't know quite what had happened. He was unable to offer any explanation of this episode. It was unclear whether he had subjectively experienced violent physical pain, nameless unpleasant feelings, or both. As he was being helped to his bed, still pale and shaky, he collapsed completely again and had to be carried to his bed. His pulse, however, continued good and the therapist was not unduly alarmed by his condition. He told him

[8] Dr. Barnet Sharrin, at that time a resident at Winter Veterans Hospital, Topeka, Kansas.

to close his eyes and go to sleep, and that he would feel much better on awakening. These latter suggestions were carried out. The next day the patient, in spite of this experience, said he would like to try again. Dr. Gill was invited to come over and witness this second attempt. *This time the patient proved unhypnotizable.* Dr. Gill now tried to hypnotize him; he also failed. Subsequent attempts were made to hypnotize him with the adjuvant use of seconal and sodium amytal. These met with complete failure.

Thus we see a good example of the patient's successful defensive "answer," as it were, to the threat of again permitting a serious loosening of his ego-functioning. This was all the more striking in view of his *conscious* wish to go on with the hypnosis and his voluntary effort to continue to cooperate with the several attempts to hypnotize him.

Although further scrutiny of data drawn from hypnotic induction and from the established state is necessary, it is our distinct impression that while affective outbursts of a kind not found in the subject normally do occur in both, the outburst during induction is usually more diffuse, more fluid, and less idiosyncratic in character than that in the established state. Again we must emphasize that our observations of the latter are largely restricted to a therapeutic context.

## SPONTANEOUS CHANGES IN THE AVAILABILITY OF THE MOTOR SYSTEM

Before we leave our presentation of the data providing evidence for a generally changing ego state in the hypnotic subject during induction, we should like to mention briefly one last kind of phenomena, namely changes in the availability of the musculature, in particular the spontaneous appearance or disappearance of hysterical symptoms.

A young woman who had come for the treatment of a depression had been voluble and articulate during the initial history-taking, conducted in the normal state. When the attempt was now made to test her hypnotizability, she began to give all signs of being a fairly good hypnotic subject. When the hypnotist asked her a routine question during the induction process, her mouth began to twist; she pursed her lips, protruded her tongue and in all ways made it clear she was trying without success to answer him. The hypnotist, after a few moments, again checked her ability to speak and found that she was quite unable to do so. Curiously enough, she did not appear to be alarmed (although the hypnotist was somewhat) and seemed to await further developments. In very short order, the hypnotist brought her back to her normal state with strong direct suggestion for the return of her voice. She seemed now a trifle confused, even dazed, and soon began to talk normally.

In another instance:

A young woman given to what she called "fits" or "blackouts"—obviously hysterical in nature—came for treatment of these. Following a general psychiatric examination and history, she was tested for her hypnotizability. After only a few seconds, her body began to twitch and shake and she spontaneously reported that her sensations were "exactly like I feel in a blackout or a fit." Her body moved in a peculiar (semisexual) manner which she identified also as characteristic of her hysterical attacks. At this time, she had no awareness of the sexual quality of her movements.

We observed such changes in available motility in *non*-patients as well, during the induction period. We include examples of these data now lest it seem that clinically established pathology is a *sine qua non* for the emergence of this phenomenon.

A psychiatric resident, taking part in a study of hypnotizability, found after just a few minutes that he had lost control of his tongue and lips, although this was not suggested to him by the hypnotist. This became apparent to the hypnotist who observed the abortive efforts to move the tongue and lips. The subject later described this as a "frozen" feeling.

Another extremely interesting bit of data on the subject's response to the hypnotist's efforts to gain control of the motor apparatus came from a resident in psychiatry, also a volunteer for a general hypnotizability study:

During a routine induction, the hypnotist had established to his own and the subject's satisfaction that the latter was unable to open his eyes. The hypnotist now turned his attention to the subject's arms, announcing that they were getting heavier. At this moment the subject reported, "My eyelids are fluttering and I am feeling alarmed, as though they are going to open." When he was questioned about this, he said, "It's as if the sudden shift from my eyes to my arms leaves the eyes unprotected by you."

The use of the word "unprotected" is curious. It is not quite clear whether the subject meant that the eyes were threatening to get out of the hypnotist's control and return to normal voluntariness, or to get out of the hypnotist's *and* his own control.

Again, as in the other phenomena, it is our impression that changes in motility which involve the *direct* expression of repressed conflict in highly personal terms occur more frequently, at least more observably, in the established hypnotic state. Later, we will present examples which show this difference.

We have summarized the responses of the subject which suggest that the hypnotist's effort to upset the normal equilibrium of ego functions—largely by techniques of deprivation—is succeeding: the changes in bodily experience, the availability of strong feeling, and the loss of motor control, all attest to this fact. It is a little more difficult to demonstrate the subtleties of the extraordinary change which takes place in the subject's relationship with the hypnotist.

Certainly the most obvious and most sweeping change which *begins* during induction, and becomes then the leading characteristic of the established hypnotic state, is the progressive willingness of the subject not only to do as he is told by the hypnotist, but also to see, hear, feel, think, and recall at the specific direction of the hypnotist, and at his direction alone. Aside from the spontaneous changes we have described, this abdication to the hypnotist of personal activity, responsibility, initiative, voluntariness is, of course, what led Clark Hull (119) to say that "hypersuggestibility" is the *only* characteristic of hypnosis which distinguishes it from other states. All of this starts observably the moment the subject makes a "positive" response to any routine suggestion given during induction ("You will find now your eyes are getting heavy— heavier— They are closing now . . ." etc.). The remarkable fact is that a good hypnotic subject, with certain exceptions we will mention, will respond with this abdication of his independence to *almost anyone who casts himself in the role of the hypnotist*. If for a moment one does not take this rather well-known datum for granted, it is an astonishing thing that the potential hypnotic subject responds in about the same way to the experienced psychiatrist, the fraternity colleague, the vaudeville performer, the student in his class of abnormal psychology, or the army captain in the medical corps. To be sure, the reality factors in the situation play some part, but apparently are not the main determinant. There are occasional instances where a subject has responded positively to a student and *not* to the professor (*sic*), or where the nature of a social or institutional situation raises the percentage of hypnotizable people, as in an army hospital, or where an unresponsive subject becomes a good subject following a significant (for him) psychological exchange with the hypnotist. In fact, one of our psychiatrist subjects who was initially quite unresponsive turned into an excellent hypnotic subject after a free-association interview with one of us during which he allowed an unusual flood of private feeling to be observed. We mention these exceptional happenings only to document the fact that to some extent reality factors play a role in the induction process. It remains, however, the more remarkable fact that these *are* unusual happenings and that by and large a "good" hypnotic subject responds similarly to the hypnotist regardless of the sex, age, experience, prestige, etc., of the hypnotist.[9]

Corollary to this is the occasional (not frequent, but not singular) instance when the potential subject shows all signs of going into hypnosis *before* the hypnotist has begun his active efforts to bring about sensory deprivation and changes in bodily awareness. In these subjects, the overwhelming, often unconscious, wish to go into hypnosis is so strong that the usual parallel process we have described of loosening reality-moorings is quite unnecessary.

One of our nonpatient subjects reported he was in "a partial state of hypnosis" two or three minutes after he had entered the room and *prior* to any routine induction efforts by the hypnotist. He reported spontaneous changes in his bodily experience (". . . a tenseness in my abdomen . . . and something going on in the fingertips . . . body is shrinking, chest smaller, legs thinner, chair smaller, but arms bigger and heavier . . . no connection between ankles and thighs, feet off out there . . ."). He admitted that he was quite conscious of an unwillingness to maintain what he called "full contact" as an equal and found great pleasure—sexually tinged—in "being cradled" in hypnosis. Interestingly enough, each time he started to think "reasonably" about what was going on, he found himself "coming out" of his "partial hypnosis."

Experiences of this kind brought into sharp focus the fact that the strange process which issues in the hypnotic state may start either with changes in ego function of the sort we have described—where reality stimulation and muscular freedom are sharply circumscribed by the hypnotist—or with an intense wish to abdicate temporarily adult human relationships, as in the above instance. But no matter which half of the process comes first, the other half shortly appears. By this we mean simply that if the subject starts with changes in his

---

[9] Although there is frequent mention in the literature of the importance of the overt sexual fantasies which emerge during induction, we do not feel this phenomenon is, in any sense, specific for hypnosis. To be sure, some of our subjects have reported such fantasies, but with no greater frequency than in equally intimate, nonhypnotic situations.

general ego-functioning brought about by sensory deprivation, etc., he shortly finds changes also occurring in his relationship to the hypnotist, usually of an infantile sort; conversely, if he starts with the regressive infantile need, he is shortly experiencing changes in all of his ego functions. The two are so intertwined it is sometimes difficult to say which is which.

In some instances the intertwining of factors was such that we could not attempt to pigeonhole them as "transference" changes or as "alterations in ego function."[10] These complex phenomena may range from a sense of perplexity or "unrealness" to what one subject described thus:

> I have so contracted that . . . I am just the essence of myself here . . . the outside of my body doesn't exist . . . I remember having had this feeling as a child when I had a high fever . . . or again as an adult in great fatigue or with a hang-over . . .

In spontaneous regression, which we have described in detail elsewhere (100), we see an even more complex phenomenon emerging, involving factors of transference as well as changes in ego function.

On the basis of our experience and, more recently, theoretical extrapolations, we have concluded that the induction process of necessity involves *not only* maximal attention (145) but also a specific kind of relationship to a real or fantasied human being. The *general* changes in ego function initiated by sensory and motor deprivation may issue in any one of several nonhypnotic states: a "brown study," a presleep state, a trancelike self-absorption as in yoga, a diffuse feeling of un-

---

[10] Indeed this distinction is in any case somewhat loose conceptually. This lack of strictness is made possible by the fact that the concept "transference" remains as yet somewhat cloudy in the literature of psychoanalysis. Sometimes it is used as if it were a constellation of defense mechanisms: projection, identification, introjection, etc. At other times it is used as if it represents essentially libidinal or aggressive drives. The phenomena usually labeled as "transference" are more likely complex, organized configurations which are the outcome of the interplay of multiple layers of drive and defense, specifically in relation to other individuals or to personifications of organized groups (school, country, army, church, etc.).

reality (as reported by a sailor movelessly watching regular signal lights on a dark sea), a transient feeling of depersonalization or derealization, a burst of creativity, or countless other allied shifts in ego organization, some of which we will later discuss in detail. Each of these states acquires its own special form by the addition of "something more" than the initial changes in ego function. For that peculiar relationship called hypnosis, where one human being is temporarily and within definite limits "controlled" by another *in a setting of such an initial alteration of ego function*, the specific "something more" that is needed appears to be a relationship of an archaic kind (largely unconscious) to another person: in short, transference.

# 2

# THE HYPNOTIC STATE

Almost from the very start of our research when we put to ourselves the question, "What is the nature of the hypnotic state?" we knew that we would need to approach this problem with a variety of techniques. Our earlier review of the literature (25) had demonstrated clearly that although the victory of the "suggestionists" had once and for all shown that the hypnotic state was *not* brought about by the physical manipulations of the hypnotist, this victory became a kind of dead end. What had historically been a significant psychological advance, namely, the concept "suggestion," was now used as an explanation which needed no further elaboration. Even the standard psychoanalytic theories of hypnosis, while certainly not sterile like the suggestion concept, seemed to us sketchy and incomplete. Not until the theory of Kubie and Margolin (145), which we will present and discuss in detail later on, was there any systematic attempt within the general framework of psychoanalysis to inquire into both the psychological and possible physiological aspects of the hypnotic state.

It seemed to us that for a comprehensive investigation of the nature of the hypnotic state it would be necessary to try both of these avenues: and so we did.

Surveying our amassed data, it is clear to us that the results of our physiological studies are by far the more difficult to interpret of the two, and so far, from the point of view of theory, the less valuable. This latter statement is particularly true with regard to any positive findings. With regard, however, to the negative results of the physiological studies, a few controversial issues in the literature on hypnosis are perhaps more finally settled by our results than they have been to date. We omit detailed discussion of these studies here inasmuch as we will present them later, in Chapter 6. Even there we dispose rather quickly of our excursion into a physiological approach to the question, "What is the nature of the hypnotic state?" essentially because this work stands in a certain isolation from the rest of our experience and subsequent thinking. The only general theoretical link which was suggested by these studies is the possibility that hypnosis as a variety of ego-functioning stands somewhere between physiological sleep and the normal *alert* waking state, and *may* be physiologically distinguishable from both.

While we do not feel that on the psychological side our data and theoretical conclusions are definitive, we do think there has been a progressive development in this area of our inquiry which stands in some contrast to our physiological work. It is our purpose here to trace in some detail the vicissitudes of this psychological inquiry, leaving our most recent theoretical extrapolations for a later chapter.

Very early in our work, when the "therapeutic short cut" stood at the center of our research, we duplicated Freud's classic observations of the dramatic reliving of repressed traumatic memories together with their painful and conflict-laden feelings (101). At that time, we made the rather primitive formulation that ". . . in the hypnotic state the ego and the resistances can be temporarily suspended to gain repressed material and that then, within the hypnotic state, this material can be reintegrated into the ego" (p. 171). This, obviously, is a statement which emphasizes what hypnosis does to the *defense mechanisms* as one aspect of ego-functioning; its essential concern is with the *alteration* of those defense mechanisms in the service of shortening the course of therapy. Its only merit as a budding theoretical statement lay in its emphasis on the fact that hypnosis does not "obliterate" ego-functioning, a view held up to this time by most writers on the subject, and emphasized by Anna Freud in *The Ego and the Mechanisms of Defence* (75). Our position was, and remains, that there occurs a complex and subtle change in ego-functioning which issues in a continuing fluctuation of the organization of the ego, and, accordingly, in its over-all functioning. We indicated also that while it was clear that hypnosis significantly alters the defense mechanism of repression, it remained to be seen whether it had any discernible effect on the other defenses. During the next several years, our studies were largely concerned with this issue, more in practical therapeutic terms than in theoretical ones, and with the question of which categories of patients are hypnotizable, again a therapeutic problem—though one with theoretical implications (26, 29, 31, 32, 102).

At this time also, we made a small beginning on the problems of clinical research in general, and research in psychotherapy in particular (22, 23).

Our unpublished research reports written during this therapeutically oriented period reflect nevertheless a continuous wrestling with the problem of the nature of the hypnotic state, marshaling on the one hand a kind of data which we subsumed under the heading "transference data," and on the other hand a parallel but independent body of data which we gradually began to identify as "hypnosis as an altered ego state." For a long time, these two approaches ran along side by side without a satisfactory logical bridge between them. It was only in the preparation of this volume that it became possible to establish such a bridge. Before we present these two kinds of data we should like to discuss first that phenomenon which, because of its extremeness, seems to distinguish the hypnotic state from the other allied states which we have mentioned and will later elaborate. This phenomenon cannot be readily classified simply as "a change in ego function" nor as a change in the "transference" relationship. We refer to that alteration of the hypnotized subject which *appears* to turn him into a passive, subservient automaton whose actions and even whose perceptions are "controlled" by the hypnotist.

As central to any person's sense of "I-ness" as anything else about him is his *subjective feeling* of what has been variously termed "will power," "voluntariness," "personal responsibility," "spontaneity," "initiative," or "independence." These terms do not exhaust the list, and although each contains a subtle difference from the others, their commonality assuredly lies in that inner experience optimally possessed by a normal person in a reasonably good state of adjustment which he *feels* as his "free will" (see 132). Every layman knows that the abdication of this aspect of self-awareness together with the temporary loss of independent action is the key happening in hypnosis.

Leaving aside the extravagances of such fantasies as the Svengali-Trilby legend, it is nevertheless no accident that these characteristics of the hypnotic state should be chosen by literary and lay people as the *essential* qualities which distinguish hypnotic from nonhypnotic states. Inasmuch as our previous publications have dealt only peripherally with this issue, we will devote relatively more space to it here than to some of the other problems.

First, let us review the most obvious phenomena in connection with the hypnotic subject's *relative* loss of his capacity to make what we will now loosely call an "effort of the will." It is a universal observation—leaving aside the artifacts of extreme lethargy, immobility, drowsiness, and the like, frequently suggested by the hypnotist—that the good hypnotic subject, be he lethargic or sharply alert, characteristically *waits* for the hypnotist to tell him directly or indirectly what is expected of him. The extent to which he does *not* do this (and this varies from subject to subject and even within the same person) is a direct measure of his still operating ego-functioning, defensive and reality-adapted. That the passive waiting is perhaps the most singularly distinguishing characteristic of a good hypnotic subject is reflected in the fact that White (226) makes this the core of his definition of hypnosis as a ". . . goal-directed striving, its most general goal being to behave like a hypnotized person as this is continuously defined by the operator and understood by the subject" (p. 483).

We attempted a series of controlled observations on this point, the results of which strongly suggest that the sense of compliance is the crucial characteristic for the subject. Our procedure, using a nonpatient population, was as follows: first, we would induce hypnosis in someone previously established as a "good" subject; then we would ask him how he knew he was in hypnosis. He might reply that he felt relaxed. Now we would suggest that the relaxation would disappear but that *he would remain in hypnosis*. Then we would ask again how he now knew he was in hypnosis. He might say because his arm "feels numb"—so again, we would suggest the disappearance of this sensation. We continued in this way until finally we obtained the reply, "I know I am in hypnosis because I *know* I will do what you tell me." This was repeated with several subjects, with the same result.

It is perhaps more pertinent to the psychology of the hypnotist than of the subject that in recent years most writers on this topic (ourselves included) have chosen to gloss over the phenomena of the hypnotic subject's passivity and to focus attention on the fact that he does *not* actually become a robot or an automaton. One feels in this effort to restore the dignity of the subject the hypnotist's own unconscious need to deny that he is enslaving anyone. On a less subjective level, to be sure, the contemporary investigator of hypnosis feels it important to counter the myth that the hypnotic subject loses all of his normal capacity to appraise outer reality and to maintain his capacity for "choice." If we are to begin to understand the phenomenon of hypnosis, however, we must scrutinize carefully *both* sets of observations: those which reflect the subject's *abdication* of his "voluntary" I-ness, and those which reflect his sporadic and fluctuating efforts to maintain himself as a separate person who can make independent efforts of the will.

We have made numerous systematic observations on both sides of this problem. In this section we shall sum up briefly those which relate to that alteration of self-awareness involving a relative loss of "will," leaving for a later discussion the issue of the play of forces brought to bear against this.

In the first series of such observations, we decided to see what would happen if we made explicit to the subject in hypnosis that we did not expect him to be a robot, and that in fact he was "free" to be as spontaneous as he wanted to be or could be: in short, we refrained from specific suggestions. This simple, closely observed situation was set up with several nonpatient college students, all excellent subjects, selected from large groups at the University of Illinois, initially with the prime purpose of studying the physiological concomitants of hypnosis. The studies we are now describing were, of course, conducted separately from the physiological investigations. In our first exploratory observations of this kind, both of us watched the subject, and found that, in the absence of any specific suggestion, he usually expressed his "spontaneity" by opening his eyes, getting up from the chair, roaming aimlessly around the room, carrying out a few awkward and obviously artificial acts (for example, looking out of the window at nothing, leafing through a magazine), and shortly thereafter sitting down again only to sink back into a passive immobile state—sometimes closing his eyes, but more often just sitting in a rather depressed and quiet torpor. Usually, when we questioned him at this point about his thoughts and feelings, the response would be a slow and halting, "I don't feel like doing anything." Sometimes he would then ask what he should do.[1]

It was only when we pushed this situation to its logical extreme that we could begin to formulate some of the subtler observable aspects of the hypnotic subject's relative abdication of his "voluntariness" and independence. We set up a new situation in which each of us in turn worked with a subject alone, the essential directive to the subject being that he would alternate his hypnotic with his normal state, defying the other hypnotist (who would now re-enter the room) to tell whether or not he was in hypnosis. At the beginning of this study, we both found to our great chagrin that each of us was as frequently wrong as right in judging whether or not the subject was in hypnosis.

It might be argued that the reason for this lies in the fact that the subject's presumably "normal" state was in fact still a variety of hypnotic state. This may be. However, the fact that our correct judgments rose as we isolated the behavioral cues of the apparently normal but actual hypnotic state suggests that there was a real and observable difference between the two states.

These cues were indeed subtle and, at first, difficult to see. However, as we watched we noticed in the hypnotic state split-second hesitations of response under the cross-examination of the hypnotist who had been out of the room, hesitations not normally characteristic for the subject. We noted also momentary lapses into somewhat stiff or frozen postural

[1] The behavior of the hypnotic subject in this situation was a kind of focused caricature of the familiar behavior of an analysand who is struggling with the problem of a defensive and compliant passivity: such a patient quite routinely will attempt to carry out (in and out of the analytic situation) behaviors which appear to be "spontaneous" and "normal"—presumably in order to please the analyst—maintaining all the while a relentlessly slavish position, waiting for cues if not for actual directives from the analyst. Ordinarily in our experience this defensive passivity, often found in masochistic characters, simultaneously protects against a hostile, devouring, needy set of impulses—greatly feared by the patient—and expresses a spiteful mock obedience. We will pursue further the implications of these psychodynamics in our later discussion of the psychology of the hypnotic relationship.

attitudes, giving a slightly static feeling to the person, or sometimes an impression of a slight slowing down of the pace of bodily movement. Along with these cues, we noticed a fleeting glazing of the eyes, the "unseeing look" normally found in reverie or a "brown study." Occasionally the subject in hypnosis would give himself away by flashing a covert glance at his own hypnotist when the conversation did not, on the surface, warrant this. The final and decisive observation came when the "cross-examining hypnotist" would pursue the subject in hypnosis with an uninterrupted series of questions and logical cross-questions in an effort to determine whether or not he was in hypnosis. If the subject were in a hypnotic state, his initially covert glancing at the hypnotist became increasingly overt, until he might look almost beseeching for direction, and sometimes even began to look foggy. If he were in a normal state, he might become a little confused in his replies and exasperated, but he did not appear to be leaning on the hypnotist for direction, nor did he slow down and begin to look languorous or immobile. It was by one or more of these signs, all indicating a fundamental absence of a feeling of independent "I-ness," that we began finally to be able to discern (most of the time) when the subject was in hypnosis.

Another rich supply of data on this same problem came from our clinical observations of patients treated in a modified analytic therapy where hypnosis had been introduced from time to time. In three long-term cases, we made a systematic effort throughout the treatment to analyze the meaning to the patient of the hypnotic relationship, the hypothesis being the following: if the unconscious motives for being hypnotizable in the first place are sufficiently analyzed, then the patient's hypnotizability will lessen. For the purpose of the present discussion of the sense of personal responsibility, we present a circumscribed portion of these data, the study of which has led to further hypotheses rather than to unambiguous conclusions.

The procedure was the following: toward the end of the treatment—that is, after many months of analytic therapy, which included the analysis of the hypnotic relationship—the therapist tried to hypnotize the patient, following the procedure of the successful early induction sessions, challenging the patient as he went along to break out of the hypnosis. There ensued in all cases an observably painful and intense conflict in the patient, resulting in a peculiar unreliability and unpredictability of the hypnotic state in these initially excellent subjects.

The ambiguity of this result lies in its being open to at least two possible interpretations. If this change were indeed the outcome of a successful analysis of the unconscious motives underlying the initially good hypnotizability, we could say that the patient had reclaimed, as it were, certain portions of his ego-functioning and was therefore now a more independent, autonomous human being with less potential area for the abdication of his sense of personal responsibility or "free will." This is of course the thesis we had set out to demonstrate. However, it can certainly be argued that this lowering of good hypnotizability resulted rather from the patient's being quite uncertain now as to what the hypnotist-therapist *truly* wanted from him. On the one hand, he knew from the analysis of his motivations for being a good subject that the therapist regarded the acting out of regressive impulses as in a sense suspect, and would therefore be secretly hoping that the patient would now be relatively freer of such motives and not hypnotizable. On the other hand, he observed the therapist making an apparently sincere effort *to* hypnotize him once again. If, in fact, there had been *no* deep change in his hypnotizability, he would nevertheless thus be thrown into just such an intense conflict as we observed, simply by dint of not really knowing what was expected of him.

From the internal evidence, it is our own conclusion that first one and then the other of these two alternatives commanded the patient's behavior, depending on the balance of forces at any given moment. Perhaps a more clear-cut result could be gotten if after a period of psychoanalysis of a good hypnotic subject, the subject were then tested by a hypnotist previously unknown to the subject, and in a setting far removed from the therapeutic situation.

As a general conclusion we hold to the conviction that: *although the person in hypnosis has a sense of personal responsibility or capacity to make "spontaneous" efforts of will greater than has been generally believed, his relative loss of this ego function is a central aspect of the hypnotic state.*[2]

Knight (132) has set this ego function (the sense of free will) in a frame of reference which accents that intrapsychic balance which issues in a *subjective feeling* that one's general behavior as well as specific decisions and choices are free. Perhaps we can understand the feeling of the hypnotic subject by contrast. Knight says:

> In the healthy person, there is a harmonious interrelationship between the various parts of the self and with the environment, and one of the important by-products of such harmonious integration is a subjective sense of freedom. Viewed in this way, the feeling of freedom is also determined, and is possible to be experienced only to the extent that there exists within the individual a harmonious integration of his instinctual drives, his superego standards and restrictions, his ego perceptions, and discriminative faculties, and the possibilities provided by the environment. Such a theoretically healthy, integrated person will then feel free, and, to some extent, will be "free." That is, his *flexibility of adaptation* [italics ours] will be greater than

[2] Moreover, his tendency to abdicate his voluntariness in this way probably does not disappear even after a reasonably successful psychotherapy. However, paradoxical as it may seem, when a good hypnotic subject in psychotherapy is persuaded by the hypnotist that the latter truly wants from him the production of normally unconscious material—whether impulse or defense—the *content* of this material seems to be genuine, relevant, and highly specific to the patient. The exception to this occurs, of course, when the hypnotist-therapist is rigid in his own formulations and "leads" the patient to his own preconceived ideas. The difference here between hypnotic therapy and ordinary psychotherapy is not qualitative.

that of the neurotic person, and what behavior he "chooses" will conform to the laws and standards, internal and external, which he accepts, but his choices will *feel* free [p. 376].[3]

The precise description in theoretical terms of what constitutes the "harmonious integration" of the parts of the self remains a task to be done; but it does not seem too bold an assumption that where we observe a gross loss in this sense of freedom (as in the good hypnotic subject) we can presume something radical has happened, however temporarily, to whatever degree of "harmonious integration" the person normally possesses. Inasmuch as we have no reason to suppose that this alteration stems from an important change in the nature or strength of the instinctual drives, we presume it arises from some shift in the functions of the ego or the superego, or both. This presumption is bolstered by our observations of the manifold alterations in ego function as described in this entire section, as well as by our systematic observations of the hypnotic subject who is told to be "free"; most notable in both observations is the very loss of the *flexible adaptation* which Knight has described as one of the leading indices of a freely functioning ego. It is as if the good hypnotic subject hands over,[4] at least in some measure, to the hypnotist the "authority" to exercise all of those faculties ordinarily part of his ego-functioning (perception, discrimination, judgment, etc.). We will see that the similarity of such an abdication to a person in love has been discussed by Freud in his *Group Psychology and the Analysis of the Ego* (88), albeit in somewhat different terms.

[3] Knight discusses also those exceptional pathological instances where a subjective sense of freedom is not matched by the flexibility of adaptation discussed here. It is striking that frequently in those instances, as in hypnosis, this loss of flexibility is reflected in literalness or humorlessness.

[4] We are deliberately avoiding here the use of such terms as "introjection," "projection," "identification," and even the more neutral term "externalization," because of the general unclarity of the interrelations of all of the defense mechanisms—a lack of clarity which remains despite a few pioneer efforts to make some conceptual sortings (see Knight, 133; also Rado, 176; Sperling, 213).

The alterations in the function of the superego of the hypnotized person seem to us only a corollary of this same process. We have persuasive evidence from the clinical data of patients that their subjective feeling of "not caring what I say—nothing is embarrassing," or "it's not really my fault if I talk about taboo things," is high, and that the sense of "responsibility" in this connection goes down. Also, from experimental work, one of us has shown that, within limits, the sense of guilt about normally forbidden acts is significantly lessened in the good hypnotic subject (21).

It appears to us, in sum, that if indeed we make a sharp theoretical distinction at all between ego- and superego-functioning, the phenomena we have been discussing variously as "voluntariness," "sense of freedom of will," "sense of personal responsibility," and so on, must be thought of as functions which are subsumed simultaneously *under both ego and superego concepts*, with much overlap among them, some shading more into the realm of the ego, others into that of the superego.

Although there are other complex phenomena which we will come to—phenomena which could not easily be classified in either one of our admittedly arbitrary groupings of data—none of them is so uniquely characteristic of hypnosis as this abdication of "will." Precisely because of its special character we have presented this loss of voluntariness first and by itself. We return now to the two sets of data we have gathered over the years: A. Hypnosis as a state of altered ego-functioning, and B. Hypnosis as a transference phenomenon.

## Hypnosis as a State of Altered Ego-Functioning

For a number of years we had been observing a great variety of spontaneous experiences in both patients and normal hypnotic subjects which we regarded at first as quite incidental curiosae, without any discernible relationship to one another. We have already reported a small sampling of the peculiar and sometimes bizarre changes in bodily sensation and body image which occur mainly during induction; presently we will report another kind of change in bodily feeling which seems to occur more frequently in the established hypnotic state, especially during psychotherapy. Along with these, we began to observe unusual kinds of thinking and quasi-hallucinatory experiences (not suggested by us); also, again especially during induction, outbursts of diffuse strong feeling or motor discharge—with a more personal kind of emotional flooding in the established hypnotic state. Finally, in 1947 we published a paper entitled "Alterations in the State of the Ego in Hypnosis" (27), in collaboration with Dr. Frederick J. Hacker. In that paper we said that ". . . certain changes which occur in a highly fluctuating and variable fashion in people in hypnosis are systematically related to each other in that they are each a resultant of a change in the state of the ego of the person" (p. 60). Clearly, the point suggested here was that the systematic relationship which these variegated phenomena bore to one another was to be found by reviewing the general functions of the ego and seeing how some alteration of each was directly reflected in the phenomena observed.

Before detailing examples drawn from the hypnotic state data, it will not be superfluous to mention briefly the kinds of functions we then included when we spoke broadly of "ego functions," leaving later additions and theoretical extensions for a subsequent discussion in Chapter 5 of this volume. They were: (1) "self-awareness"; (2) the function of "toning down" intensive drives (usually instinctual in nature); (3) the function of delaying the gratification of an impulse and/or the postponement of its motor expression; (4) processes of perception and thought.

At the time of this first paper we made no distinction between the phenomena of the induction period and those of the established state, nor did we tie together the changes we observed as integral parts of a regressive process. In the illustrations we now offer we will try to show differences in the phenomena of the hypnotic state from those we presented in our section on induction.[5]

## CHANGES IN SELF-AWARENESS

Aside from the profound change in the subjective feeling of voluntariness which we have described, the most important shift in self-awareness in the hypnotic state lies in the *bodily experience* of the subject. We commented in our section on induction that the initial changes in body awareness "do not appear to have an important personal or individual symbolic meaning, but have rather a more universal character that appears to be relatively independent of differentiated unconscious content; they occur in hypnotic subjects of widely differing temperament and experience" (p. 18). It is our impression that *this* diffuse kind of change in body image decreases, by and large, in the established hypnotic state; it gives way, at least in the context of psychotherapy, to a kind of change which appears sporadically and seems to be a statement in "body language" of a significant personal, idiosyncratically expressed conflict. For example:

A young woman, reared in the backwoods of Kentucky, came for help with her acute anxiety and depression; she was accepted as a research case and treated with a combined technique of hypnosis and psychoanalytic psychotherapy. During one session she was reluctantly recalling her "Uncle Joe . . . a deeply religious man . . . who had had sex relations with his own daughter . . ." As she got this last out, she reported that she felt her body twisting and said, "I'm being drawn toward the wall." Actually she was on her back, motionless. She went on to say: "People . . . they don't have any understanding of kids . . . I wonder if I were a grown-up person and there were . . . oh somebody like I was when I was little . . . if I could understand them . . ." Her further associations indicated that her bodily experience of twisting away from the

[5] Again we remind the reader that the distinctions between induction and the established hypnotic state are not so clear as an organized presentation would make them appear.

therapist toward the wall was at least on one level a statement of simultaneous shame for her wretched background and anger toward all "grownups"—now the therapist—for their cruel indifference to the needs of children. At the end of the session, when the hypnosis was terminated, she was astonished to find herself still on her back, having become certain she had *actually* twisted to the side.

This example, though grossly simplified for the present purpose, suggests what we mean by an "idiosyncratic" change in body image, in contrast to the generalized changes reported during induction.

Another illustration will show the difficulty in making distinctions between the induction-changes and the state-changes in bodily experience:

A married woman, among whose presenting symptoms were fainting spells, spontaneously announced during a hypnotic session that a ". . . complete blackness is closing in on me . . . little waves of white light are striking against my eyelids, rising to a peak and then beginning again . . . I am falling . . . I'm getting awfully tense . . . I'm falling fast into a dark nothingness . . . want to go to the bathroom . . . need to urinate." (The patient was now extremely disturbed, began to tremble and to grab the side of the couch.) ". . . This is different from anything I have felt before in hypnosis . . . My head feels all closed in . . . constricted . . . this is how it usually feels just before I faint . . ."

We know that the experience of a descent is extremely common during hypnotic induction and that a loss of equilibrium—even dizziness—often accompanies it. In fact, this patient had reported such bodily feelings initially. However, the present description is significantly different from the familiar (usually much quieter) accounts of descent during induction. It is as though the diffuse feeling of "going down" links up with her actual hysterical symptom; other conflicts are released, the wish to urinate being a bodily expression of one of these, and the end result is a duplication of the bodily feelings she experiences during a fainting attack.

It is not at all infrequent that the experience of bodily changes which we have called "contentless" or "undifferentiated" link up in this way with something quite individual and specific to that person. Another example from a study carried out by our early collaborator Hacker (unpublished ms.):

A young male patient reported the swelling of his hand. The surrounding context made it quite clear that this experienced swelling represented in part an effort by the patient to deny to himself the smallness of his penis (as he thought of it) and to develop on a magical level a large, impressive "appendage."

As we reported in the chapter on induction, the experience of "swelling" is quite commonly reported by subjects of varying personalities and with a wide range of personal problems. But here the change in body image links up with the more organized unconscious content, probably of a later vintage in the individual's psychological development when idiosyncratic interaction with the environment has issued in higher-level organizations of body image.[6]

Another important change in self-awareness most easily observed in the established hypnotic state is the general reduction in the self-consciousness of the subject. We mean this now in the popular sense of the word. That quality which normally makes most of us acutely aware of where and how we are holding our hands or feet, which makes us take care of how we appear to other people, and which puts definite limits on how we move through a room, is greatly reduced in the hypnotic subject—not obliterated, but reduced.

This change seems to be related to another, namely, the subjective sense of a certain loss of *normal* diffuseness, with the development of a curious "one-track mindedness," described by some of the patients in analytic psychotherapy where hypnosis was from time to time introduced into the treatment. Comparing their experience during the normal-

[6] See Schneck (209).

state sessions with those conducted in hypnosis, they characteristically report in the latter a peculiar capacity, if not
compulsion, to focus on a current problem with an intensity
and clarity which they normally do not feel. One patient tried
to describe the difference by saying that normally in therapy
she felt she was driving down a rough dirt road which made
many twists, turns, and detours, but that in hypnosis it was as
though she were traveling on a broad, smooth highway that
made "direct connections."

We presume that the meaning of such a report must be the
subjective experience of a certain loss of established layers
of defense and adaptation in their complex interplay with
unconscious impulses. To be sure, this relative simplification
and loss of subtlety has many implications, both positive and
negative, for the progress of a therapeutic process. We are not
concerned here, however, with that problem. We include this
datum only as further documentation of an observable change
in the functioning of the ego. In the relative loss of self-
consciousness, as in the subjective sense of being on a single
track, we see changes not only in "ego-functioning" in the
most general sense; we see also something which in an important way has to do with the subject's feelings toward the
hypnotist. We include it in this section because it is so often
reported by the subject as a change in self-awareness without
reference to the unconscious material we know must be there.

CHANGES IN THE QUALITY OF AFFECT RELEASED

The second phenomenon we have chosen for this presentation of hypnosis as "a state of altered ego-functioning" is the
appearance of vivid and intense outbursts of feeling, occurring, as we have seen, frequently during the process of induction, and sporadically thereafter. The standard literature is
replete with examples of this phenomenon during hypnosis,[7]

[7] See in this connection the interesting clinical work of Harold Rosen
(197).

and we have made reference to it at other places in this volume, most particularly in connection with the *alteration of defense mechanisms* during the course of psychotherapy where hypnosis is used. We regard such sudden releases of strong affect as one of several indications that defenses in hypnosis are indeed to some extent changed (in some instances definitely weakened), and that this alteration of defenses is in turn one of several signs that the hypnotic state is among other things a state of altered ego-functioning generally. The classic phenomenon of hypermnesia seems to be in part the result of this loosening of defenses, especially repression. Other indications that the organization of defenses (as part of the general regressive process of hypnosis) is weakened lie in the changes in the thought process and in the nature of available motility, the phenomena of which we will discuss subsequently in this section. Before going on to these, however, we include examples of the particular quality and strength of affect which we have seen released during hypnotic sessions. For instance:

A suave, well-poised physician, hospitalized for alcoholism by his relatives, had maintained a façade of impenetrable glibness and self-control throughout the general examination. In his first hypnotizability interview, when it appeared that a hypnotic state had been established, he was told he would have a "dream"—a dream which might seem to him meaningless. He adopted a supercilious attitude at first, which slowly turned into a "scientific curiosity about this process," and finally (as the hypnosis deepened) the patient's face became flushed, he began to breathe heavily, and suddenly burst forth with his dream. He began: "All of a sudden there is a monster . . . it's choking me . . . it has a great body and lots of legs, trying to crush me . . ." As he continued this description in the present tense, he developed a panic and began to flail his arms and breathlessly grappled with his imagined assailant until he finally fell to the floor and spontaneously emerged from the hypnotic state, looking a trifle dazed and sheepish.

Direct questioning and free association at this point indicated clearly that this explosion was related to this man's intense conflict over his underlying fear and passivity, normally well-defended against. More specifically, the violent feeling and the primitive image of the monster trying to crush him seemed to be an expression of his archaic, repressed terror of his mother as the incubus or succubus—described by Jones (124)—who is trying to dominate, and indeed to destroy him.

In this example, the flood of intense feeling occurred in the setting of a nightmarelike experience with images very like those in dreams. Outbursts of powerful affect do not always occur in the hypnotic state in this form. For example:

A young woman who came into therapy with "frozen feelings" said, during the hypnotic sessions, that she was ". . . overwhelmed with tenderest love for you [the therapist] . . . like nothing I ever felt before . . ." As she said this she burst into deep sobs and after a while added, ". . . and I feel somehow that you love me too." She reported that in her normal state, "I go about with my usual crust and feel nothing . . . I have to face reality then and know that you think of me with the same interest as you have toward any other patient . . . Sometimes I feel I would rather die in the hypnosis chair than wake up and face the real, adult world . . ."

Interestingly enough, as her therapy progressed, she became increasingly ambivalent toward hypnosis[8] and said on one occasion: "I don't want to go to sleep because I want to *really* feel all these things [discussing both her tender and her angry feelings toward the therapist] when I'm awake the same as I do when I'm asleep . . . I mean I do want to go to sleep but I won't permit it . . . Used to be I had to have the curtain of hypnosis to hide behind . . . protected . . . not ashamed of my feelings . . . Hypnosis has helped me find out a lot of things I wouldn't have found out otherwise, I'm sure . . . but I don't want to have that desire to go to sleep all the time . . . I want to enjoy [without hypnosis] bursting forth with my feelings . . ." She added that there is something

[8] In this case, as one of our research variations we alternated periods in the normal state with hypnotic sessions.

"deceitful" or "cheating" in restricting her strong feelings to the hypnotic state.

There is a curious paradox in the fact that the very thing which at first made it possible for her to experience intense affect, namely, the hypnotic state, now issued simultaneously in a feeling of "spuriousness" and "unreality." It is as though the altered functioning of both ego and superego,[9] with the concomitant infantile bond with the therapist, makes her strong feelings suspect and ". . . not really mine."[10]

There is a great variety in the form and range in which the affect level is heightened in the hypnotic state. In those instances where the difference between the normally experienced feeling and that in hypnosis is not so great as in these examples, but where the patient in hypnosis feels simply "more involved" or "much clearer about my feelings," he does not in our experience have consciously the sense of "deceit" or "hiding behind hypnosis," as did the young woman we described.

As we indicated earlier, the generally greater affect availability in hypnosis came to our attention early in our work because of its frequent and dramatic appearance during non-therapy induction sessions, and its high frequency in the hypnotic state in the various forms we have mentioned. We have several times commented on the fact that we observed the heightened emotional level in the hypnotic state *in a psychotherapeutic context*; it will be evident in Chapter 11 that the affect availability in a psychotherapy *which uses hypnosis* is generally greater than in one which does not. We mean by this to underscore the fact that the psychothera-

[9] See discussion of "free will" (pp. 35-43).
[10] We will discuss the general therapeutic implications of all this in Chapter 11. In line, however, with our effort throughout this volume to establish continuities with nonhypnotic phenomena, it was of interest to us to hear from Dr. Hanna Fenichel (personal communication, 1952) that she has seen similar though less extreme instances where patients have used the psychoanalytic situation as a screen, patients who in their everyday life had adopted a defensive need to "hang onto reality" as their only way of living.

peutic context alone does not seem to account for the affective outburst. We believe, rather, that it becomes manifest as an expression of the altered ego-functioning in the established state when the hypnotist, acting as therapist, behaves in a manner which calls it forth. It is as if a strong potentiality for violent feeling is present in the established state, but requires a trigger to set it off. When the hypnotic subject is participating in an experiment (e.g., our physiological studies), where the release of strong affect would be irrelevant to the intent of the hypnotist, these explosions do not occur. It has been repeatedly demonstrated in the literature, however, that even in nontherapeutic contexts when the hypnotist permits or, better, encourages the release of strong feeling in the hypnotic state, outbursts of the kind we have described certainly do occur (34).

## CHANGES IN MOTILITY

This area of our observations of the changed functioning of the ego in hypnosis is even descriptively, let alone theoretically, more difficult to set down than the others; this is partly because of the great variety of its overt manifestations, and partly because of the complex and little-understood character of the relationships between unconscious wishes and available motility.

Let us begin with stating the range and varieties of phenomena we have observed. At one extreme lie the classical phenomena of the induction process, described in Chapter 1: the apparent abdication on direct suggestion of the *control* of all normally voluntary, usually automatic, bodily movements (e.g., opening and closing the eyes, raising and lowering the extremities, clasping and unclasping hands, etc.). This control, moreover, for all practical purposes is gradually handed over to the hypnotist during induction. Thus, on the one hand, when he says, "Now you *can* open your eyes, move your arm, lower your leg," the motor act in question is carried out. If, on the other hand, he decides to bring within his orbit of control the big toe on the left foot which has, up to this point, been wiggling freely—the toe muscles will contract in response to his suggestion and now become paralyzed. These manipulations of the control of the motor apparatus are of course standard procedures to determine whether or not a given individual is going into hypnosis.

What seems—on the surface at least—to be the other extreme of this range of phenomena is the appearance during the hypnotic state of the *motor expression* of normally unconscious impulses which occur in the absence of any direct suggestion from the hypnotist. For example:

A patient, a married woman, discussing the pros and cons of divorce in the hypnotic state, suddenly seized her wedding ring and flung it across the room.

Or again:

A woman in intense conflict regarding a masochistic attachment to an overbountiful lover (and who consciously felt mainly guilt and gratitude toward him) sat up during a psychotherapy session in the course of which hypnosis was used, stripped her fingers systematically of several expensive rings he had given her, and threw them into a corner. She then sat back, discovered her wrist watch, also a gift from her lover, took it off and sent it after the rings.

The following is a more extreme example which illustrates excellently the regressive character of the hypnotic state, with its attendant archaic symbolism, as well as the direct motor expression of infantile impulses. This material has been selected from the original research summaries[11] of the treatment of a young *nonpsychotic* woman, wrestling in her ther-

---

[11] These summaries were written by the therapist from verbatim recordings long before we had any systematic notion of the changes in motility in the hypnotic state. The motor outbursts were triggered by a variation in the hypnotist's instructions: the patient was told that on this occasion as she went into a deep hypnotic state her arms would feel "lighter" instead of "heavier" as they usually did.

apy with the problems of her relationship to a mother whom she saw as prudish and inhibiting:

Suddenly she remarked that her hand was becoming very light . . . Now her right arm began to circle round and round. When I asked her what it meant she wasn't sure. Her right arm was extended in what appeared to be a pleading gesture. She thought maybe she was pleading with herself to give in to her own feelings. Now she commenced to bend back her fingers at right angles to the palm of her hand and said, "This is to keep me from doing something . . ." After a long series of struggles of this kind . . . her right hand went between her legs and she began to masturbate . . . "Now I am thinking about my left thumb. It seems cold and all by itself . . . Then it feels extremely hot . . . it has become dark red and is larger than the rest of the fingers . . ." At this point she popped her left thumb into her mouth and began to suck it violently, her right hand remaining inactive in her vagina . . . Later she commented that when she picked up her skirt to masturbate, *she felt as if someone else had actually lifted it.*[12]

On the following day, the patient reported some consternation over the fact that the impulse to put her thumb into her mouth had carried over somewhat beyond the hypnotic session,[13] but that smoking and chewing gum had helped curb it somewhat. Hypnosis was again induced with the following results:

She immediately announced that the thumb on her right hand (not the one she had been sucking) tingled. . . Now her left hand and arm began to move but *away* from her body not toward her mouth. This was replaced by both hands being crossed on her chest. She told me that was the way her mother looked in her coffin. . . Now an exceedingly dramatic struggle took place between her right and left arms, as though the right arm were actually fighting with the left. Her left fist tightened until the

[12] See discussion of "free will" and the abdication of personal responsibility (pp.35-43).
[13] This may well be an instance where a "regression in the service of the ego" threatens to become a regression proper.

knuckles were white and she beat her right arm with great fury. At first she could not tell me what this was all about but after a bit suddenly exclaimed: "I am doing this because I masturbate with my right hand." However, she wanted me to see that she was holding her left hand now away from her mouth and said her mother should never have made her stop sucking her thumb. Suddenly now her right hand took hold of her left wrist and began to twist it back in a ruthless fashion as though she were trying to break it. . . She said that "now the right hand is trying to prevent the left thumb from going to my mouth." [This is a pallid account of a surrealist performance.] Toward the end of this session, she said that if she tried to get her hands under her skirt, I must bring her out of hypnosis lest she injure herself internally. After a little while, the dramatic motor struggle abated . . . she quietly extended the index and middle finger of her left hand, remarking, "V for victory." Now she curled up in the chair, her knees almost touching her chin, and gently began sucking her left thumb. She felt happy now, her thumb glowing and "I don't have to fight any more." This thumb-sucking quite clearly represented to her her victory over her mother's prohibitions.

We say that such examples are at the other end of the continuum only on the surface, because we can presume that although the hypnotist has not explicitly suggested the content of any of these behaviors, he has throughout given permission, indeed encouragement, to the "letting go" of those ego functions which normally control, defend against, and modulate such impulses. In this sense, he controls the *expression* of movement quite as much as he does its *inhibition* (as in the suggestions for motor paralysis). This statement leaves unanswered, of course, the problem of why the combination of loosened moorings in reality with explicit and/or implicit encouragement from the hypnotist to "take the lid off" issues sometimes in outbursts of affect, other times in motor explosions, on other occasions, as we shall see, in symbolic visual images, and sometimes in a dramatic combination of all of the phenomena discussed in this section.

A subsidiary, though theoretically important, problem is raised by our observations of instances where a person carries out movements during hypnosis *without any awareness that he is moving*. For instance:

A married woman, in obvious conflict about her ambivalence toward her husband, children, and parents, fantasied that she was looking into a grave. As the fantasy became more vivid, more concrete, and more directly visual, she *actually* began to sit forward in her seat and to crane her neck as though she were trying to look into the open grave without falling into it herself. Her eyes remained closed during all of this, and direct questioning revealed that she had no awareness of any bodily movement.

In this example, the general feeling conveyed to the observers was very similar to that of a sleepwalker—an important actual difference being that our patient is protected, as it were, by the presence of an outside source of control, the hypnotist, while the sleepwalker is on his own. This fact brings us back to the difficult theoretical issues briefly alluded to at the beginning of this discussion of the changes in motility during hypnosis.

We know that, in the normal individual, unconscious wishes are constantly trying to "force their way by way of the preconscious system to consciousness and to obtain control of the power of movement" (76, p. 567); the powerful counterforces relax only at night and permit some of these impulses entrance into consciousness, but even then this freedom is limited by the fact that the impulses are heavily disguised and the "gate to motility" is closed. Freud, speaking of the action of unconscious wishes, says:

No matter what impulses from the normally inhibited Ucs. may prance upon the stage, we need feel no concern; they remain harmless, since they are unable to set in motion the motor apparatus by which alone they might modify the external world [76, p. 568].

He points out, moreover, that in two conditions this "safe" relationship of unconscious wish and available motility does not exist: in psychoses and in somnambulism (76, 84). He says psychosis may occur under two conditions: when there is a "pathological enfeeblement of the critical censorship" or a "pathological reinforcement of the unconscious excitations," either of which may bring about a state in which "forbidden" unconscious impulses and potential motor expression exist simultaneously. He feels that we do not know what conditions create the phenomenon of somnambulism, and wonders why it does not occur more frequently. No systematic answer has been suggested by subsequent research, and the problem stands substantially as challenging as it was when Freud called attention to it.

In the hypnotic state, while the "gate to motility," as we have seen, is not actually closed, forbidden impulses are permitted entrance into consciousness presumably because the subject or patient believes—whether rightly or wrongly—that their expression will be limited by the hypnotist; the subject thus feels essentially "safe" from setting the motor apparatus going in a direction which might be dangerous. It is as if the hypnotist here is the functional equivalent of the barrier to motility which is set up by the normal sleep mechanism. The latter, of course, does in fact "close the gates to motility" via a wholesale withdrawal of the body cathexis of the sleeping dreamer.

## CHANGES IN THE THOUGHT PROCESS

The example of the married woman hallucinating an open grave might well serve as illustrative material for this section of our observations on the frequent (though again by no means invariable) alterations which occur in the modes of thought of the hypnotized person. The standard literature on hypnosis is, again, rich in detailed clinical accounts of this kind.[14]

In all of this material we see a significant departure from

[14] See Wolberg (229). Also, in Chapter 11 of the present volume, on the use of hypnosis in psychotherapy, there are several additional illustrations.

normal, *waking* modes of thought: instead of a relatively stable, logical kind of thought—which for the most part employs words as its material—we see the emergence of fluid, archaic forms which often employ visual images and symbols as material, forms which do not follow the ordinary rules of logic, and which moreover are not bound to realistic limitations of time and space. Obviously this distinction between the logical or "secondary-process," and the "prelogical" or "primary-process" kinds of thinking corresponds roughly to the usual distinctions between normal waking thought and that variety which is operative in sleep in the form of dreaming. Although we do not propose here to expand the psychological similarities and differences between hypnosis and sleep, there can be little question that there is an important overlap between the two in regard to the alteration in thought process,[15] this alteration being, we presume, in both instances an outcome, in different forms, of the regressive changes in ego function.

Our observations confirm the investigations of Kubie and Margolin (143, 144), who have shown that a deep hypnosis is not prerequisite to the production of this fluctuating change. They have reported strikingly similar material issuing from their work on the hypnagogic reverie. In their work, such "primary-process" production emerges spontaneously *without* any direct suggestion of "dreams," "visions," or anything else. The following is a good example from our own records of the spontaneous emergence of such material:

A young unmarried woman who had devoted most of her life to the care of a sick mother was, during the course of a psychoanalytic therapy using hypnosis, deeply involved in an effort to resolve her intensely ambivalent relationship to her mother, now dead for several years. Understandably, she held her mother largely responsible for her own present spinsterhood and loneliness. This feeling, early in the therapy, was quite unconscious.

[15] See also Chapter 6.

This patient was a fairly good, though not an excellent, subject. During one of the hypnotic sessions, as she continued to struggle with her conflict about her feelings toward her mother, she spontaneously *saw* herself descending into an open grave, and proceeded to describe in the present tense her strenuous efforts to pull off her mother's wedding ring. This "vision" was accompanied by an outburst of feeling such as we have described in the previous section, with a wild and unmodulated quality ordinarily restricted to nightmares and psychoses. As her efforts to pull the ring off did not avail, she despairingly gave up the effort and now saw herself trying to pull her own body out of the mother's grave.

All of this symbolic, dreamlike material was orally reported, with the patient remaining motionless. We mention this because it contrasts sharply with the form of expression of motility in hypnosis previously described.

Further indication of the altered thought processes in the hypnotic state lies in all of the well-known hypnotic phenomena producible by direct suggestion: negative and positive hallucinations, hypermnesia, experimentally created delusions, quasi dreams, and the like. One of the most dramatic phenomena which in a highly complex way seems to reflect, among other things, a change in the quality of thought is the occurrence of a spontaneous regression.[16]

## VARIABILITY OF CHANGES

We have discussed under four major headings alterations of ego-functioning which can occur in hypnosis—self-awareness, affect, motility, and modes of thinking. We want to underscore the fact that one or another of these cuts across the others and that the interweaving complexities of all of these functions are such that, in fact, mutually exclusive categories are probably nonexistent.

[16] We do not use the word "regression" here in the restricted theoretical sense, but rather in the technical sense in which it is used in the standard literature on hypnosis, i.e., a reliving of past (often partially or totally repressed) events, usually reported by the subject in the present tense. One of us has reported such an instance in detail elsewhere (100).

In closing this summary of those data we have subsumed under "hypnosis as a state of altered ego-functioning," we want to emphasize the extreme variability and fluidity of all of the described phenomena, both from subject to subject and within the same person. A given subject may show with clarity only one of the changes of ego function we have discussed; another may illustrate several; a third may exhibit the entire range of regressive ego function. These changes, moreover, may be partial and fleeting from moment to moment within the same individual: he may report spontaneously that he feels as if he is "floating, dreamy, and far away," and within a few minutes announce that all of these feelings have left him so completely that he can detect no significant difference from his normal-state feelings or thoughts. We have to regard *the very fact of this fluidity* as an additional indication of a generally changed state of the ego: such a range and fluctuation of subjective experience is not characteristic for a normal waking ego.

### Hypnosis as "Transference"

In introducing the problems of the "nature of the hypnotic state," we stated that for many years we had considered our observations on the psychology of the relationship between hypnotist and subject as being separable from the phenomena just described under "hypnosis as a state of altered ego-functioning." Although we now believe that in the preparation of this book we have succeeded in establishing at least a bridge between these two bodies of data, we have decided to reserve the discussion of this "bridge" for the conclusion of this chapter, and to present first the kinds of data we have marshaled under the oversimple heading, "hypnosis as transference."

In this connection we must mention again our view that hypnosis is at least in part a dovetailing of the unconscious fantasies of the two people involved, and that strictly speaking one should not speak of "the hypnotic state" but rather of "the hypnotic relationship." This hypothesis obviously necessitates some discussion of both contributors to the relationship. For this reason we include here data on the hypnotist as well as the subject.

For the purpose of convenience in data presentation, we have arbitrarily divided our material into seven parts. We do not intend to imply that these divisions represent dynamically distinct kinds of data, but only a practical separation with regard to the source of our material:

(1) Observations of shifts in hypnotizability and in the depth of hypnosis; (2) the occurrence of spontaneous hypnotic states; (3) reports by hypnotic subjects of their experience of the process of hypnosis; (4) data on the nature of the hypnotic subject; (5) the intensive analysis of the hypnotic relationship in long-term psychoanalytic therapy where hypnosis was used as an adjuvant; (6) data on the nature of the hypnotist; (7) the interplay of subject and hypnotist.

## OBSERVATIONS OF SHIFTS IN HYPNOTIZABILITY AND IN THE DEPTH OF HYPNOSIS

We first began to take serious note of spontaneous changes in hypnotizability when we were considering the hypothesis that individual hypnotizability rests on some undefined physiological basis, perhaps of a constitutional nature. In the context of such a hypothesis, observations which showed that a given person's hypnotizability could change in relation to a discernibly meaningful change in his *psychological* situation became, if not conclusive evidence against a physiological hypothesis, at least significant data. Such instances were not our run-of-the-mill experience. As a matter of fact, we were rather surprised by the relative consistency of hypnotizability (or lack of it) which most subjects showed. Usually, if a person did not respond well in a group screening process, he was also a poor subject when tested individually. Similarly, if one of us failed to hypnotize a given subject, the other did too. The same usually held for our good subjects. During the course of our work, we encountered no more than a dozen occasions where there was a significant change in hypnotizability; thus we tried to pursue these shifts wherever we could, in the effort to see what was "the difference that was making the difference." One of the most striking instances of such a change was in a patient hospitalized at a veterans' facility:

This man, suffering from an acute "traumatic war neurosis," commented in the course of a routine history that he had been an excellent hypnotic subject in high school where the principal of the school, whose hobby was hypnosis, had frequently used him for demonstration purposes. The first several attempts we made to hypnotize this man met with no success whatever. He was as unresponsive as any poor subject we had ever encountered. In view of his history, however, we continued to try. After several further efforts, he began to show a few minimal signs of being hypnotizable, but would break off each time he seemed to be developing a hypnotic state, in an outburst of acute anxiety which he reported as "unbearable." Now the therapist decided to abandon temporarily the direct effort to improve the man's hypnotizability and began, instead, to attempt to deal therapeutically with his anxiety. Using the minimal signs of hypnosis, together with his increasingly good relationship to the therapist, several "abreactive" sessions of his war experience were brought about during which the patient recounted with a good deal of feeling the worst of the traumatic episodes. It was of special interest that although these sessions did not at this time reduce the acute symptoms which had brought him to the hospital, he became in very short order an excellent hypnotic subject, as he once had been.

Another instance of change occurred in a group hypnotizability session being conducted by a resident who, under the supervision of one of us, was learning the technique of hypnosis:

One of the members of the group who had responded not at all spontaneously commented that had he been able to "let go," he would have gone into hypnosis. In spite of the fact that our general experience had shown, curiously enough, that relative inexperience in a hypnotist usually made no striking difference in results, the supervisor now decided to try the entire group again, using a far more forceful approach than had the resident, in order to see what would happen to this subject. This time, the subject in question responded very well, showing all the classical signs of a deep hypnotic state. The effort to pursue this phenomenon systematically in individual follow-up was blocked by his adamant refusal to participate further in *any* hypnotizability studies.

This unusual episode was especially valuable in highlighting the delicate balance of forces which must have existed in this person initially, a balance so even that he successfully resisted the efforts of the inexperienced hypnotist—whose prestige, incidentally, was no doubt far less than that of the supervisor. That he should spontaneously invite—by implication—further efforts to hypnotize him, "give in," and then totally reject them, seems to us further testimony to what must have been an active conflict, which by its nature we were prevented from pursuing. Despite the fact that we were thus unable to learn the content of this conflict, it was still another small piece of evidence to question the hypothesis that hypnotizability is a "given" which cannot radically change with a change in the total psychological situation.

We come now to those data we have collected on spontaneous smaller shifts in the depth of hypnosis occurring within the same psychotherapeutic session in a given individual. We have studied these data in painstaking detail and have reported them elsewhere (28). A summary will suffice here.

At first we paid scant attention to these depth fluctuations, taking them for granted as inherent aspects of the hypnotic state. Thus, if a patient in the midst of a discussion would report, "I'm going into a lighter hypnosis," or "I'm coming out of hypnosis," we would simply try to help him to restore the previous level of hypnosis. We regarded a change in the opposite direction—"I'm going deeper into hypnosis"—simply as an aid to our therapeutic researches.

It was only when our research interest began to focus on the problem of the nature of hypnosis, and in particular on its relationship to, broadly speaking, "transference" problems, that we began to watch closely the occurrence of these fluctuations and to try to discern their meaning.

We should like to summarize the three main steps in our thinking about these data:

At first we proceeded on the assumption, generally accepted in the standard psychoanalytic theory of hypnosis, that the hypnotic state is no more than a special form of transference relationship in which infantile, passive (masochistic) wishes are gratified. Accordingly, we expected spontaneous changes in depth to accompany fluctuations in the transference relationship, particularly those fluctuations involving the ebb and flow of infantile receptive needs. Continued observation soon showed us that this hypothesis had only partial validity.

The second step in our thinking issued directly from the fact that we observed many reports of a change in the depth of hypnosis when the surrounding material contained an *increase in hostility* toward the therapist. For example, the patient might go into, and report, a deeper hypnosis in order not merely to entrench himself further in a position of infantile libidinal gratification, but essentially to deny his hostility by exaggerating his passive submission. In retrospect we saw that this second step in our thinking marked the beginning of our emphasis on the *defense* in the hypnotic relationship, in addition to its libidinal aspects. However, at that time we were unable to synthesize into a unified hypothesis the observation that changes in depth seemed to occur sometimes in a context of an increased infantile need and sometimes in a setting of covert hostility.

As a result of a change in our technique of studying these data (a change described in detail in our published report), we emerged with our third hypothesis which brings together the first two: *We can expect a spontaneous change in the depth of hypnosis when there is evidence—accompanied by indices of conflict and anxiety—that an existing impulse-defense balance is being threatened.* This threat to the existing balance may occur either as the result of an upsurge of a passive need or as the result of a hostile wish against which the ego is insufficiently defended. The patient in hypnosis attempts to deal with the resultant anxiety by a change in the depth of hypnosis. This shift may thus be an attempt either to gratify the impulse or to defend against it. Usually it is both. We do not know as yet what determines the *direction* of the change, although we have speculated a great deal about it. We have observed the same patient deal with anxiety sometimes by going deeper and at other times by disrupting the hypnosis entirely.

It is as if the established hypnotic relationship is itself a compromise formation like a dream or a symptom; and the main function of a spontaneous change in depth is that it is one of a number of possible ways of attempting to deal with the anxiety which is released by a temporary breakdown in the existing equilibrium. If, in a given sample of material, there is evidence that a forbidden impulse *is* being adequately defended against by one or more of the usual mechanisms of defense, we do not expect a change in the depth of hypnosis. It is economically unnecessary. If, on the other hand, there are indications that an intense need *or* a hostile wish is breaking through, we expect a change in depth as a spontaneous effort to re-establish an equilibrium, an equilibrium which will provide a maximum of gratification and a minimum of anxiety. Obviously, this hypothesis takes it for granted that a person's defensive operations are by no means obliterated in the hypnotic state.

We gradually began to define the indices of a threatening breakdown of an impulse-defense balance, and conversely the indices of ego-functioning sufficient to obviate a change in depth. For example: shifts in topic, blocks in speech, "pressured" speech, outbursts of affect, etc., are some of the more obvious indications of conflict in the context of which a change in the depth of hypnosis may be expected. Conversely, evidences of strong defensive operations (displacement, denial, reaction formations, etc.) provide a context in which no change is expected. On a "formal" level, the existence in the material of metaphor, humor, self-reflectiveness, continuity, etc., speak against a change in depth; when a patient reports a change, these qualities are relatively lacking. We have presented detailed case illustrations for this third hypothesis in our previously mentioned study (28).

The importance of these data on spontaneous fluctuations in depth of hypnosis lies in the fact that they provide a portion of the bridge between "hypnosis as a state of altered ego-functioning" and "hypnosis as transference." We do not mean to imply that this material "proves" anything conclusively; but taken together with the other data we are presenting, there is an increasing accumulation of evidence that *not only does the hypnotic state alter ego-functioning, but also, conversely, changes in the transference—more specifically in the impulse-defense balance—alter the depth of hypnosis.*[17]

## The Occurrence of Spontaneous Hypnotic States

Another kind of phenomenon we came to subsume under "a transference theory of hypnosis" was the *spontaneous* occurrence of hypnotic states, sometimes within the therapy session and sometimes away from it. On these occasions the patient would suddenly give every appearance of being in hypnosis and/or report all of the subjective sensations usually accompanying his own characteristic hypnotic state—all of

---

[17] Freud's view of transference in 1912 was ". . . the state of readiness in which the *libido* [italics ours] that has remained accumulated about the infantile imagos exists . . ." (79, p. 318). We have come to take it for granted not only that *aggressive* drives are also involved in "transferences," but a complex configuration of *defensive* operations as well.

this either in the absence of any direct suggestion from the therapist or, on occasion, in direct opposition to his stated wish. Again such data, standing alone, are not conclusive, but they are certainly suggestive when they occur in a context which on scrutiny appears to be psychologically meaningful in the patient's relationship to the therapist. We were not, on all such occasions, able to discern the meaning of the emergence of the spontaneous hypnotic state. We will present a small sampling of those numerous episodes where we were able to make sense of the incident. It is our impression that part of the meaning of such a spontaneous hypnosis usually derived in some measure from the *immediate* drives and defensive maneuvers of the patient, in relation to the therapist. For example:

A highly intelligent and sophisticated attorney presented himself to the Outpatient Department of the Menninger Clinic for treatment of various psychosomatic symptoms. For administrative reasons he could not be accepted for therapy at that time, but he was told that if he were willing to participate for a period of ten days in the hypnosis research project, we could evaluate his total situation at the same time and then put him on a waiting list for treatment. He agreed to do this, and, although he was not in the standard sense a good hypnotic subject, his responses both in and out of the therapist's office were most striking. During the hypnotic sessions, his productivity was phenomenal; the content was of such a nature that if we had not known him as a functioning and responsible lawyer in his normal state, we would certainly have thought him psychotic. Even more arresting were his reports of his experiences outside the office when he was alone, with no professional duties at hand. He would lie down and find himself in a spontaneous hypnotic state during which he had vivid hallucinatory experiences and would find himself engaged in automatic writing. The content both of the hallucinations and of the automatic writing was highly relevant to his underlying conflicts, and extremely helpful to us in formulating a picture of him. About a year later, when he was accepted for long-term treatment, he began again just where he had left off: although no effort was made to hypnotize him, he would go into spontaneous hypnotic states during his therapy sessions and at home. For a variety of reasons, the decision was made to treat this man with standard psychoanalytic technique; he was informed of this decision. The analyst paid little attention now to the *content* of his strange hypnotic experiences and dealt with these experiences in the context of this man's general character trait of needing to please and to be compliant. The patient began to express some of the resentment he had felt in the first place at being "used" as a research case, resentment never mentioned during his initial ten-day evaluation. Very rapidly, as this analysis proceeded, the spontaneous hypnotic states decreased and soon vanished entirely. The treatment continued in standard analytic fashion, with the usual ups and downs of any analysis.

The significance of this entire sequence seemed unmistakable: as long as the patient felt his spontaneous hypnoses (plus their dramatic content) were in the immediate service of pleasing and exciting the intellectual interest of the therapist, he produced them. When it became clear that they were not needed for this purpose, he could dispense with them. Indeed, it could be argued that his *giving up* of these experiences represented another level of the characterological compliance of this patient: "If you want them, I'll deliver them; if you don't, I won't."

Another instance of the appearance of spontaneous hypnosis is taken from the records of a patient whose case we have reported at length elsewhere (30):

The patient was a kindergarten teacher in her late thirties who came for the treatment of acute phobic symptoms. Up until her illness, her essential role in life had been that of a strong (even tyrannical) mother. The eldest of seventeen children, she had, upon her mother's death, dealt with her own needs to be taken care of by denying them and ministering instead to her numerous siblings. Her choice of profession extended her role of the maternal "rock of Gibraltar" to her pupils. The patient managed a fairly comfortable though narrow existence until a mismated man twenty-five years her senior took her on first as a protégée, later as a mistress.

We have described in detail in our published report the systematic breakdown in this relationship of her well-established reaction formations against her dependent needs, and the consequent onset of her illness. Most important for the present discussion was her childlike helplessness and her acute anxiety whenever there was no "grownup" with her. The Staff Conference decided that she was far too disorganized at this point to commence with expressive psychotherapy and that, at least for a time, an attempt should be made to meet her need for complete dependence rather than to try to give her insight into its nature: in short, to let her be the "little girl" she had never been. She was accepted as a research case and, at first, hypnosis was used as an auxiliary in implementing the treatment plan.

During this first phase of her treatment it soon became clear that she was trying to establish with the therapist the same kind of tyrannically dependent relationship she had had with her lover. There can be little question that the regressive character of the hypnotic relationship temporarily encouraged this. After a time, when she had improved considerably, the decision was made to withdraw the hypnotic sessions gradually and to attempt to help her rebuild defenses against her need to be a helpless child.

Her reaction to this change in therapeutic strategy demonstrated dramatically her wish to maintain herself overtly as a dependent little girl (and the therapist as the all-powerful, all-giving parent): *she would go into spontaneous hypnotic states in spite of the explicit statement from the therapist that she should talk now in her normal state*; during these she would whimper like a child and sometimes sob piteously. That she regarded these spontaneous hypnoses as (among other things) a hostile demand was clearly shown by her expressions of fear and guilt whenever she brought one about.

Although it is difficult to establish unequivocally the nature of the surrounding context of such a spontaneous hypnosis, it appears to us after a detailed study of the verbatim records that she would develop a hypnotic state whenever she felt threatened by an upsurge of need or of conflict-laden anger. Often, for example, when it appeared that she was about to become aware of her intense hostility toward her lover, or toward the therapist, she would report, "I am dropping off now." This kind of event was in marked contrast to her spontaneous *disruption* of hypnosis when she wanted to express an angry feeling about which she did not feel guilty: for example, her rage at a nurse who had brought her a cold breakfast egg. In one such instance she said, "I want to feel sore at that bitch while I'm myself and wide awake."[18]

Although such spontaneous hypnotic states were not an everyday occurrence during the course of our research, they happened with sufficient frequency that we began to amass them as part of that body of data we came to label "hypnosis as transference." Although the difficulties of establishing clearly the psychological significance of each such instance— even from verbatim records—are mammoth, it is our distinct impression that the spontaneous hypnotic state, like the change in depth of hypnosis, occurs when there is a threat to an existing impulse-defense balance. There is some evidence that the emergence of a spontaneous hypnotic state may sometimes serve as an immediate anodyne for the accompanying anxiety[19] via the concomitant alterations in ego-functioning (perhaps as alcohol or drugs do for some people). This function is at least theoretically separable from the other two functions of hypnosis, namely, as the vehicle for specific gratification and/or defense on the one hand, and on the other as a direct or fantasied appeal to the hypnotist to "take over" responsibility.

[18] Compare this with the similar statement from the young woman who commented that she sometimes wanted to "enjoy bursting forth" with her "real" feelings *without* hypnosis (p. 50).

[19] One of the most striking instances of this occurred in the teacher just discussed, directly after her father's death. For several days her anxiety mounted until it reached panic proportions. When she felt she could no longer tolerate this, she found herself developing a spontaneous hypnotic state before she arrived for her therapy hour. She came in announcing, "I am drugged now and sleepy—and I feel a little better." As long as she could maintain her spontaneous hypnosis, her acute anxiety, guilt, and grief were muted.

## Reports by Hypnotic Subjects of Their Experience of the Process of Hypnosis

*Hypnosis and "hysterical" mechanisms.* Efforts in one form or another to link hysteria and hypnosis are an old story, the most extreme of these being the conclusion that hypnosis is an "artificial hysteria" (40). Although there have been many data brought forth which suggest the relationship is not a simple one, the general impression has persisted that on some level there are overlaps which are significant. Our own experience bears this out. Our most important data of this kind have come from the scrutiny of our case records of patients, some diagnosed as "hysterics," others including "hysterical mechanisms" as an incidental postscript to a different diagnosis.

In this connection, Schilder (206) says the following:

The differentiation [of hypnosis] from hysteria, and from the hysterical special state, is not difficult either. In the hysterical special state, the patient transforms his fantasies into reality, and it is his wishes that are fulfilled; in hypnosis, the subject's relationship to the hypnotist dominates the picture. Otherwise, there are many common characteristics. In hypnosis too, infantile erotic attitudes are revived. The hypnotist becomes the archetype of the father; he both arouses love and demands unquestioning submission—precisely the father's attitude toward the child. If hysteria is a breakthrough of infantile erotic attitudes, then the boundary-line between hysteria and hypnosis cannot be sharp; indeed, at times we see hypnotic somnambulism change into a hysterical twilight state. . . The transition is entirely fluid from normal hypnotic somnambulism . . . to pathological somnambulism. . . [pp. 258-259].

Although this statement by Schilder is somewhat oversimplified, in our opinion, our experience suggests that, broadly speaking, he is right. We offer some examples:

A young married woman in her early thirties came for the treatment of "spells" in which she appeared to be drugged or in a stupor and felt herself to be a kind of automaton. In these "spells," she initiated no spontaneous action, but would obediently do as she was told. Normally, she was an active, intelligent person who held a responsible position as an executive secretary in a law firm. She commented that during her "spells" she had the curious feeling of being a "cheat." On the one hand she felt that she could not help her bizarre behavior, and on the other hand she wondered whether she had really tried hard enough to "break out of the spell." *Without any stimulation from the hypnotist-therapist* she volunteered the fact that "I have precisely the same feeling of being a cheat in hypnosis here." She found it extremely difficult to explain what she meant, saying, "It is as if there are two wills working against each other in both cases. When you asked me to try to unclasp my hands in hypnosis, I tried until the beads of sweat stood out on my forehead . . . and still I couldn't pull them apart. Yet later I wondered if I had really tried hard enough." She felt certain that she was not "actually pretending" any more than she was pretending in her "spells," and yet she could not escape the feeling that "somewhere, somehow" there was some pretense involved. She spontaneously added that during her episodes of acute hysterical behavior, her predominant feeling was, "I just don't care," and that this, too, seemed strikingly similar to her feelings in hypnosis.

The kind of subjective feeling we have just described was by no means an isolated instance. In at least a half dozen cases, patients reported, in various forms, striking subjective commonalities between spontaneous hysterical episodes and/or symptoms, and hypnosis. Frequently, though not invariably, the sense of pretense accompanied these descriptions. In one case, it was only in retrospect that the subject reported a "feeling of doubt about the genuineness of my hypnotic feelings." At the same time, she reminded herself of the "things I felt and did in hypnosis . . . and I am certain I could not possibly have done all that in my normal condition."[20]

[20] This was the patient who indulged in various infantile behaviors during several hypnotic sessions, ranging from thumb-sucking to open masturbation (see pp. 53-55).

It appears to us that there exists a broad continuum, with numerous gradations, between pretense and unconscious dramatization in both hysterical mechanisms and hypnosis. Where repression is especially severe, the conscious experience of "cheating" or "faking" does not occur.

A particularly striking example where symptom and conscious "role-taking"[21] shaded into each other is shown in the following:

A young woman came with the complaint that frequently, without warning, she would have what she called "seizures" during which she would lapse into baby talk, lose all contact with everyone around, and sit on the floor "like a little girl." Most often she would have amnesia for these episodes and be told later what had happened. On one occasion, after she had been in therapy for some time, the following events transpired: she tried to induce a young prize fighter to have intercourse with her; when he refused she flew into a rage and cut him with a piece of glass from her compact mirror which she had broken for this purpose. Immediately following this outburst, she had a transitory amnesia for her identity and began wandering about town looking for her home. While doing this, she was picked up by a policewoman who found her behavior peculiar. By this time, she was "coming to" and quickly regained her identity. *However, she now consciously feigned a loss of personal identity and let the police spend several hours questioning her in the presumed effort to restore her memory for who she was and where she lived.* She felt "peculiarly thrilled" by the drama of the whole situation and, with considerable inner reluctance, allowed the police to "bring back my memory." She indicated that fluid transitions of this kind were familiar to her in hypnosis.

The occurrence of transient, quasi-hysterical symptoms as *communications* to the hypnotist are also evidence for some overlap between the two states. An example:

A depressed woman in her middle forties spontaneously developed a glove anesthesia during a hypnotic session. The at-

---

[21] Sarbin has discussed the relationship of "role-taking" and hypnosis in an interesting paper (201).

tempt to uncover the meaning of this short-lived "symptom" brought back to her a dream (unclear whether an actual night dream or itself a product of hypnosis) in which she shyly extended her hand to the therapist. He refused to take it "because you recognize something bad in me." Her further associations suggested that the "something bad" was sexual in nature and that by rendering her hand senseless she attempted to deny the original wish.

Although we have no doubt that there are areas of overlap between the mechanisms of at least some of the hysterias and the hypnotic state, we cannot leave this brief section without emphasizing the fact that the precise mapping of this overlap and of its limits has by no means been accomplished. We have seen *bona fide* hysterics, with conversion symptoms, who, though hypnotizable, *produce no other spontaneous symptoms during the hypnotic state*—and perhaps most important of all: the majority of hysterics, like the majority of psychiatric patients, cannot be classified as good hypnotic subjects. Thus we must conclude that the tangled complexities of the relationship between hypnosis and hysteria remain to be unraveled.

*The fantasy of "magic power."* [22] One important aspect of the transference which emerges in hypnosis is the fantasy of the limitless power of the hypnotist. To be sure, this fantasy is frequently held consciously or unconsciously by patients in nonhypnotic psychotherapy. However, in hypnosis this, like many other regressive phenomena, is brought into high relief. A few examples:

A man in his middle forties, diagnosed as a borderline schizophrenic, came for the treatment of depression and acute anxiety. He had been in psychotherapeutic treatment of one kind or another for over twenty-two years, having been the patient during this long span of some of the most eminent psychoanalysts in this country. He complained of "endless rumination about myself" and thought that if he could only stop trying to deduce his

[22] This issue has been discussed by Wolberg (229).

unconscious motivations, he would be well. From the very first, he wanted to be hypnotized and expressed in a variety of ways his belief that only something which was "beyond the rational" could reach him. Although he was not a particularly good hypnotic subject, he was accepted on a research basis for trial interviews. During the first several sessions he was "given permission" to stop trying to reason out his motivations. The immediate result was nothing short of a miracle, albeit a temporary "miracle": he became relaxed, regained his lost appetite, was able to sleep, and felt he had been touched by a "magic wand." His comments made it quite clear that he regarded his dramatic remission as proof that he had been right in his plea for "nonrational therapy." However, as time went on and the somewhat negative goal of "not thinking about myself" began to wear thin, he tried to extend the therapist's "magic power" into the assumption of complete responsibility for his life. Since this latter task was obviously not an achievable one, he gradually took up again his torrential account of his "psychological mechanisms," thus blocking all further attempts to hypnotize him.

We have included this instance essentially because of the nakedness of this man's fantasy of the omnipotence of the hypnotist and because of the clearly observable relationship between this fantasy and the remarkable though short-lived remission which took place. It is likely that the "miracle cures" which occur at shrines and then remain permanently are to be understood in similar terms, but occur in a personality for whom the gains of illness have become less important than the gains of health.

The following account is taken from the record of the hysterical young woman mentioned earlier:

This patient, from the very beginning, has given every evidence of believing not only that the hypnotist is an all-powerful person, but also that the therapist [actually a woman] is a man. It appears to be her feeling that she has been trying through her creative writing to achieve just such power, but without success. Moreover, it now emerges that one of her deepest reasons for being willing to be treated under the auspices of the "hypnosis research project" has been that she would gradually acquire this power via hypnotic treatment. The reason, thus, for her growing anger is the fact that this has not come about.

Shortly after the above note, the patient began to frequent the dressing rooms of young prize fighters to pick out the one who seemed to her the most powerful, and to proceed then to attempt to seduce him. When her efforts met with success, she became elated and extremely expansive. When they failed, she frequently had an aggressive outburst, one of which we have described, followed by a hysterical "spell." The effort to make fools of the local police force in feigning amnesia when she no longer had any doubt of her identity was in all likelihood yet another attempt to capture the power which still eluded her.

Although it was not possible in all patients to observe the operation of the fantasy of the magic power of the hypnotist, we have seen sufficient evidence of its presence in a wide enough range of cases to presume that it is in all likelihood universally present.

DATA ON THE NATURE OF THE HYPNOTIC SUBJECT

Although some of the material in this section is of a somewhat different order from the rest of the data we have collected in connection with a "transference hypothesis" of hypnosis, we have decided to include it here because our later discussion of the hypnotic relationship rests in part on these data. During the course of our research, the question, "What kind of person is most likely to be a good hypnotic subject?"[23] was a major one we put to ourselves. The answer has been and remains, for the most part, elusive. Although we have

[23] To be sure, hypnotizability is not an all-or-none matter. People range in their response to the effort to hypnotize them from a slight feeling of lethargy to the subjective feeling of a total loss of volition, including such extreme phenomena as posthypnotic amnesia, the capacity to experience hallucinations, and all of the classic phenomena of a deep hypnosis. When we speak of a "good" subject, we refer to those people who respond with the most extreme phenomena on the hypnotic scale (48).

learned a few things about hypnotizability which we will report in this section, we still cannot predict with any reliability
who will be a good and who a poor hypnotic subject; moreover, we do not know of anyone who can, although many
maintain that this feat is possible. We, like all other investigators of hypnosis, have had our intuitive hunches in individual instances which have proved correct; we have had them
also proved incorrect. Our efforts to systematize these hunches
by detailed studies—to be described—of good and poor hypnotic subjects have issued in but meager findings. Nonetheless, it is of importance to report these studies, if only to
suggest some of the difficulties in pinning down the kind of
person capable of developing the particular transference attitudes which appear to play an important role in becoming
hypnotized.

So-called "suggestibility" tests as instruments for predicting
hypnotizability are highly successful in so far as they are
actually small attempts to hypnotize the subject. In short,
such tests lead to the less than remarkable finding that if you
can hypnotize a person, he is probably a good hypnotic subject.

Our first effort to narrow the problem of who makes a
good hypnotic subject came from the impression of one of
us who had earlier worked with large groups of college students that the percentage of good hypnotic subjects seemed
strikingly higher than in the patient population with whom
we were currently working. Accordingly, with the collaboration of Dr. Gerald Ehrenreich we pursued systematically the
hypothesis that "normal" people are on the whole better
hypnotic subjects than patients. A patient population was
compared with a "normal" population of secretaries, nurses,
and aides. Our initial impression was borne out: the employee group yielded a significantly higher percentage of good
subjects. Yet the difference between this employee group and
the patients did not appear quite so great as we had expected.
We wondered then whether employees of a psychiatric hospi-

tal (and we do not exclude here the professional staff) might not be a self-selected group in that the amount of conflict and inner disequilibrium in people attracted to working in a psychiatric institution is greater than in the average "normal" group.

This supposition clearly dictated the next step: the selection of a new "normal" group with which to compare the patients. Practical necessity limited this choice to a group of university students, still not a cross section of the average population, but apparently a close enough approximation; in this last group the percentage of top-notch hypnotic subjects was again strikingly higher than in the patient group and closer to the frequently quoted impression that the proportion of good hypnotic subjects in the general population is approximately one in five (unpublished ms.).

This series of studies then permitted us to say, no longer impressionistically, that psychiatric patients are on the whole poorer subjects than those judged by ordinary standards to be "normal." Having established that "normals" are on the whole better hypnotic subjects than patients, we now tried to narrow the issue still further. Dr. Ehrenreich under our supervision studied the hypnotizability records of the following: 447 psychiatric patients who had been seen at the Menninger Clinic; 270 patients (psychiatric and nonpsychiatric) at the Winter Veterans Hospital in Topeka, Kansas; 75 psychiatric residents; 26 employees of the Menninger Foundation; and a mixed group of 79 subjects including medical students and a variety of professional persons. This study had as its main purpose the investigation of a possible relationship between hypnotizability and psychiatric syndrome.[24] It had become somewhat tiresome to read repeatedly in the literature the unverified impressions that "hysterics are usually excellent hypnotic subjects" and that "schizophrenics cannot be hypnotized." We found no clear-cut evidence which would establish a correlation between particular nosological categories

[24] It was briefly reported by Dr. Ehrenreich in 1949 (52).

and hypnotizability. Interestingly enough, however, in spite of the fact that the *majority* of our hysterical patients were *not* hypnotizable, there were more good hypnotic subjects in the group of hysterics than in any other single psychiatric category. We are thus left with the somewhat paradoxical finding that while the frequently held belief that the presence of hysteria is a guarantee of hypnotizability is untrue, nevertheless there is some important relationship between the dynamics of at least *certain* hysterias and hypnotizability.[25] Our hysterical group was not large enough to permit of a systematic breakdown of subtypes within the group. On the other hand, while our investigation did show that most schizophrenics, like most other patients, are not hypnotizable, one of our very best hypnotic subjects was a schizophrenic girl.

It has become our conviction that these data point not only to the necessity for a closer study of the hypnotizability of large groups of patients but also to the more general problem of developing a more precise nosology. At any rate, it became clear that the attempt to establish a simple correlation between psychiatric syndromes as they now stand and hypnotizability is likely to prove a fruitless endeavor.

This conclusion led now to our next attempt to unravel the mystery of hypnotizability: on the assumption that specific personality organization would be a more sensitive and "truer" basis for establishing groups of various "kinds of people" than nosological categories had been, we decided to study groups of patients and of normal people—including good and poor hypnotic subjects—to see whether any clear differentiations could be seen at the extremes.

The first such effort was a careful study of a wide variety of cases, conducted by Dr. Roy Schafer in 1946 (203), using a comprehensive battery of psychological tests. We chose 19 good and 19 poor hypnotic subjects, sending them in random order to Dr. Schafer for testing. He, of course, did not know in advance which was which. After he had completed the 38

25 We have presented clinical evidence for this proposition on pp. 71-74.

qualitative reports, we sorted them out into the "good" and "poor" groups and Dr. Schafer now scrutinized his reports to the end of establishing what, if anything, distinguished the good subjects from the poor ones. Although he found significant personality trends shared by the poor subjects, it was much more difficult to pin down the good subjects. In other words, he was able to see more clearly those factors in personality organization which seem to interfere with being hypnotized than those which provide a favorable setting.

In the most general sense, he found that those people who were unable in a deep way to engage in free participation in human relationships were our poorest subjects. For example, it was difficult or impossible to hypnotize those whose tests showed *marked* obsessional or compulsive tendencies, inclination to use projection as a major defense, overt aggressiveness and emotional unadaptability, narcissism and devotion to the unconscious effort of denying their passive needs. These characteristics were on the whole infrequent in the good hypnotic subjects, who were, however, characterized relatively often by a strong repressive tendency. This finding substantiates Rosenzweig's "triadic hypothesis" (200). Positive indications of a high capacity for "free participation" could not be pinned down.

A restudy of these 38 cases in 1954 (unpublished ms.) was undertaken by Dr. Schafer at our request, with the specific aim of establishing whether or not our good hypnotic subjects are distinguished by their strong masochistic trends. It seemed reasonable to suppose that if the standard psychoanalytic theory of hypnosis as essentially a "masochistic surrender" (67) is true, persons with outstanding masochistic trends would be among our best subjects. Although Dr. Schafer did indeed find such trends in some of our best subjects, he found them also in some of our poorest ones; he concludes:

> Masochistic trends, in so far as they are reflected in test results, do not correlate significantly with hypnotizability if the trends are considered by themselves. It is entirely possible

that *in the presence of certain other conditions* masochistic trends may contribute to hypnotizability, but, assuming these test reports have any validity for this problem, it would seem that blatant masochistic trends *per se* are neither sufficient nor necessary conditions of hypnotizability.

It is not a simple matter to draw conclusions for the psychoanalytic theory of hypnosis as a "masochistic surrender" from these findings. It may be that the test indices of "masochism" reflect only in part the clinical constellation we have given this label. It may also be that the notion of a "masochistic surrender" is an oversimple summary of a far more complex phenomenon.

Following our effort to pin down the characteristics of good and poor hypnotic subjects via studies of personality structure provided by psychological tests, we proceeded to attempt a test of the hypotheses put forth by Dr. Schafer: this time we decided on a *clinical* study of a group of good and a group of poor subjects. We thought it possible that the crucial characteristics might emerge more sharply in clinical interviews than they had in the battery of tests. In this we were mistaken. A brief description of this clinical study is in order at this point:

The research population was a class of approximately 100 psychiatric residents. This was a fairly homogeneous group: young men between the ages of twenty-five and thirty-five, all of the same educational background, a narrow range of (high) intellectual endowment, and all having elected to enter psychiatry as a specialty (whatever significance this may have for shared psychological structure). A clear advantage in working with so homogeneous a group lay in the presumption that the extremes of good and poor hypnotizability could be more readily related to specific personality characteristics than in a group varying in age, sex, intellectual achievement, and occupational choice. The large group was divided into subgroups with about 15 in each. One of us conducted group hypnotizability sessions with these subgroups, selecting then the 12 best and the 12 poorest subjects from the entire group. These 24 men selected for further intensive study were then seen individually by the same investigator—in order to recheck their hypnotizability, the group hypnosis having been mainly a screening process.

Now, without informing the second member of the research team which were the poor and which the good hypnotic subjects, all 24 men were sent in random order to participate first in a general psychiatric interview and then in a "free-association" session. They were asked also to write an autobiography. The aim, of course, was for the second research member to sort the group into the best and poorest subjects on the basis of some clear-cut differences between them. Regrettably, his task was made all too easy by various of the subjects who, despite warning, inadvertently revealed their good or poor hypnotizability by some indirect comment.

When it became obvious that the groups had sorted themselves out into good and poor subjects, the fundamental task remained: to discern the significant differences between the two groups. This proved an even more difficult undertaking than the detection of differences on the psychological tests.

A close study of the data from the psychiatric interviews, the "free-association" sessions, and the autobiographies revealed no unequivocal differences in personality structure between the good and the poor subjects. To be sure, there were strong indications here, as in Dr. Schafer's psychological-test study, of the factors which interfere with hypnotizability: in the "poor" group there were strong evidences of general negativism, evasiveness, truculence, minimal capacity for emotional adaptiveness—and above all a striking effort to deny passive needs. This last was well illustrated by the fact that although the men in the "poor" group were on the whole no better adjusted than those in the "good" group, they did not in general reach out to the examiner for any kind of personal aid or comfort during the investigation. This general attitude stood in striking contrast to the good subjects who almost without exception did so reach out, whether by some direct appeal to the examiner (weeping, asking for advice) or by oblique reference to their strong wish to arrange for a personal analysis at some time. Another characteristic frequently though not universally present in the good subjects is a tendency to exploit feeling in a somewhat histrionic manner.

It is striking that, despite the relative rareness of both sleepwalking and homosexuality, 2 of our 12 good subjects have a sleepwalking history and 3 have some history of overt homosexuality, whereas none of the poor ones do—or at least none admitted it. Three of the good subjects were currently in analysis and none of the "poors" was. Obviously, none of these facts in so small a sample can be considered significant. We mention them only as possible areas for further investigations.

An additional source of information about the "structure of the subject" has been the intensive study of a very few patients who proved to be highly hypnotizable in group hypnosis sessions and who subsequently entered long-term treatment with one or the other of us. To be sure, this source of data is again limited by the smallness of this group; yet the leads offered by these intensive single-case studies have been more provocative than any of the larger studies.

From the study of these few patients, the good hypnotic subject emerges as a person with an intense unconscious need to be passive, and aggressively demanding; these needs are, however, rarely expressed directly. On the contrary, they are relentlessly defended against both by a denial and usually a powerful reaction formation, so much so that the overt personality was most frequently (with varying degrees of success) that of a self-sufficient, independent human being who —sometimes professionally and sometimes informally— "looked after" other people, and who appeared to get along well with them except for occasional feelings of resentment at being exploited.

Another characteristic of our good subjects, especially of

the women—a characteristic undoubtedly related to what we have called the "need to be passive"—is the frequent and striking evidence of some variety of oral conflict: in several it took the form of obesity; in two others of strict dieting and/or anorexia with resultant thinness; in yet another, an addictive trend plus a duodenal ulcer. One of our best male subjects was an alcoholic. Our experience with these patients provides some support for Fenichel's suggestion that hypnosis represents a nostalgic reversion to that phase of life when "passive-receptive mastery" represented the primary means of coping with the outside world: that period when security was achieved by participation in a "greater unit," the all-powerful parent. Fenichel comments further that the regressive longing to revive this lost sense exists in all of us, particularly when "attempts at active mastery fail"; moreover, it is his impression that this longing is not equally developed in all persons, and is produced most intensely by what he calls "the oral type of patients" (64, p. 561), a view which fits in very well with our observations of our good hypnotic subjects.

Further confirmation of Fenichel's hypothesis comes from our repeated observation, reported earlier in this chapter, of the occurrence of spontaneous hypnosis in our good subjects precisely at those moments when "attempts at active mastery" are failing.

It is not enough, however, to say that the good hypnotic subject is a person in whom these regressive longings are intense. There are assuredly many patients in whom they are intense who are *not* good subjects. Such a "pull" toward regression is usually offset in a fluid way by the complex defensive operations we have described, resulting in a peculiarly poised impulse-defense balance which can be tipped by the hypnotist's intervention (the initial attempt to hypnotize). It may even be that still another necessary ingredient is a special form of ego development which readily allows for the kind of limitation of sensory intake we have described, plus the capacity for ready alterations of bodily awareness. We do not yet understand the nature of this ego development.

## THE INTENSIVE ANALYSIS OF THE HYPNOTIC RELATIONSHIP IN LONG-TERM PSYCHOANALYTIC THERAPY WHERE HYPNOSIS WAS USED AS AN ADJUVANT

In the same way that it is difficult to pin down the structure of the hypnotic subject, so is it difficult to isolate the unconscious fantasies of the subject in regard to the hypnotic relationship, especially on the basis of data from a handful of intensively studied "single cases." We have, off and on, toyed with the idea that perhaps there does not exist a least common denominator for all subjects in this relationship, and that the psychodynamics are as various as the individuals themselves.[26] Undoubtedly the particular form of the transference as it develops in a therapy which uses hypnosis does vary a good deal, and the difficulties of sorting out those attitudes which are *specific* for the hypnotic relationship from those which would have developed without hypnosis are great. Nonetheless, there has emerged a relative consistency of configuration which has led us to the tentative conclusion that the kind of person who is a good hypnotic subject in the first place reveals transference attitudes which, to be sure, are characteristic for him as an individual and which would have appeared, though less sharply, in nonhypnotic therapy, but which simultaneously become part and parcel of his hypnotic relationship. Although it is possible to make a theoretical distinction between the transference underlying hypnotizability and the "normal" transference which would have developed in any case, the two become exceedingly difficult to separate in any clinical study. Nevertheless, we have made the attempt.

Before we proceed with examples, we want to comment on the fact that in every instance where we made a serious effort

---

[26] This view is, for the most part, held by most investigators and has been most clearly expressed by Wolberg (229).

to subject the meaning of hypnosis to analysis, the patient resisted strenuously: on a conscious level by pleading that this topic be dropped, and on an unconscious level by attempting a series of defensive maneuvers intended to block the emergence into consciousness of the relevant material. One patient went so far as to suggest a bargain: she would ". . . *promise* never to be hypnotized again if only you'll stop asking what it means to me . . ." While, to be sure, this extreme reluctance to explore the meaning of the hypnotic relationship made our task more difficult, it provided a datum of real significance: the subject had all along been regarding the underlying meaning of hypnosis as a secret, one which is usually held intact by the hypnotist's stopping short of the analysis of that aspect of the transference which has *specific* reference to the hypnotic relationship itself. The gradual clarification of the nature of "the secret" became, for us, the significant extension of the commonly held views of the nature of the "hypnotic transference."

In the illustrative material to follow, we have restricted ourselves to excerpts from one intensively studied case, partly because of the exceptional clarity of this patient's productions, and partly because of the technical difficulties of integrating fragments taken from verbatim records of different patients. This seemed an especially important issue here because of the complex organization of the unconscious material which makes up the "meaning" of hypnosis. This meaning, as we distilled it, appeared to be the same in its general structure in the four cases intensively studied; naturally, there were individual variations in the specific content.

Before we commenced the systematic pursuit of the "secret" of the hypnotic relationship, the young woman we have chosen as our example spontaneously offered a wealth of data which confirmed some of the more standard views of hypnosis. For instance, if there were any doubt about the fact that hypnosis involves, in part, what has loosely been called an "incorporation" of the hypnotist, she provided ample material to substantiate this idea:

Early in her treatment, she was talking about the strange ease of "talking about uncomfortable things" in the hypnotic state and made what at first she regarded as a "meaningless" slip of the tongue: she said, "Somehow I never mind what I am saying when *we* are in hypnosis . . ." (italics ours). When she was pressed about this slip, she said that she had vaguely known for a long time that ". . . all the time when I go into hypnosis, I feel that I take you down with me . . . that you go down inside of me *with* me. . . It's a nice feeling to be down here where it doesn't make any difference. . ."[27] Later on she elaborated this idea to include the fact of spontaneous fluctuations in depth: ". . . somehow you didn't sink with me today. . . I left you 'way up on the cliff . . . it's as if I were being lowered into the valley . . . and we remain two separate people. . . When we both go down, it sounds strange but it's almost as if I were in the room alone and completely out of the world. . ."

That the "incorporation" of the hypnotist is not of a real person but of a childishly fantasied one is made clear by her reflections about the hypnotist. Her thoughts in this connection certainly substantiate the standard hypothesis that the subject in hypnosis regards the hypnotist as an omnipotent being.[28] For example:

The patient observed a lecture demonstration in hypnosis given by a psychiatric resident, a trainee of the therapist. She reported

[27] We have commented in Chapter 1 on the frequency of the entry into the hypnotic state as some variety of descent. This patient later presented the idea that this "going down" was somehow linked with the feeling of *falling* asleep, adding that in both instances there was some sensation of going down into an all-enveloping medium ". . . like water or soft feathers . . ." Depending on a variety of (undetermined) circumstances, the descent into such a medium might be ". . . comforting and soothing . . . or it might be smothering." Perhaps the difference depends on the experienced safety or danger of the temporary regression, even as in falling asleep or *"sinking into slumber"* a person may welcome the sensation if he feels no hazard, or conversely may have to wake *up* if he feels in psychological jeopardy.

[28] This is the same point as that discussed earlier under "The fantasy of magic power" (p. 74 ff.).

this experience with considerable bitterness, saying she felt it was an impertinence and a presumption on the part of the resident to give such a lecture at all. She went on at great length, criticizing his technique and finally burst out with, "You see in a way he was trying to take your place . . . so I wanted to ask him who he thought he was, anyway . . . God? . . ." As soon as she had said this, she fell silent for a moment, a little astonished at what she had said. At first she wanted to regard it as a slip of the tongue, but finally admitted that she had had fleeting fantasies that ". . . you are kind of a supreme person or something . . . like you were my mother up in heaven or something. . . You see?"

We see the same underlying fantasy in another form in the following:

The patient happened to see the therapist in a department store and reported the next day that she was "shocked to see how tiny you are. . . I realize that in hypnosis you seem very, very big to me and I feel very little . . . kind of shrunk . . . but when I'm awake I feel kind of equal to you or with you, or something."

This experience is not different in quality from that of the psychoanalytic patient who is surprised at the youth or small stature of the analyst when there occurs a chance encounter outside of the analytic hour. The regressive fantasy, though less extreme in analysis than in hypnosis, is undoubtedly the source of this distorted perception in both.

The fantasy of incorporating an omnipotent, Godlike person emerged fairly early in the treatment and thereafter sporadically; it was discussed quite casually each time it came up, and in no way occasioned the intense anxiety, shame, and withdrawal which accompanied the divulging of the "real secret" of the hypnotic relationship. The latter was pursued by us relatively late in the therapy and became the nub of a serious crisis. We have selected excerpts from notes of the few days during which this crisis developed:

Early on Saturday morning, the patient telephoned to say that she urgently needed a special (unscheduled) appointment. When she came in, she said she needed to see me urgently because at last she understood what hypnosis really meant to her and felt she *had* to tell me. It had "come clear" to her that ". . . in hypnosis I feel that I really love you very deeply and that you love me too." Having announced this, she stopped lamely and said, "I suddenly have no idea why I had to see you." I asked her why she had felt so urgent a need to come and tell me this. She said she didn't know and now "I feel very foolish to have put you to all this trouble for nothing at all." She had made me make special arrangements and now has "nothing to say." She tried frantically to fill in with various things that had disturbed her. Yet none of them "hit the spot." She kept repeating, however, "But I know I just *had* to see you." She seemed more puzzled than disturbed and so I soon terminated the appointment, telling her perhaps we could pursue this on Monday during her regular appointment.

On Monday, she came in consumed with anxiety, saying, "I'm so upset, I just feel on fire. . . ," adding she had felt this way all week end. She had kept reminding herself that I had not seemed angry with her on Saturday and sometimes that would help a little. She had somehow expected to find me angry. I asked her to lie down (not in hypnosis) and to free-associate. At first she thought about a boy who had run away from home over the week end and had been found drowned. Then she said: ". . . now I'm thinking about hypnosis . . . and I feel very guilty about something. . . I don't know what it is. . . I feel extremely guilty . . . like I've told you a big lie, and I don't know what the lie is. . . I don't know why I'm guilty . . . my throat feels just scorched with anxiety. . . I keep trying to tell myself I haven't done anything . . . there's no need to feel guilty or anxious and no reason to stay awake all night. . . *I keep telling myself I'm not going to hurt anything and nothing's going to hurt me. . .*" As she talked she began to feel languid and ". . . tempted to go into hypnosis," but she ". . . doesn't really want to, because now that we have begun to talk about what it means to me, it just falls flat." She had wanted to tell me this on Saturday and to tell me then that she didn't want to go into hypnosis any more and would *"promise"* that she wouldn't.

She tried now to veer away from the topic but when I brought her back to it she said, "I know I feel there's something bad and hostile about hypnosis . . . when I used to just love it and crave to go to sleep. . . I feel now I hate it and I'd rather give it all up than go into it and see *why* I feel this way. . . I didn't even want you to ask me what it meant to me. . . I don't want to think about it because I do feel like I've been doing something that's dishonest, disloyal or something. . ."

Within the next several days, with utmost reluctance and with continued intense anxiety, she disclosed step by step the ramifications of her "guilty feelings" about hypnosis. She began by saying that although the "complete love" she felt in hypnosis was, in a way, real and deeply satisfying, it was at the same time a "terrible sham." The sham and the "dishonesty" consisted in the fact that she felt a relentless, devouring tyranny in this "love," that it "was like eating you up alive." She had had the fantasy that if she could get me to hypnotize her, she could thus prevent me from going on vacation. The translation of this fantasy seemed clear enough: if she could force me to become part of her by "us both going into hypnosis together," she could immobilize and control me. As she put it, "In hypnosis, I've got you in my clutches and I won't let you go." As she elaborated this aspect of her fantasy, it became clear that she regarded it as predatory and potentially destructive of me, and all "under the cover of" a mask of loving, childlike obedience and submission.

The irony here became evident to both patient and therapist: that whereas on the surface the hypnotic relationship appears to be one in which the hypnotist elicits automatic obedience from the subject, the latter is trying to "devour and control." This is very different from her earlier formulations of a tender, benign incorporation of a powerful loving mother. Those earlier comments had not caused her anxiety, conflict, or shame. Now she felt truly "unmasked" and continued to feel that she must never be hypnotized again. The hostile wish to "steal your tool,[29] your power," and thus "to indulge myself in all kinds of strong feelings . . . and have you under my thumb" had been the source of her sense of deceit or "disloyalty." At last it became clear why she had kept telling herself on that Saturday afternoon that ". . . I won't hurt anything and nothing will hurt me" and had felt relief to see that in reality the therapist did not appear to be angry with her. She had unconsciously expected some devastating retaliation from the therapist for her hostile impulses, and had thus urgently felt the need to come in for a special appointment to say that ". . . in hypnosis I feel I love you very much and that you love me too. . ."

In brief then, the "real secret" of the hypnotic relationship which this patient fought to protect was the fact that *under the cover of the classic obedience of hypnosis, there lies an intense and hostile wish to turn the tables and to "devour" the hypnotist, thus stripping him of all power.* This is a very different matter from the classic formulation of "sharing the hypnotist's power by identification."

## DATA ON THE NATURE OF THE HYPNOTIST

We come now to the other major participant in this process: the hypnotist himself. Our information about this other member of the "group of two" (88) is derived from several sources: the introspection of a number of hypnotists supervised by us in a resident-training program; material gathered from psychoanalysts who have had hypnotists in treatment, or who themselves work with hypnosis; and finally, responses by a small group of experienced workers in this field to a written inquiry from us.

---

[29] Space limitations preclude our detailing the fascinating sidelines of this fantasy. In numerous dreams, it became clear that the vast power of the hypnotist was seen as an essentially masculine attribute and that a part of the unconscious "plot" was to seize the symbol of this power, in short to steal the female hypnotist's penis, leaving her helpless—as "helpless" as the subject usually appeared to be in hypnosis.

That there has been almost no significant discussion of the psychology of the hypnotist is in part a function of the general reluctance in all of us to consider or discuss the infantile, or even the unconscious, motives in our professional work; in addition to this, the assumption that hypnosis is something that happens to the subject, alone, has made such considerations as the motivations of the hypnotist appear to be irrelevant to a theory of hypnosis. Yet another reason for this paucity of discussion issues from the belief held by several leading psychoanalyst-hypnotists that there are no specific driving motives common to all practicing hypnotists, and that, to quote one respondent, the individual meaning of inducing hypnosis is "contingent on specific personality needs and conflicts . . . and that the individual responds to the use of hypnosis the way he does to other things in life." He concludes ". . . to tell you about my own unconscious attitudes toward hypnosis would be merely to tell you my own unconscious attitudes toward anything else." While we can agree that the hypnotist certainly does not fall easily into a single, stereotyped personality pattern, any more than does the subject, it is nonetheless our impression that there are certain important characteristics shared by those who practice hypnosis, and moreover by those who try it and quickly abandon it, both for therapeutic and for research purposes.

There can be little question that the process of inducing hypnosis touches off important and intense feeling in the hypnotist as well as in the subject. Curiously enough, it has been our observation that whereas the first attempt to induce hypnosis is usually attended by acute anxiety in the operator, this is an exceptional happening in the potential subject who is being tried for the first time. We have speculated that the reason for this difference in experienced anxiety in a situation where we presume both members of the partnership are, among other things, acting out infantile fantasies, lies in the fact that, at least overtly, the "goings-on" are the responsibility of the hypnotist and not of the subject.

Further evidence that important motives are brought into play in the induction procedure is the fact that success and failure in hypnotizing the subject are regularly attended by an exhilaration or a disappointment in the operator greatly disproportionate to what Schilder called "the business at hand" (208). Both the initial anxiety and the extreme reactions to success and failure have been regularly reported by the hypnotists who cooperated in this study; these two reactions are, however, no more than indices to important motivations in the hypnotist, some of which we shall attempt to describe.

Pardell (173), in one of the few significant discussions of this problem, suggests that ". . . the hypnotist is a person who is willing, and perhaps desires, to accept the position of the controlling and omnipotent parent-figure and who at the same time is willing, and perhaps desires, to allow the patient to satisfy the regressive longing that is characteristic in hypnosis" (p. 486). This hypothesis is good as far as it goes, and is unquestionably confirmed by our data in so far as most of our responding hypnotists recognize in themselves an important need, however well or poorly disguised, to control other human beings. This need may express itself variously, ranging from an overt energetic tyranny (in both hypnotic and nonhypnotic situations) to an all-giving position which seeks to control by engendering dependence.

When, however, such strivings are for one reason or another unacceptable to the aspiring hypnotist, his anxiety becomes intolerable and he shortly gives up the effort. One of our respondents, a particularly honest and self-searching psychoanalyst, says:

I gave up hypnosis as a regular procedure very early in my career because I am aware of the fact that for me personally, it was an unhygienic situation. Without elaboration of details, I may now say that my decision to hypnotize a man was motivated ultimately, with almost immediate awareness, by some almost sadistic impulse to dominate him and with the female, the comparable situation manifested itself in the form of an erotic impulse. In my emotional economy therefore I have to look upon hypnosis as an acting-out with implications ramifying beyond even the aware phenomena which I have stated.

It is of incidental interest that Freud's own reminiscences suggest that he abandoned hypnosis in part because the procedure made him uncomfortable. His feeling that ". . . such treatment savored of injustice and violence" (35, p. 66) came after he watched a particularly tyrannical session conducted by Bernheim in 1899.

Another of our psychiatrist informants, who stresses as one of the infantile components of the wish to hypnotize the need for a magical omnipotence, adds rather wryly: ". . . but we must not forget that such motives undoubtedly play an important role in the initial decision to become a physician at all, and certainly in the specialty choice of psychiatry. The only trouble is that with the use of hypnosis this all becomes so naked." It is precisely this "nakedness"—made doubly so in recent years by the deliberate introspectiveness of analytically trained workers—that has had certain important influences on the technique of induction itself. Whereas the classical hypnotist like Bernheim (or the stage hypnotist) apparently felt no embarrassment at such overt tyranny as has been described, the average young psychiatrist or psychologist today cannot allow himself such liberties, and usually tries to reassure his patient that the whole procedure is extremely "rational," if not cut and dried; in this way he tries to outmaneuver his own unconscious, and to make palatable to himself that part of his motivation which is essentially infantile and which he could probably not tolerate in its nakedness. With a few notable exceptions, the obviously theatrical "Svengali" approach has vanished from the professional scene; this is in keeping with the temper of the times which demands "rational magic" and regards as amusing a Svengali who is trying to be frightening.

We indicated earlier that it is far from complete to sum

up the unconscious motivation of the hypnotist as "the wish to be an omnipotent parent-figure who allows the patient to satisfy regressive longings." We would like to add to this the hypnotist's more deeply hidden wish to satisfy such regressive longings in *himself*; this he can do via an identification with his hypnotic subject. It is difficult to document this crucial aspect of the structure of the hypnotist, because it cannot be both adequately disguised and at the same time persuasively discernible. We are sufficiently convinced, however, of the importance of the hypnotist's unconscious regressive yearnings to have built our theory of "the psychology of the hypnotic relationship" in part on this assumption.

The question now inevitably arises: are there not numerous professional undertakings characterized by the wish to be magically omnipotent and yet (by identification) regressively satisfied? Indeed there are. This means then that far from having arrived at any pattern of motives which are *specific* for the structure of the hypnotist, we have outlined only a scaffolding. We have some important hints from our data as to what some of the other ingredients are, but only hints.

For example, it is our impression that just as our good hypnotic subjects have a histrionic "streak" in their personalities, so do our good hypnotists. In recent years this ingredient has all but disappeared in the observable induction technique of most professional workers, with a few exceptions, for reasons we have already indicated. Nonetheless, the frank discussions offered by our informants strongly suggest a vivid interest in the high drama of hypnosis (". . . it is always a good show") and a sense of participating *with* the subject in a kind of game or play. It is no accident, we believe, that the reports describing the experience of hypnotizing so often include comparisons to theatrical situations; for instance:

> . . . regarding the use of the word "seductive" to describe the experience of hypnosis: I think of it only in terms of the situation and not that it is the subject who is being seductive. I tend to think of seduction or of my being seduced in terms

*of artful seduction, in contrast with attack or open offer; I think of it in terms of someone so setting a stage that I move about as though I were the hero of the piece while really, as I might later discover, I was only a straight man for the real star.*

There are many interesting aspects to this statement. Not only does it contain the sense of a somewhat contrived or staged situation; it includes also an overtone of the profound (though usually hidden) passivity of the hypnotist who while "running the show" may actually feel himself to be "only a straight man." Indeed, the above statement taken by itself might easily be thought to be a notation from the subject, not the hypnotist. Although there is certainly a tremendous range of histrionic quality in our hypnotist group—with the flamboyant "ham" at one end, whose routine technique is close to that of the average stage hypnotist, and the restrained, modest, matter-of-fact "scientist" at the other—we have considerable material which suggests that, in one form or another, the hypnotist does enjoy the role-playing which the hypnotic relationship necessarily involves.

Yet another factor which seems important is the particular attachment to, and in the gifted hypnotists, the special talent for, talking; they seem to have what has been properly called "a gift for gab." Many of our good hypnotists savor speech quite consciously, particularly their own, are highly articulate individuals in nonhypnotic situations, and on the whole seem to do a good deal of talking whether or not they are hypnotizing anybody. We have speculated whether this form of "orality" in our hypnotist group is the reverse side of the orality we have mentioned in our good hypnotic subjects.

Finally, several of our informants have sharpened for us an issue which has seemed to us extremely important in the choice of psychiatry as a profession generally, but which becomes particularly clear in the hypnotic relationship: this is the paradoxical need for simultaneous intimacy and distance. One man, a psychoanalyst, writes:

I always felt in doing hypnosis that I was keeping the patient at arm's length. Despite many qualities of psychological closeness it felt nevertheless to me like an arbitrary interdiction . . . or a qualitative block in communication. It is perfectly true that it allows me to pull some stops which I would never do without it, but this still has a quality of play-acting. It sometimes is enjoyable as such and one might say it was a sincere performance, but nevertheless a performance. . .

Another informant, also an analyst, having expressed much the same sentiment, adds however:

. . . yet is this really so different from the curious situation where I sit behind my analysand who is supine and thus symbolically "helpless," who has to tell me his most intimate thoughts and feelings and to whom *in this controlled and circumscribed situation* [italics ours] I react with intimate feeling and comment—and to whom a few seconds later I behave in a somewhat cool and professional manner as he leaves my office?[30]

From the last comment, taken together with other material which we do not have permission to quote, it has seemed to us that the need to establish a close and even "merging" relationship with another human being is kept in strict and thus "safe" bounds for the psychotherapist by the professional rules of the practice of psychotherapy, whether or not he practices hypnosis; but that in those who choose to specialize in hypnosis, this paradoxical necessity to establish closeness, and yet retain firm control over the maintenance of necessary psychological distance, is of particular importance.

These few hints leave much indeed to be learned of the structure of the hypnotist; yet they are sufficient, added to the extensive material from our clinical cases, to allow at least

[30] Wheelis, in an extremely interesting paper dealing with "the vocational hazards of psychoanalysis," has discussed this problem under the heading, "intimacy" (224).

for a general outline of the unconscious interplay between hypnotist and subject.

## THE INTERPLAY OF SUBJECT AND HYPNOTIST

From analysis of the two sets of data, on subject and on hypnotist, it appears to us quite clear that hypnosis is a complex dovetailing relationship between the two participants wherein the overt role taken by the one is the covert fantasy of the other. Thus, while the hypnotist is *overtly* being the powerful figure, whether as a domineering tyrant or a boundless source of "supplies," he is *covertly* on the receiving end of this power and/or bounty in his fantasy. On the surface he says, in effect, "*I* will assume responsibility now for you; in exchange, you must do, feel, and think as I want you to." He offers thus not only the opportunity for emotional gratification of various kinds (". . . in hypnosis I can feel intensely that I love you . . . and you love me too") but also the gift of guilt-relief for a wide range of infantile erotic *and hostile* impulses.[31]

As we have seen, on the other side of this coin, the hypnotic subject takes *overtly* the role of the obedient, supercompliant puppet; *covertly* he is not only sharing in the hypnotist's presumed omnipotence, but is pushing this in fantasy to the point of the hypnotist's having to abdicate completely. This fantasy was stated quite sharply by the patient discussed in the preceding section:

> . . . I had a dream [about hypnosis] . . . in which I was munching on an old piece of lamb, but I was really saving the delicious beef that had just been butchered. . . Makes me think

[31] One can only speculate on the similarity between this bargain and that which is tacitly made by the rulers of a totalitarian state with their "subjects." The way in which a sudden reversal of the overt relationship may take place has been dramatically expressed by Thomas Mann in "Mario and the Magician" (163), which ends with the fatal shooting of the hypnotist by the subject. Mann has Cipolla, the hypnotist, say that "The capacity for self-surrender . . . for becoming a tool, for the most unconditional and utter self-abnegation [is] but the reverse side of that other power to will and to command" (p. 553).

of a dog who buries a bone and doesn't want to share it. . . In hypnosis, I am just like a hoggish animal . . . that isn't really love, is it? . . . to have you on the inside of me. . . Then comes a picture that I have you so tight in my clutches, you *can't move*.[32]. . I am clamped on you like a leech and my fingers are so tight on your arm, the blood just runs down. . . Now I have the idea that none of your patients but me means anything to you. . . Funny how in hypnosis I feel at my most powerful. . .

After this last, the patient burst into tears and pleaded for reassurance that the therapist would not hate her now and terminate the treatment, again saying she never wanted to be hypnotized again.

One unresolved question which has presented itself in connection with our hypothesis concerning the hypnotic relationship is this: if it is true that the hypnotic relationship involves important *two-way* transferences, should there not be some alteration of ego function in the hypnotist as well as in the subject? Obviously, we would not expect such extensive changes as in the subject inasmuch as the sensory and motor deprivations of the latter are so much greater. On theoretical grounds, however, we would expect some. Our data on this point are meager. However, there are indications that there is some alteration in the hypnotist's "sense of reality." We have a few reports where the hypnotist speaks of feeling "somewhat dreamy and removed," especially during induction. There are a few indications also of the hypnotist's being more "emotionally touched" by the subject's productions than in ordinary psychotherapeutic work. This latter point, however, is not clear-cut inasmuch as the hypnotic subject's productions in therapy are in truth rawer, and at times awesome in their intensity. In any event, we can assume that despite the existence of unconscious fantasies in the

---

[32] Compare this with the motor paralyses usually suggested by the hypnotist in any standard induction procedure.

hypnotist, these are no doubt held in abeyance far more than in the subject, even as in all forms of therapy.

### The Relationship Between Hypnosis as a "State of Altered Ego-Functioning" and Hypnosis as "Transference"

We mentioned early in this chapter and in our discussion of induction that, for a long time, we found ourselves in the somewhat uncomfortable position of amassing two parallel bodies of data which appeared to be quite independent of each other: those which could be unified under the general heading "alterations in ego-functioning," and those which seemed best summed up under the concept "transference." We stated that an important stumbling block to the unification of these two sets of phenomena has been the lack of clarity in the concept of transference. Our emphasis now is on the fact that transference phenomena *are*, in part, functions of the ego—i.e., they are probably resultants of unconscious impulses against which have been brought defensive maneuvers, the latter certainly a function of the ego; whereas current usage of the idea "transference" frequently implies *only* the expression of some *unconscious impulse*, libidinal or aggressive.

More important, however, for the integration of the two sets of phenomena has been the hypothesis that hypnosis is a particular kind of *regression* which affects all areas of functioning. Thus, on the basis of this hypothesis we would expect to see the development of an archaic quality not only in those ego functions which we are accustomed to thinking of as such—sensory, motor, ideational—but also in that impulse-defense balance we call "transference."

We have offered evidence that these two sets of function are not, in fact, separable, most particularly: *the observation that the regressive process of hypnosis can be initiated either by an attack on the sensory-motor-ideational level or by the stimulation of an intense transference.* The curious fact that when one of these has been accomplished, the other soon occurs, suggests the thoroughgoing nature of a regressive process. Our most important data in this connection have come from our analysis of spontaneous hypnotic states, where we have seen that sometimes the one, and sometimes the other, stimulation (or deprivation) has triggered the regressive process. An example:

A patient, seen in a follow-up interview after termination of therapy, reported that frequently while watching a ping-pong game or a tennis match she would find her eyes riveted on the ball, and be acutely aware of the monotonous "ping" of the ball as it hit. She would feel as if she were going into hypnosis at such a moment, but could quickly stop it by changing the focus of her attention. She noticed also, however, that *if at such a time she had been anxious and vaguely wishing for the "protection of therapy," the process would be much harder to arrest.*

In our previous account of spontaneous hypnotic states we saw numerous instances where the regressive process was initiated without sensory monotony or the like, but where the failure of an "attempt at mastery" was sufficient to invoke the image of the therapist and then all of the subjective sensations of the hypnotic state we have been grouping under "alterations in ego-functioning."

## Observations Indicating the Persistence of Some "Attunement to Reality" in the Hypnotic State

Although the burden of this chapter has been the presentation of the ways in which the hypnotic state differs from the normal, it is of prime importance to underscore the fact that none of the changes we have described is absolute; i.e., it is our conviction that to some extent the hypnotic subject maintains throughout an appreciation of the total reality situation via a maintenance of at least some portion of his normal ego-functioning.[33] To be sure, the degree of change

[33] We include here not only his normal processes of perception, thought, and motility, but also his unconscious defenses.

varies with the depth of hypnosis, the personality of the subject, and a host of other factors we have yet to unearth.

We, along with many other investigators, have repeatedly
observed the "blind" hypnotic subject avoiding obstacles as
he crosses a room, or more subtly, the subject who has been
instructed to develop a selective blindness averting his eyes
ever so slightly from the person he is "not seeing."

One of our most striking experiences in this connection occurred when we successfully induced a chronological regression, in the usual hypnotic sense, in a woman with a severe
anxiety hysteria. She was reliving, with utmost vividness, an
episode when she had actually fallen from her high chair as
a small child. Her re-enactment of this experience was initiated by a piercing scream and then the following:

> I am falling. . . I am falling. . . Oh, please please catch me
> [screaming in between sentences]. . . Oh, *doctor* [italics ours],
> please catch me. . .

The blurting out of such an "anachronism" as this direct
address to the therapist does not usually occur in a hypnotic
regression which is more complete than this one was; we
have chosen this instance because of the great disparity which
existed between the obviously genuine character of her panic
as she was "falling" from the high chair and her realization
of the therapist's presence. Where the hypnotic regression is
more complete, such gross indications of reality attunement
do not occur, but *they are always present in some form.* If
they were not, communications with the hypnotist would
necessarily disappear entirely. This rarely happens, even
temporarily.

Another area of observation classically offered as evidence
of the maintenance of the subject's reality contact is that of
the limits which the hypnotic subject places on behavior
which might threaten his sense of privacy or his moral standards. This is a more complex and controversial issue than the
others we have been discussing. We do not doubt that some

young women will break out of hypnosis rather than disrobe before a group of medical students (Janet's famous subject); we also do not doubt, however, that other young women *who would not in the normal state disrobe* will do so in hypnosis, given an adequate technique. The problem here is the interplay between the appreciation of reality, the subject's own impulses (normally defended against), and the immense shift of the sense of personal responsibility to the hypnotist. The patient who masturbated openly before the therapist was certainly not a person who, imaginably, would do this under any other conditions. No doubt there are other patients who would not have masturbated openly even while in hypnosis.

Similarly, there is no doubt that some subjects would "stab" the hypnotist with a rubber dagger but refuse to slap him with an actual palm. There are others, however, who will not permit themselves outbursts of aggression or petty larcenies in the normal state, but will in hypnosis (see 21).

In short, we see condensed in the question of the limits on antisocial behavior of the hypnotic subject, all of the problems of the interplay of the various vectors at work in the hypnotic state: the alterations in general ego-functioning, the regressive core of the transference relationship, and the maintenance of a significant (varying) degree of reality attunement.[34]

## The Posthypnotic State

Before we close this chapter we would like to add a few observations on the posthypnotic state which tend to support the idea that the way back to a normal from a hypnotic state is transitional in the same sense in which the induction period appears to be. The classic phenomenon of posthypnotic amnesia, though not universal, is one of the most striking evi-

---

[34] Rosenberg and Gardner (199) have recently published a very interesting clinical study which shows the interaction of these vectors in posthypnotic compliance, the basis for which must, after all, be closely related to hypnotic compliance or, more generally, to hypnotic behavior.

dences of a kind of hiatus between the hypnotic and the normal state. More frequent are the less dramatic evidences of the need to establish a new equilibrium—e.g., the confusion and temporary disorientation so often seen directly after the hypnosis has been officially terminated. The retrospective distortions in judging elapsed time are extremely common in this transition, the most common error being the subjective feeling that the hypnotic state had been much shorter than in fact it was.

The frequent posthypnotic denial that there has been any hypnosis (or anything unusual at all) seems a more complex phenomenon: perhaps a combination of the great "shake-up" in general ego-functioning, plus a defensive need to repress the entire experience.

One of the most striking and frequent indicators of the transitional character of the posthypnotic state is the fact that there appears to be a fleeting reinstatement of the hypnotic state at the moment of carrying out a posthypnotic suggestion. This observation, described systematically by Milton Erickson (54), is one of the most potentially fruitful for the further pursuit of the nature of the transition. It is difficult to pinpoint, because it happens so quickly: the subject, now apparently back in his normal state, may be talking quite naturally and with animation, perhaps leaving the room; the hypnotist gives the signal and a host of lightning-quick changes occur. The subject's eyes may glaze, his general tempo and rhythm may slow down, or he may begin to look slightly depressed. Then he carries out the posthypnotic suggestion, and instantly he is back to where he was a few minutes earlier. Much is condensed in these few minutes, probably a recapitulation of the entire process in capsule form.

# *3*

# THEORY OF HYPNOTIC INDUCTION

Taking as our point of departure the phenomena we have described in Chapter 1, we will now discuss the psychoanalytic theory of hypnosis. We will especially take note that some of the phenomena have not been marshaled in support of the theory as well as they could be, while others are unexplained or neglected. In addition, we will discuss certain related *nonhypnotic* phenomena, an understanding of which can buttress a psychoanalytic theory of the hypnotic phenomena. A discussion of these topics will lay the groundwork for our own theory, which we regard as an amplification and extension of the psychoanalytic theory of hypnosis, particularly in the realm of ego psychology.

Psychoanalytic writing on hypnosis generally fails to distinguish between the induction period and the established state, nor is it explicit on the distinction between hypnosis as an altered ego state and hypnosis as a changed human relationship. Our own presentation will be organized according to these distinctions.

The psychoanalytic theory of hypnosis clearly implies, where it does not explicitly state, that hypnosis is a form of regression. This thesis will be our first guideline, in relation to which we will show how the phenomena of hypnosis we have observed provide evidence for this theory. But here we introduce our own distinction: *induction is the process of bringing about a regression, while the hypnotic state is the established regression.*

For clarity of presentation we will reverse the order in which we discussed the phenomena of the induction period. There we described first the manipulations by the hypnotist and then the reactions of the subject. Here we will discuss the reactions of the subject first, to try to demonstrate that a regression is actually being brought about, and then the manipulations by the hypnotist to show how these are designed to this end.

## Reactions of the Subject

### EVIDENCES OF REGRESSED ALTERED STATE DURING INDUCTION

It is a well-accepted principle of psychoanalytic theory that in the course of development the impulse life is progressively "toned down" and braked. A complex system of derivatives of primitive impulses, defenses against, controls of, and adaptive expressions of these impulses is erected. A regressive process is one in which the balance of forces shifts so that freer and more primitive impulses come to expression, while the control system likewise becomes more primitive and relatively less stringent and determining of the course of psychic life vis-à-vis the impulses. Regression is not only a matter of previously hidden content coming to the fore, but also an alteration in the mode of functioning of the psychic apparatus, what we are calling here an altered state. There are a number of responses of the hypnotic subject during the induction period which are evidence that a shift in the impulse-defense balance is occurring, that impulses are relatively stronger vis-à-vis the defenses and controls; in other words, that a regressive course is being pursued. We will discuss these as freer expression of repressed affect and ideas, the availability of motility to repressed impulses, the appearance and disappearance of hysterical phenomena, spontaneous regression, changes in body experience, and feelings of depersonalization.

In psychoanalytic theory, the two major instinct representations are the affective and the ideational, the so-called quantitative and qualitative representations respectively (82, pp. 152-153; 83, p. 178). In our presentation of the phenomena of the induction period, we have offered examples of outbursts during the induction phase which reveal regression in the affective sphere of instinct representation, while in our presentation of the phenomena of the hypnotic state we have seen instances of regression which show both an increased emotional discharge *and* the appearance in consciousness of derivatives closer to repressed ideation as compared with the nonhypnotic state in the same individual.

We have likewise offered examples of motor expression which indicate the availability of motility to impulses which are unable to achieve such motor expression in the nonhypnotic state. The fact that such repressed impulses can gain access to the apparatus of motility is an evidence of the relative weakening of defense in relation to impulse, and again is evidence of a shift in a regressive direction.

There are many reports in the literature in which a hysterical symptom—like aphonia—disappears on the induction of hypnosis and reappears when the hypnosis is terminated. Such a disappearance of hysterical phenomena is ordinarily explained as a "transference" or "suggestion" effect, whether or not an explicit suggestion has been made. We do not dispute the role of "transference" factors. However, since we ourselves have noted the contrary phenomenon—the appearance of an aphonia on the induction of hypnosis—this is some evidence that there is also an altered state, that the weakening of control may in some instances lead to the disappearance, in others to the appearance of hysterical phenomena. Where an aphonia disappears, a possible mechanism is the freer access to the motor apparatus of a repressed impulse which previously had led to an inhibition of all speaking. Where an aphonia appears, the balance of forces may be such that with the threatened emergence of a repressed affect or idea, a defensive effort is intensified. According to this last formulation, both impulse and control have been heightened, the result being a movement toward regression.

The phenomenon of spontaneous regression is a dramatic outburst of emotional, ideational, and motor expression of previously repressed mental contents. In the hypnotic literature, "spontaneous regression" refers to the partial reinstatement of an earlier life event, relived with vivid intensity. As we have discussed in an earlier paper by one of us (100), and as we shall discuss in more detail in connection with the relationship between hypnosis and the traumatic neurosis, the reliving in the present tense is indicative of a regressive shift in the synthetic functioning of the ego.

Changes in bodily experience further bespeak the occurrence of a regressive movement during induction because of the similarity of these alterations to those which have been described in psychoanalysis as aspects of archaic ego states.[1]

In *The Ego and the Id* (90), Freud advanced the proposition that the ego is first and foremost a body ego. Extensive psychoanalytic work has demonstrated that early mental life is primarily concerned with processes intimately related to body function (56, 138, 139, 140). With subsequent development, there is the establishment of hierarchies of organization on various levels of derivation from primary drives, and at varying distances from elementary perceptual and motor patterns. Interests, strivings, and attitudes may become as thoroughly bound up with ego feeling (61) as are the primary body processes.

The body image, the mental representation of the body, develops early. Schilder (205) has demonstrated how in various regressed states, early bizarre forms of the body image come to light. W. Hoffer has discussed the role of hand and mouth in early ego development (117). As we described in

---

[1] Freud discussed "organ language" or the expression of psychological content by subjective alterations in bodily sensations in the regressed state schizophrenia in "The Unconscious" (83, pp. 198-199).

our chapter on phenomena, alterations of hand and mouth sensations loom especially prominent in hypnosis.

Perhaps the most widely known of the alterations in body image in regressed ego states is the Isakower phenomenon,[2] which in its fully developed form seems so clearly a regressive revival of the nursing experience. Though we have never heard a classical example of an Isakower phenomenon related by a subject during the induction phase, the existence of so many abbreviated forms of the phenomenon (152) makes us suspect that such instances as the lips feeling so swollen that the subject can scarcely speak may be truncated examples of it.

Isakower has described the regression during the process of falling asleep as a disintegration of various parts and functions of the ego and a diminution of its differentiations.

Of the cathectic energy withdrawn from the external world, a relatively greater quantity streams into the bodily ego than into the perceptive parts of it, and, at the same time, the

---

[2] "The phenomenon in question is closely akin to certain well-known hypnagogic manifestations, and this mainly by reason of the fact that it very often occurs when the subject is on the point of falling asleep . . . The principal bodily regions concerned are the mouth, the skin and the hand. In many cases there are, as well, distinct sensations of floating, sinking and giddiness . . . Some of our informants state that they could on occasion produce the condition intentionally; others, that they voluntarily retained it, once it had set in—partly out of curiosity, in order to study it. (Here by the way, it differs from most hypnagogic phenomena, which usually vanish as soon as attention is focussed on them.) . . . Most striking of all is the blurring of the distinction between quite different regions of the body, e.g. between mouth and skin, and also between what is internal and what is external, the body and the outside world . . . The visual impression is that of something shadowy and indefinite, generally felt to be 'round', which comes nearer and nearer, swells to a gigantic size and threatens to crush the subject. It then gradually becomes smaller and shrinks up to nothing . . . The auditory impression is of a humming, rustling, babbling, murmuring, or of an unintelligible monotonous speech. The tactile sensation is of something crumpled, jagged, sandy or dry, and is experienced in the mouth and at the same time on the skin of the whole body. Or else the subject feels enveloped by it or knows that it is close at hand. Sometimes it feels as if there were a soft yielding mass in his mouth, but at the same time he knows that it is outside him . . . And finally, there is the behaviour of the subject during and in relation to the experience: his evident attitude of self-observation" (Isakower, 120, pp. 331-333).

cathexis of that side of the perceptual system which faces out-
wards is relatively depleted, while the side which faces towards
the ego is more abundantly cathected [120, pp. 336-337.]

The regressive nature of the presleep state is characterized
as follows:

> . . . as a result of the regressive diminution of differentiation
> which occurs when we are on the point of sleep, the body ego
> reverts to the stage we have been describing: it revives an
> archaic phase of development [p. 338].

Recent writings by Greenacre on fetishism (106, 107) and
on changes in body image, especially in body size in the writings of Swift and Carroll (109), offer further evidence of the
relation of altered body image to regressed ego states.

The spontaneous changes during induction in body sensation, the most common of which are the sensations of floating, dizziness, and descending, provide further evidence for
the revival of archaic states. Incidentally, disturbances of
equilibrium may also be part of the Isakower phenomenon.

The bulk of evidence linking these body sensations to
archaic ego states comes from the data which associate them
with regressive revivals of pregenital sexuality. Fenichel (64)
finds that equilibrium and space sensations are essential components of infantile sexuality and may therefore come to
represent infantile sexuality in general. He believes these
sensations are especially likely to occur during falling asleep
and when sexual excitement arouses anxiety. It may be that
only in people in whom the excitement arouses anxiety do the
sensations appear in consciousness. Fenichel (p. 71), like
Schilder (207), mentioned earlier, suggests that the connection between anxiety and equilibrium may originate in the
infant's fear of losing stability. Fenichel, however (p. 202),
suggests further that a reason for the close connections between sexuality and anxiety is that sensations of equilibrium
are an essential part of both. Persons with no conscious
memory of infantile masturbation may remember games and

fantasies involving the situation of the body in space—
changes in size of the body, or of certain parts of the body,
impressions of the bed being turned around, or still vaguer
sensations. (Compare some of the descriptions by people during the induction phase.)

Fenichel finds various sensations of changed equilibrium
specific for being overwhelmed by excitation (p. 215), and
notes that in falling asleep archaic types of ego feeling are
regressively experienced before consciousness is lost, and that
a high percentage of these archaic ego feelings are felt as
sensations of equilibrium and space. He believes that normal
people are not much bothered by these sensations, but that
among people whose infantile masturbation is mainly represented by these sensations there is a minority who enjoy the
experiences as a masturbation equivalent and a majority who
are afraid of and repress them, and who may suffer severe
sleep disturbances because of them. It is possible that a similar explanation may account for the appearance of such sensations in some people during the induction of hypnosis, and
not in others. It may be that in some people who are afraid
of these sensations, their appearance may lead to a breaking
off of the developing hypnosis.

Incidentally, it is interesting to note that Fenichel finds
that the eroticism of sensations of equilibrium in the fear of
one's own excitement plays an important role in the traumatic neurosis (p. 545), the relation of which to hypnosis we
will discuss later.

French, in his paper on disturbances of vestibular function
in dreams, has speculated on a possible early libidinal invest-
ment of the experience of passive motion (74). In view of
the fact that the infant's first experience of locomotion is
that of being carried about passively, it is tempting to speculate that the experience of floating is a regressive revival of
such sensations.

Isakower has proposed that a hypothesized early close connection between perception and motor intention is main-

tained during the state of falling asleep only in the vestibular apparatus, a sense organ which he regards as one of the most important intermediaries between the internal and external worlds.

And, as a last note, the occasional appearance during hypnotic induction of depersonalization feelings, which are generally acknowledged to be manifestations of regression, is further evidence that a regressive movement is occurring. Mayer-Gross reports that parts of the head are often affected in depersonalization, and that hands and arms were affected in all of his patients who did experience bodily change (164).

## TRANSFERENCE REACTIONS

The development of transference reactions of any intensity is of course itself evidence of a regressive movement. We have already indicated how strong these transference reactions are by emphasizing that the subject's response is usually the same to operators of different sex, prestige, technique, and experience, and that moreover the response may in some instances be immediate and deep even before any *active* effort has been made by the hypnotist.

Psychoanalytic theory generally lays heavy emphasis on transference as an explanation of hypnosis, but without any distinction between induction and the established state. Since the manipulations of transference during induction are, we believe, simply continued into the hypnotic state, we will reserve our extended discussion of transference for that section. Kubie and Margolin, who do distinguish between induction and state, and who agree that transferences begin in induction and are carried over into the state, nevertheless argue that they are not essential to hypnosis.

Ida Macalpine (161) believes that hypnotizability involves the immediate establishment of a transference relationship analogous to that which develops more slowly in the ordinary course of a psychoanalysis, and that in both situations the transference is established by essentially the same means. We will return to Macalpine's thesis later on.

## EVIDENCES THAT INDUCTION IS A REGRESSIVE MOVEMENT

So far, we have presented evidence only of regressive phenomena; we have yet to demonstrate that the induction period is a regressive *movement*, as against the established state which is a regressed *state*. Perhaps the most obvious indication that the induction period is a regressive movement lies in its transitional character; it fails to stabilize and disappears.

We indicated earlier the practical difficulties in demonstrating conclusively that the induction phenomena disappear as the induction period shortens; nevertheless, our experience suggests that the hypothesis is a likely one. The sharp reduction in the time required to hypnotize a trained subject is a well-established finding. We assume therefore that the disappearance of the more obvious phenomena of the induction period, as a subject becomes more experienced, bespeaks the transitional character of the induction period for which we will later offer a metapsychological explanation.

The essential argument here is that the phenomena of the induction period are similar to those phenomena characteristic of other states which are obviously transitional. The clearest example is the similarity between the phenomena of the induction period and of falling asleep. Later, in Chapter 6, we will discuss this relationship in detail; here we are merely emphasizing that both are transitional intervals on the way to established states of regression: hypnosis and sleep.

The hypnagogic state, transitional to sleep, is analogous to induction in an inexperienced subject. The phenomena produced by Kubie and Margolin (144) in hypnagogic reverie show similarities to phenomena of the induction phase. In Silberer's work on hypnagogic symbolization (211), in which either the psychic state itself, or specific thoughts just prior to the onset of the state, become represented in concrete symbols rather than in abstractions, we again see similarities to induction-phase phenomena. The changes in body sensation in induction may not only reflect archaic ego states but may also be concrete representations of the induction phase itself. The induction phase is one of loss of moorings, and the vestibular sensations may be a concrete representation of such loss. For example, the common experience of descent during induction may concretely represent the withdrawal from the external reality situation. The related state—falling asleep—is frequently described in terms of descent—"falling asleep," "sinking into sleep," "going deeply asleep." We have also remarked on dizziness as a common experience in the posthypnotic period *transitional* to the secure reinstatement of the normal nonhypnotic state. Perhaps even the general instability of body image is a concrete representation of the fluid character of the induction process.

The similarity of some of the phenomena of the induction phase to those typically described in depersonalization lend further support to the view that induction is a transitional phase. Depersonalizations are fascinating but, despite a fairly extensive literature, little understood. Our argument here is restricted to the suggestion that depersonalization phenomena are also evidence of a *transitional regressive period*.

It is commonly held that depersonalization phenomena are precursors of any severely disturbed mental state (172, 205), and thus are transitional to the more stable regressed state itself. To be sure, there are instances in which depersonalization phenomena become chronic, but these instances do not disprove the hypothesis that depersonalization phenomena are evidence of a transitional state, inasmuch as there are mechanisms by which a transitional state itself can become stabilized. It is not impossible that the balance of psychic forces in a particular person may remain such that he fails either to regress more definitively to an established state, or to recover from the regressive movement under way. It is also possible that apparently chronic depersonalizations are no longer depersonalizations, since when such patients lose their depersonalization symptoms, they feel strange and the world seems unfamiliar.

Depersonalization phenomena are transitional in the sense that they represent the emergence of one type of organization of the psyche (with the threatened eruption of repressed material), while the usual organization still remains in the ascendancy. This has been expressed by Ackner (2) as follows: "The depersonalization types of complaint arise as a result of a relative failure of integration of experience into the total organization of psychic functioning, while the latter remains relatively intact."

*Déjà vu* (regarded by Freud as the "opposite" of depersonalization [96]) is also a transitional, or at least a transient, state. It too seems to occur when repressed material threatens to erupt, and in this sense is related to a regressive movement, though it more likely is not a regressive movement itself but a defense against one.

Hypnosis has been described by many as an "uncanny" phenomenon. Freud attributes uncanniness to the threatened return of the repressed, in the case of hypnosis the phylogenetic memories of subjection to the primal-horde chieftain. A reading of his essay on "The Uncanny," however, shows that on a more formal level he finds an essential ingredient of the uncanny to be the conflict between two frames of organization. A fairy story, for example, if it is clearly set forth as such and we accept the fact that we are in the framework of magic, does not give rise to a feeling of the uncanny. But if the author fails to let us clearly settle on being either in a magical or a rational framework, he can, with regard to certain contents, awaken in us the sensation of the uncanny:

> . . . for, as we have learnt, that feeling [of the uncanny] cannot arise unless there is a conflict of judgment as to whether things which have been "surmounted" and are regarded as incredible [infantile anxieties] may not, after all, be possible;

and this problem is eliminated from the outset by the postulates of the world of fairy tales [86, p. 250].

The uncanny, then, like depersonalization, emerges from the conflict between two simultaneously present frames of reference and is therefore also evidence for the transitional character of hypnosis, though we must admit that we do not have evidence that uncanny feelings are more prominent in induction than in the established state.

The aura of an epileptic attack frequently reveals the emergence into consciousness of disturbances of the body image and body sensations. The phenomena of smell in the uncinate fit are well known. Despite the fact that in epilepsy we are dealing with a phenomenon with basically organic etiology, the aurae may also be looked upon as phenomena of a regressive movement on the way toward a regressed state, namely the fit and unconsciousness itself. Beck and Guthrie (13) have recently studied the psychology of the aura and have demonstrated—especially to be emphasized in view of our present thesis—that the aura can be recaptured and studied during the hypnotic state.

Dizziness at the end of an analytic hour seems to be a phenomenon allied to dizziness on emergence from the hypnotic state as well as on entering it. The analysand is in a transitional state between the emotional organization (partial regression) of the analytic session, and his resumption of his usual role. Ruling out the possibility of an organic dizziness on the basis of blood-pressure changes incident to arising, here again is one of the sensations which occurs in the induction phase of hypnosis—and in the transition to the posthypnotic state—appearing in a state transitional between two types of psychic organization, one of which is regressed relative to the other (68).

We have now completed our presentation of the reactions of the hypnotic subject which offer evidence that *during induction a regressive movement is occurring, and that the induction phase is a transitional one.* We will next take up the manipulations by the hypnotist and attempt to show that they are designed to bring about this regressive movement.

## Manipulations by the Hypnotist

### OTHERS' VIEWS ON THE ROLE OF MANIPULATION IN INDUCTION

In taking the position that the manipulations of the hypnotist are important in themselves, we are departing widely from the usual psychoanalytic view that they are of no importance except as a vehicle of the transference. We have suggested that the advances in ego psychology make it possible to demonstrate that the manipulations of the hypnotist do play an important role in bringing about a regression. In a more general sense, it may be said that our emphasis on these external manipulations is part of the increased emphasis that psychoanalytic thinking is placing on the environment. However, since the influence of the environment is still relatively underemphasized in psychoanalytic writings, data gathered from other fields are especially desirable in this connection; for this reason, among others, we are buttressing our argument with data obtained in situations quite different from the psychoanalytic or the hypnotic.

There are, however, two recent psychoanalytic contributions which emphasize the importance of the manipulations by the hypnotist, and which should be mentioned before we pass to the development of the generally accepted psychoanalytic theory.

One is the important paper by Macalpine (161). She emphasizes the active role which the analyst and the analytic situation play in bringing about the development of transference—which she calls an adaptation by regression. Among the "factors which constitute this infantile setting" she includes: "Curtailment of object world. External stimuli are reduced to a minimum (Freud at first asked his patients even to keep their eyes shut). Relaxation on the couch has also to be valued as a reduction of inner stimuli. . ." (p. 523). She also mentions "the constancy of environment" (p. 524), a concept analogous to that of sensory adaptation as discussed by Kubie and Margolin.

The other is Fisher's very interesting study of dream suggestions to patients in analysis (72). The central idea of his experiment was that if analysis is a state of induced regression as is hypnosis, phenomena producible in hypnosis should also be producible in analysis. He states that "during the process of hypnotic induction, certain ego functions, especially consciousness, motility and perception, are manipulated" (p. 431).

Our discussion of the hypnotist's efforts to reduce both external and internal stimuli as conducive to the initiation of a regressive movement parallels Macalpine's and Fisher's views.

Freud's rarely quoted remarks on the significance of the manipulations by the hypnotist are germane here also. Whereas most psychoanalytic theorizing has been directed toward an elucidation of the hypnotic state itself rather than of the process of induction, a number of provocative remarks made by Freud in this connection are well worth following up and will be found, we believe, to be adumbrations of the theory we propose.

In his discussion of hypnosis in *Group Psychology and the Analysis of the Ego* (88), Freud remarks on how little we know about how hypnosis is brought about: "There is still a great deal in it which we must recognize as unexplained and mysterious. . . The manner in which it is produced and its relationship to sleep are not clear. . ." (p. 115). A few pages later he suggests, as evidence for the derivation of hypnosis phylogenetically from a primal horde and primal chieftain, that hypnosis is induced by the gaze of the hypnotist and that "it is precisely the *sight* of the chieftain that is dangerous and unbearable for primitive people, just as later that of the Godhead is for mortals" (p. 125).

Freud then explicitly discusses fixation and monotony as factors in inducing hypnosis:

It is true that hypnosis can also be invoked in other ways, for instance by fixing the eyes upon a bright object or by listening to a monotonous sound. This is misleading, and has given occasion to inadequate physiological theories. In point of fact, these procedures merely serve to divert conscious attention and to hold it riveted. The situation is the same as if the hypnotist had said to the subject: "Now concern yourself exclusively with my person; the rest of the world is quite uninteresting." It would of course be technically inexpedient for the hypnotist to make such a speech; it would tear the subject away from his unconscious attitude and stimulate him to conscious opposition. The hypnotist avoids directing the subject's conscious thoughts towards his own intentions, and makes the person upon whom he is experimenting sink into an activity in which the world is bound to seem uninteresting to him; but at the same time the subject is in reality unconsciously concentrating his whole attention upon the hypnotist, and is getting into an attitude of *rapport*, of transference onto him. Thus the indirect methods of hypnotizing, like many of the technical procedures used in making jokes, have the effect of checking certain distributions of mental energy which would interfere with the course of events in the unconscious, and they lead eventually to the same results as the direct methods of influence by means of staring or stroking [pp. 125-126].[2]

2 "This situation, in which the subject's attitude is unconsciously directed towards the hypnotist, while he is consciously occupied with monotonous and uninteresting perceptions, finds a parallel among the events of psycho-analytic treatment, which deserves to be mentioned here. At least once in the course of every analysis a moment comes when the patient obstinately maintains that just now positively nothing whatever occurs to his mind. His free associations come to a stop and the usual incentives for putting them in motion fail in their effect. If the analyst insists, the patient is at last induced to admit that he is thinking of the view from the consulting-room window, of the wall-paper that he sees before him, or of the gas-lamp hanging from the ceiling. Then one knows at once that he has gone off into the transference and that he is engaged upon what are still unconscious thoughts relating to the physician; and one sees the stoppage in the patient's association disappear, as soon as he has been given this explanation" (Freud's footnote, p. 126).

We see that though Freud insists that physiological theories are misleading, and that the essence of the process is an unconscious transference onto the hypnotist, he does ascribe a "technical" function to the manipulations, "checking certain distributions of mental energy." We will return to this "technical function" and refer to other discussions by Freud when we take up the role of the manipulation of attention in inducing hypnosis.

The only serious attempt to deal with the problem of the hypnotist's manipulations in the induction phase by psychoanalytic writers which we know is the one made by Kubie and Margolin (145). We shall refer to their theory in a number of different connections, inasmuch as it is a fairly comprehensive one. We would like to remark here that it has had an undeserved fate. Though thoughtful and dealing with many issues often scarcely raised, it has been largely ignored in the literature, both psychoanalytic and general. This is probably because, though the theory emphasizes ego-psychological issues, it describes them in physiological terms and, in addition, the theory essentially rejects the role of transference.

With regard to the restriction of sensory intake, Kubie and Margolin come to a conclusion in some ways diametrically opposed to that just quoted from Freud, despite the fact that at first glance the similarity seems strong, since they too appear to regard the relations with the hypnotist as crucial in induction. Whereas Freud sees the manipulations as technical maneuvers but not of the essence of the procedure, Kubie and Margolin see the essence of the induction phase as lying in the manipulations designed to alter the sensorimotor relationship between the subject and the outside world. In their discussion of emotional factors in induction, they say that the hypnotist's psychological relationship to the subject is important only in so far as it makes the subject comfortable, willing to be not alert, and most importantly, "*to concentrate attention on one field of sensation and to withdraw attention from all others"* (p. 617). In other words, one might say they regard the emotional relationship with the hypnotist as having only a "technical function." In the Kubie-Margolin theory, it is not a general restriction of sensory stimuli which is emphasized, but the concentration of all attention on one field of sensation. They discuss monotony and rhythm in sensory stimulation as a way of withdrawing attention from "other" fields of sensation. As a result of sensory adaptation, monotonous and rhythmic stimuli are, in effect, no stimulation. Yet the one field of sensation to which all attention should be directed is not so impersonal as one would expect from Kubie's and Margolin's conclusion that "such an extension [to hypnosis] of a normal process [maximal attention] should be attainable . . . without the agency of suggestion, or even of any human contacts" (p. 620). For the one field of sensation is the hypnotist!

In the initiation of the process there is a progressive elimination of all channels of sensori-motor communication between the subject and the outside world, with the exception of the channels of communication between the subject and the hypnotist. As a consequence, during this phase the hypnotist becomes temporarily the sole representative of and contact with the outside world [p. 620].

Kubie and Margolin refer to this latter phenomenon as "a fusion of subject and hypnotist" (p. 620). They hold that when an individual is related to the world by only one "active sensory modality," there is an erasure of ego boundaries and a fusion between subject and the one active modality—in this instance the hypnotist. It is this inability to distinguish between self and hypnotist which they hold responsible for the "apparent" suggestibility during induction.

It is this dissolution of Ego boundaries that gives the hypnotist his apparent "power"; because his "commands" do not operate as something reaching the subject from the outside, demanding submissiveness. To the subject they are his own thoughts and goals, a part of himself [p. 612].

It must be asked, of course, whether it is legitimate to equate the concept of "one sensory modality" with the concept of the hypnotist as the sole representative of and link to the outside world. We too believe that the presence of a hypnotist is indispensable, but do not believe that he is simply analogous to any other sensorimotor contact, as Kubie and Margolin appear to believe.

It will be noted that the major ego-psychological concept Kubie and Margolin employ is the concept of ego boundary, which they define as follows:

> The term Ego boundaries, originally introduced by Federn, refers to the boundary between an inner and outer world which evolves slowly in the life of each individual, which constantly changes, and which like the Ego itself is partly conscious and partly unconscious [p. 612].

What they describe as the "erasure of ego boundaries" is apparently what is ordinarily described as "incorporation." But they also use the concept of ego boundary to differentiate between induction and the established state, regarding the former as a contraction and the latter as a partial re-expansion of ego boundaries. They do not explain, however, how this contraction and expansion comes about.

We want to emphasize that although Kubie and Margolin suggest that attention is withdrawn from all sensory modalities but one, whereas we describe the activity of the hypnotist as directed toward the restriction of sensory intake generally —and hope later to show that, in so far as a reduction of stimulus in hypnosis plays a role in initiating regression, the reduction refers to all avenues of intake—Kubie and Margolin were the first to give a prominent role in the theory of hypnosis to the *limitation of sensory intake* during the induction phase. Whether they overplayed their hand on the one side by denying the importance of transference factors in induction, and on the other side confuse the issue somewhat by regarding communication with the hypnotist as a sensory modality, remains to be seen.

## REDUCTION OF SENSORY INTAKE

We turn now to some recent experiments which, though not psychoanalytic, buttress the hypothesis that a reduction of sensory intake facilitates the onset of a regression.

In a by now famous experiment reported from Hebb's laboratory by Bexton, Heron, and Scott (17), a number of healthy adult college students were subjected to sensory restriction. They were put in a small cubicle and allowed out only for toilet and meals. Their vision was cut down to formless light by opaque goggles, and their hearing limited to communications from the experimenter by headphones, set in sponge-rubber head fittings, which cut out all other auditory stimulation. Their skin stimulation was cut down by encasing hands and arms up to above the elbow in cotton wool kept in place by cardboard cylinders. Subjects were paid twice as much as they could earn in other work, but several refused to stay even as long as 24 hours. At first most subjects slept, and then, in some subjects, came the development of spontaneous phenomena similar to those which we have described as occurring during induction. Most of the phenomena were visual. They ranged from geometric figures—usually the first to appear—to fully formed hallucinations, such as squirrels marching purposefully across a field of snow. The subjects who had such hallucinations usually came to call them "dreams with your eyes open."[3]

Several of Bexton et al.'s subjects reported auditory hallucinations. Several subjects experienced changes in the body image: one, for example, reported that there seemed to be two of himself, one overlapping the other. Mental calculations attempted during the period in the apparatus were dis-

[3] Wolberg has remarked on the appearance of geometric figures during induction (230). We ourselves had a subject who saw a circular spot closing down as he went into hypnosis, and opening up as he came out.

tinctly inferior to achievements in the ordinary state, and it is worthy of note that these losses persisted for some hours after removal from the apparatus.

Bexton et al. suggest that "the maintenance of normal intelligent adaptive behavior probably requires a continually varied sensory input." It seems clear that this experimental situation reproduces one of the features of the induction period—the restriction of sensory inflow—and results in some similar phenomena, quite clearly indicative of a regressive movement.

It must be emphasized that these experiments were undertaken without any reference to hypnosis. It would of course be most instructive to study the relative hypnotizability of subjects engaging in such an experiment, to see whether those who developed the phenomena described most easily were most readily hypnotizable, and whether it is the same phenomena which develop during induction and during the experimental period in the same subject. It would also be important to study whether during the experiment or in the immediate postexperimental period there are alterations in the subject's hypnotizability as compared with his hypnotizability prior to the experiment.

Experiments on "sensory deprivation" have begun to multiply. Especially noteworthy is the work of Lilly (155) at The National Institute of Mental Health. He points out that in the experiments of Bexton et al. the aim is to reduce the *patterning* of stimuli to the lowest level, while in his experiments the objective is to reduce the *absolute intensity* of all physical stimuli to the lowest possible level. His technique is to suspend the subject, wearing a blacked-out head-mask for breathing and nothing else, in a tank containing slowly flowing water. Though the work is in early stages, some phenomena similar to those of the Bexton et al. experiments have been reported. Continuing work with these and similar techniques, with due attention to the psychological impact of the situation and to the individual differences in the subjects, should offer fascinating leads on the problem of regression and its initiation.

There are a number of naturally occurring conditions in which sensory stimulation is markedly reduced, and in which occur alterations of the kind we have described during the induction period: changes in body image, visual phenomena ranging from apparently increased sharpness and brightness to complex hallucinations, hallucinations of other senses, outbursts of affect, and depersonalization phenomena.

The reduction of stimulation may be involuntary, as with prisoners (especially in solitary confinement), or survivors of shipwrecks, airplane accidents or other disasters, or in various kinds of confining illness, or voluntary, as in the case of Arctic or desert explorers, or as in voluntarily undertaken seclusion, whether religious or nonreligious. We quote several illustrations from an unpublished paper by Watterson (221).[4]

> Critchley [42] has given a description of the psychological effects of being shipwrecked during wartime, and of suffering privation while waiting for an uncertain rescue. Immediately after the disaster, while jumping into the sea or struggling in the water, the subject may experience the visual hypermnesia described as *panoramie de la vie passée*, very similar to that recorded by Heim in the case of a falling climber. Subsequently, while drifting in small boats or on rafts, and suffering from hunger, thirst, and cold or blistering heat, the survivors may develop visual hallucinatory states, usually, but not always, in a setting of clouded consciousness. In these circumstances the peculiar phenomenon of shared hallucinations occurs, in which everyone in the same boat, literally and figuratively, may see, and live within, the same hallucinated scenes.

And, on the basis of material from David-Neel (47):

> The Tibetan monk, for instance, may seclude himself for a month or even years in a room built on a mountain face, or in

---

[4] We are grateful to Dr. Donald Watterson of Vancouver, Canada, for allowing us to use this unpublished material.

an entirely dark underground chamber—immobile. In these circumstances he experiences the same visual phenomena as those produced more aseptically in the psychological laboratory. "Men who have spent long periods of seclusion in darkness enjoy at times wonderful illuminations. Their cell becomes bright with light or, in the darkness, every object is drawn with luminous outlines; or again a phantasmagoria of shining flowers, landscapes, and personages rises before them." Such kaleidoscopic imagery may give way to rich and meaningful hallucinations (for instance, scenes from places previously visited or visions of terrestrial catastrophe), or the hallucination of a chosen human figure may be deliberately cultivated (the so-called *tulpa*). The latter kind of hallucinatory image becomes three-dimensional, and the other senses (e.g., touch) are also involved. The *tulpa* may become increasingly ego-alien, and seem to acquire characteristics and a life of its own. It may even be seen by others—an example of a phenomenon encountered in certain other situations, namely the sharing of hallucinations.

Though in the kinds of phenomena described here the situation is considerably more complex than simply a reduction of sensory stimulation, these phenomena buttress the hypothesis that sensory deprivation does act as a factor to help initiate regression. The detailed exploration of these phenomena and their conceptualization remains to be done.[5]

## THE RESTRICTION OF MOTILITY

We turn now to the restriction of motility as a second factor in the manipulations by the hypnotist which initiate a regressive movement.

[5] The work of Magoun and associates throws light on the neurological pathways by which sensory stimulation influences the cortex. Electrical stimulation of the reticular formation in the cat results in an EEG activation pattern similar to the EEG pattern in emotional tension and arousal in human beings (169). Bilateral hypothalamic lesions in cats, which cut off the influx of stimuli from the reticular formation, eliminate fast activity composing the activation pattern and result in synchronized large waves in bursts or spindles like those of normal sleep (158). The cutting off of the reticular pathway for influx of sensory stimuli results then in the cortex being "isolated" from the external environment and "beating" in an indigenously determined, sleeplike, or in our terminology, "regressed" manner.

Freud ascribed enormous importance to the role of motility in differentiating the outer from the inner world, considering it a major factor in, if not the essential determinant of, reality testing. In "A Metapsychological Supplement to the Theory of Dreams" (84) he said:

> . . . we ascribed to the still helpless organism a capacity for making a first orientation in the world by means of its perceptions, distinguishing "external" and "internal" according to their relation to its muscular action. A perception which is made to disappear by an action is recognized as external, as reality; where such an action makes no difference, the perception originates within the subject's own body—it is not real. . . This function of orientating the individual in the world by discrimination between what is internal and what is external must now, after detailed dissection of the mental apparatus, be ascribed to the system *Cs.* (*Pcpt.*) alone. The *Cs.* must have at its disposal a motor innervation which determines whether the perception can be made to disappear or whether it proves resistant. Reality-testing need be nothing more than this contrivance [pp. 232-233].

The hypnotist's restriction of the subject's motility, then, is designed to shake the subject's command of a major reality-testing apparatus, thus setting the regressive process in motion.

Kubie and Margolin in their theory of hypnosis speak generally of sensorimotor relationships, but they actually stress the sensory much more than the motor aspect. Nevertheless, they do ascribe to immobility a role equal to that of monotony as one of the "physiological" factors responsible for the "extension of the processes of normal attention," which leads to the hypnotic process, itself "the result of the creation in the central nervous system of a concentrated focus of excitation with the surrounding areas of inhibition (in the descriptive Pavlovian sense)" (145, p. 620).

The fixing of the subject's eye on a single point, which traditionally has played such an important role in the melodramatics of hypnotism, has a valid physiological basis. Pavlov showed that the "exploratory" or "investigatory" impulses of animals are basic in maintaining a state of general alertness, and that any interference with them is the first step towards the induction of the hypnotic immobilization which is described by all who work with animals, both in animal husbandry and in the experimental laboratory. . . In the human subject the eye has replaced the nose and head as the exploratory and investigatory organ; and the prolonged, voluntary fixation of the eye on a single point is physiologically homologous to the immobilization of the whole head in lower forms. When at the request of the hypnotist the human subject fixes his eye on one spot, he figuratively speaking takes himself by the back of the neck and immobilizes himself. Thereby he produces a state of relative inhibition (or at least a reduction of excitation) not in the segmental oculo-motor apparatus alone, but also in the supra-segmental levels which play upon it, and therefore in the entire sensori-motor apparatus which adjusts the human body to the roving and exploring activities of the eye [145, p. 614].

We see then that though Kubie and Margolin stress immobilization, their explanatory constructs are within the neurophysiological rather than the psychological frame of reference. Nonetheless, this discussion for the first time makes the link between so-called "animal hypnosis" and human hypnotic states *via the interference with an apparatus of the organism vital in maintaining its contact with the stimuli of the outer world.*

The previously mentioned paper by Watterson (221) synthesizes a good deal of the data on the relation between interference with motor activity, whether voluntary or involuntary, and a regressive movement. Watterson's emphasis is on the development of visual imagery as a sign of a regression due to a loss of motor activity. In line with the concept developed in this book, we would make regression the central concept and see the development of regressive visual phenomena as part of the more general picture of regression. In fact, in the Watterson case material, which deals principally with immobilization in a plaster cast, phenomena of depersonalization and change in body image play as large a role as do those of visual imagery. Similar data have been reported in patients immobilized because of cataract operations (9) and spinal paraplegia (174).

Watterson also summarizes and emphasizes the correspondence between imagery changes, body-image changes, and depersonalization phenomena as produced on the one hand by psychological factors and on the other by organic factors. He divides the latter into three groups: (a) disease of the brain (especially temporal lobe cortex); (b) various metabolic diseases and drugs which produce hallucinatory delirium; and (c) drugs which produce imagery and body-image changes and depersonalization phenomena without clouding the sensorium, notably mescaline and lysergic acid diethylamide. Watterson derives his major explanatory statements from the psychoanalytic theory of thinking, and concludes that "when action is blocked, reality-attuned thought tends to give way to primary-process thinking dominated by visual imagery."

## THE MANIPULATION OF ATTENTION

We have so far discussed restriction of sensory intake and motor output. But the induction period also includes a filling of the available channels of intake and output of the sensorimotor apparatus, and an ideational impoverishment, both of input and of spontaneous thinking, brought about by the subject's absorption with the monotonous and repetitive hypnotic patter. We believe that these two additional kinds of manipulation also occur in other nonhypnotic circumstances of impoverished or controlled ideational input such as detention in concentration camps and subjection to "brain-washing," and we will later discuss the latter as a state related to hypnosis.

In our discussion of the phenomena of hypnosis, we indicated that the hypnotist attempts to influence the employment and direction of the subject's attention. We have already quoted Freud as saying that the hypnotic manipulations have a "technical function" to "check certain distributions of mental energy." This "technical function" apparently has to do with attention distribution. An editor's footnote (88, p. 126) to Freud's suggestion that the hypnotist's manipulations serve a technical function leads us to certain remarks of Freud's on jokes, on thought transference, and on an earlier device employed by him, pressure on a patient's forehead to overcome resistance to association.

In his discussion of wit, Freud deals with "auxiliary wit techniques, which obviously serve the purpose of diverting the attention of the listener from the wit process, so as to allow the latter to proceed automatically" (78, p. 737). This is clearly analogous to his view of the diversion of attention in hypnotic induction to allow the transference to proceed "automatically."

His comment on thought transference is as follows:

> The fortune-teller's astrological activities would in that case have performed the function of diverting her own psychical forces and occupying them in a harmless way, so that she could become receptive and accessible to the effects upon her client's thoughts—so that she could become a true "medium." We have found similar distracting contrivances employed (for instance, in the case of jokes) where there is a question of securing a more automatic discharge for some mental process [89, p. 184].

Even earlier than these remarks on wit and on thought transference, Freud describes the same idea, but with direct reference to hypnosis, in *Studies on Hysteria* (33):

> In these circumstances [resistance to association] I make use in the first instance of a small technical device. I inform the patient that, a moment later, I shall apply pressure to his forehead, and I assure him that, all the time the pressure lasts, he will see before him a recollection in the form of a picture,

or will have it in his thoughts in the form of an idea occurring to him; and I pledge him to communicate this picture or idea to me, whatever it may be.[6]. . I press for a few seconds on the forehead of the patient as he lies in front of me; I then leave go, and ask quietly, as though there were no question of a disappointment: "What did you see?" or "What has occurred to you?"

This procedure has taught me much and has also invariably achieved its aim. Today I can no longer do without it. I am of course aware that a pressure on the forehead like this could be replaced by any other signal. . . It would be possible for me to say, by way of explaining the efficacy of this device, that it corresponded to a "momentarily intensified hypnosis"; but the mechanism of hypnosis is so puzzling to me that I would rather not make use of it as an explanation. I am rather of the opinion that the advantage of the procedure lies in the fact that by means of it I dissociate the patient's attention from his conscious searching and reflecting—from everything, in short, on which he can employ his will—in the same sort of way in which this is effected by staring into a crystal ball, and so on. The conclusion which I draw from the fact that what I am looking for always appears under the pressure of my hand is as follows. The pathogenic idea which has ostensibly been forgotten is always lying ready "close at hand" and can be reached by associations that are easily accessible. It is merely a question of getting some obstacle out of the way. This obstacle seems once again to be the subject's will, and different people can learn with different degrees of ease to free themselves from their intentional thinking and to adopt an attitude of completely objective observation towards the psychical processes taking place in them [pp. 270-271].

It is analogously true that different people are hypnotizable to different degrees.

Another aspect of the hypnotist's manipulations to which we have called attention is his deflection of interest generally from outside to inside, from the distance receptors to somaes-

[6] This procedure is similar to the hypnotic devices we employed in our treatment of a case of anxiety hysteria (101).

thetic sensations—to the body. Kubie and Margolin would probably argue that this deflection inward facilitates illusions and hallucinations, since Kubie has argued elsewhere that illusions and hallucinations can be produced in normal people much more readily in the somaesthetic sensations than in the distance receptors (138). Our emphasis here is rather that there is a general association between a regressive trend and attention to one's own body, as against attention to the outside world, necessarily mediated by the distance receptors. Hypochondriasis is a prime example (80) of the tendency to become preoccupied with the body and its sensations in regressed states. It is equally true that when attention is perforce directed to the body, as in bodily illness or under the pressure of unfulfilled bodily hungers, interest in the outside world is diminished and a narcissistic regression occurs. We are suggesting that the hypnotist capitalizes on this association between attention to the body and regressive shifts to help initiate a regressive movement.

It is noteworthy that self-observation is a prominent feature in several of the transitional regressive conditions described above. Hypnagogic reveries take place in a setting of self-absorption; indeed the "functional phenomenon" may itself be a concretization of the psychic state of introspection. Isakower emphasizes a subjective sense of self-observation in the phenomenon named after him. He likewise emphasizes self-perception in his metapsychological explanation of the process of falling asleep. He believes that as the functioning of the perceptual apparatus changes during falling asleep, processes in the "somatic" parts of the sensory apparatus are more powerfully cathected and become themselves objects of observation (entoptic and entotic hypnagogic phenomena).

As far as self-observation is concerned in others of the transitional states which we have described, we may note that Isakower groups together epileptic aura, *déjà vu*, and the phenomenon he described as all being characterized by a subjective sense of being able to prolong the state at will.

This extraordinary phenomenon of the subjective sense of voluntary control, so contradictory to what to the external observer looks like an involuntary occurrence, we will discuss in another connection, but here want to suggest that it implies a heightened self-observation.

And lastly, the self-observation of the sufferer from depersonalization is described as prominent by almost all writers on the subject. Mayer-Gross remarks that Schilder made self-observation the central point of his theory of depersonalization, believing that "self-observation is an opposition arising from deeper layers of consciousness. This opposition, by way of increased introspection, disturbs the genuineness and evidentiality of every psychic occurrence" (164, p. 107). Though Mayer-Gross himself doubts that self-observation is of such primary importance in depersonalization, "this turning toward their own psychic experience seems extremely unusual and remarkable to most of our patients, and normal consequences of augmented introspection are regarded by them as signs of their illness" (p. 107).

But self-observation must be viewed not only in the light of the consequences of shifting attention from the outside to the inside, but also in terms of how the direction of attention to functions themselves interferes with their functioning. We have pointed out how the hypnotist encourages the subject to focus on the processes of sensation and motility themselves. It is a commonplace of everyday experience that an automatically performed function is interfered with when attention is directed toward it. There is the classic illustration of the centipede who, when asked to describe how he is moving his legs, becomes helpless. Corollary to the idea that interference with the functioning of the apparatuses helps to initiate a regression is the hypothesis that the direction of attention to bodily and psychic functioning plays a role in such interference. We will try to explain how this employment of attention operates when we deal with the metapsychology of attention as an apparatus and the metapsychology of the disruption of functioning of the sensorimotor apparatus.[7]

The "confusional technique"[8] is yet another type of manipulation carried out by the hypnotist which works by way of interference with the employment of attention. The effort to comply with confusing instructions leads to an even fuller employment of attention than is the case with clear, easily followed instructions. We have described a similar phenomenon in the ideational sphere, in terms of a shifting of frames of reference, in our discussions of dizziness on beginning or terminating hypnosis, and in our discussion of the uncanny.

### THE HYPNOTIST'S ROLE IN BRINGING ABOUT TRANSFERENCE

We have relatively little more to say here on how the hypnotist behaves during induction to bring about the transference. Psychoanalytic writings generally follow Freud in ascribing the development of hypnotic transference to the subject while saying little or nothing about the hypnotist's role. Schilder, however, puts more emphasis on the hypnotist's behavior, saying that "gentle reassurance, shouting and a certain amount of brutality are devices used not only in hypnosis but also in erotic seduction. The technical aids of fixation or stroking—some hypnotic methods make very extensive use of stroking the subject's body—are common to both hypnosis and erotic situations" (208, pp. 85-86).

In our discussion of induction in Chapter 1, we emphasized how the hypnotist behaves in ways calculated to arouse transference attitudes in the subject. Macalpine (161) has made

---

[7] It must be emphasized that self-observation is a phenomenon of the transitional phase, not of the established state, which latter, on the contrary, is characterized by a diminution of self-observation (see p. 47). It is common for a hypnotist to encourage a subject during induction to observe bodily sensations and movements and to discourage the subject from introspecting into his own *psychic* processes. Empirical study may show that psychic introspection would also favor the development of the hypnotic state rather than retard it.

[8] See p. 9.

the same point about transference generally. She challenges the assumption that the analysand is exclusively responsible for the development of transference attitudes. She says that, on the contrary, the analytic situation and the analyst's behavior actively foster the appearance of the transference—true though it is that the transference always lies latent in the subject. The situation is even more obvious in hypnosis.

We have surveyed briefly psychoanalytic theories of hypnosis, adding to this survey some nonhypnotic data. We have provided the background from which arises our own theory which is designed to include the observations of altered ego function as well as the development of "transference" as aspects of a "regressive movement" during induction and an established regression in the hypnotic state.

*4*

# THEORY OF THE HYPNOTIC STATE

## Hypnosis as a "Transference Phenomenon"

We turn now to that chapter of the psychoanalytic theory of hypnosis which is best known—the transference theory of the hypnotic state. Before we review the development of this theory, however, we would like to make a number of observations on some of the phenomena we described in Chapter 2.

We have already pointed out that our view of the behavior of the hypnotic subject has been influenced by the fact that most of the subjects we saw in the hypnotic state were also in therapy. This same consideration led us to some knotty problems concerning the development of the manifestations of transference in the hypnotic subject. It has seemed to us that it may be possible to make a distinction between the "transference" underlying hypnotizability initially and the transference as it develops in the ensuing psychotherapy. A conclusive statement on this issue would require a detailed study of numerous cases in which a serious effort was made to uncover the unconscious dynamics of hypnotizability in each instance. On the basis of those few cases mentioned in Chapter 2 in which we tried systematically to pursue this problem we offer the following considerations.

To be sure, our patients showed differing forms of transference as treatment proceeded. If the developing transference is only a making explicit of the transference underlying hypnosis, this would mean that the transference underlying hypnosis can differ from person to person. As we shall discuss in a little more detail later, hypnotizability seems to be an outcome of the drive-defense-adaptation balance; it is possible then that the final balance may be the same even where there are differences both in content and strength of these three variables. Our clinical experience, insufficient though it is for final conclusions, nevertheless suggests a "least common denominator" in the unconscious fantasies of the hypnotic subject.

That the transference developing in therapy and the transference underlying the hypnosis do not coincide is suggested by the fact that transference attitudes can develop in therapy which significantly alter the patient's hypnotizability. We reported instances where the development of anger on the patient's part, for example, resulted in a lessening of hypnotizability. Such instances may represent the impact of an immediate feeling on hypnotizability without any change having taken place in the transference structure *underlying* the hypnotizability. Just as current emotional attitudes influence the depth of hypnosis, so does the employment of hypnosis have repercussions on the manner in which the transference develops during therapy, but this again is different from saying that the developing transference and that which underlies hypnotizability are identical.

The data we have reported on the development of "spontaneous" hypnotic states in patients likewise seem compatible with the hypothesis that there is a difference between the developing transference and the transference underlying hypnosis. Spontaneous hypnosis appeared to be precipitated by immediate needs and defenses in the ongoing therapeutic situation. The hypnotic state appeared to function like a ready-made structure with a complex but "frozen" transference meaning. We are suggesting that the *ongoing and developing* transference is fluid and shifting, specifically related to the interaction between patient and therapist, while the *hypnotic state* may be more like a fixed structure, without specificity to the therapist and the therapeutic situation.

Yet another line of evidence differentiating the two types of transference is that analysis of the transference can proceed without influencing hypnotizability. It must be remembered, however, that this can also be true for analysis of the transference attitudes related to the hypnotizability itself.

Though our discussion of the points above has anticipated some of the major concepts of the psychoanalytic transference theory of hypnosis, we turn now to a sketch of some of the high points of the development of that theory.

In 1905, Freud said in a footnote to *Three Essays on the Theory of Sexuality* (77), in discussing the overestimation of the object in "physical and psychical spheres":

> In this connection I cannot help recalling the credulous submissiveness shown by a hypnotized subject towards his hypnotist. This leads me to suspect that the essence of hypnosis lies in an unconscious fixation of the subject's libido to the figure of the hypnotist, through the medium of the masochistic components of the sexual instinct (p. 150).

In 1909, Ferenczi proposed that the hypnotic relationship was a reactivation of the oedipus complex with the subject standing in a child-to-parent relationship with the hypnotist. He differentiated "maternal" and "paternal" forms of hypnosis, the first based on love and the second on fear (67).

The same thinking was continued in Freud's *Group Psychology and the Analysis of the Ego* (88), where he similarly compared hypnosis with being in love. In fact, he argued that "everything is even clearer and more intense in hypnosis so that it would be more to the point to explain being in love by means of hypnosis than the other way around" (p. 114). The essential difference, he proposed, is that in hypnosis sexual satisfaction is excluded, and that it is also like the group, but differs in that the group adds identification with other individuals. We may note by the way that though this seems to rule out identification with the hypnotist, Freud suggests in the same work that Christianity adds to the usual constitution of group structure the requirement that the Christian "identify himself with Christ and love all other Christians as Christ loved them. At both points therefore the Church requires that the position of the libido which is given by group formation should be supplemented. Identification has to be added where object-choice has taken place, and object-love where there is identification" (p. 134).

Freud is not satisfied, however, with this explanation of hypnosis, and says: "Hypnosis would solve the riddle of the libidinal constitution of groups for us straight away if it were not that it exhibits some features which are not met by the rational explanation we have hitherto given of it as a state of being in love with the directly sexual trends excluded" (p. 115). The main unexplained elements he regards as a "paralysis" derived from the relation between someone of superior power and someone who is helpless.

But he believes he has the answer to this mystery in deriving the group from the primal horde.

> It ought also to help us to understand what is still incomprehensible and mysterious in group formations—all that lies hidden behind the enigmatic words "hypnosis" and "suggestion" [p. 125]. . .
>
> By the measures that he takes, then, the hypnotist awakens in the subject a portion of his archaic heritage which had also made him compliant towards his parents and which had experienced an individual re-animation in his relation to his father; what is thus awakened is the idea of a paramount and dangerous personality, towards whom only a passive-masochistic attitude is possible, to whom one's will has to be surrendered, —while to be alone with him, "to look him in the face," appears a hazardous enterprise. It is only in some such way as this that we can picture the relation of the individual member of the primal horde to the primal father. As we know from other reactions, individuals have preserved a variable degree of personal aptitude for reviving old situations of this kind [p. 127]. [Thus does Freud account for different degrees of hypnotizability.]

Schilder (208) follows Freud's formulations quite closely. "Hypnosis and suggestion have an erotic root" (p. 85). And: "In addition to the erotic roots in the sense discussed above, hypnosis has also another source, namely, submission to an authority" (p. 91). But there are indications that this submission has erotic components too; and the submission is regarded as equivalent in its dynamics to masochism.[1] Schilder too calls hypnosis "goal-inhibited eroticism" (p. 92), though he offers a good deal of evidence for quite frank expressions of object-directed sexuality in the hypnotic subject:

The hypnotist can often detect an expression of sexual excitement in the eyes of women before they fall asleep and after awakening. Trembling occurs similar to that accompanying erotic stimulation. The hysteriform symptoms of rigidity which may develop in the early stages of hypnosis often bear a distinct resemblance to the motions in sexual intercourse. If you question hypnotized subjects, they frequently report that they experience a pleasant sensation of fatigue, and some openly admit feelings of sexual excitation. Accusations that the hypnotist has abused his subject are the result of erotic fantasies which have been aroused by hypnosis. . . The clairvoyance of schizophrenics with respect to psychological problems applies particularly to hypnosis. Being hypnotized and being sexually influenced have the same meaning for schizophrenic patients. We must also consider here the everyday usage of language which often mentions magic and hypnosis in connection with erotic feelings. "You have hypnotized me," has practically become an expression for erotic compulsion. It is a typical fear of women that they will be raped in hypnosis. . . The fear of rape is certainly an expression of a corresponding wish aroused by the hypnosis [pp. 85-86].

Schilder's principal addition to Freud's discussion is his stress on the role of identification with the powerful hypno-

[1] Our clinical material presented on pp. 89-91 certainly supports this view if the phenomenon of masochism is understood as including a significantly hostile set of unconscious fantasies. One of us has set forth this view of masochism in a paper on teasing (24).

tist. ". . . he [the subject] projects his desire [for magic powers] onto the hypnotist and subsequently, by identification, attains magic powers which he would not otherwise be permitted to ascribe to himself" (p. 94). Schilder points out that the submission may actually provide the masochist with a little power he could not have attained otherwise (p. 93).

It is interesting to note that *Group Psychology and the Analysis of the Ego* was written after the introduction of the dual instinct theory. But even with the increasing emphasis on hostility in discussions of transference in the psychoanalytic literature, no explicit reassessment of the transference situation in hypnosis was undertaken from the point of view of aggression. Nevertheless, despite the fact that it was not so labeled, Freud's view that hypnosis combined erotic and submissive (masochistic) elements would be translatable into the view that both libido and aggression figure in the hypnotic transference. We have earlier taken the position that the concept of "transference" is not complete without considering the defensive aspects as well.

We turn now to a consideration of the handling of transference in the Kubie-Margolin theory (145). In essence, they argue that though transference manifestations appear, they are incidental to the way in which hypnosis is induced, and do not constitute a basic ingredient of the hypnotic situation:

> During the process of inducing hypnosis, a constellation of conscious and unconscious attitudes arises between the hypnotist and the subject, in which manifold libidinal displacements and substituted object relationships (*i.e.*, transference phenomena) are active. When the hypnotic state is fully achieved, an extensive carry-over occurs from this pre-hypnotic relationship into the content of the hypnotic state, comparable precisely to the carry-over into the content of any dream of the residues from the emotionally incomplete experiences of the preceding day (the so-called *"Tagesrest"*) [p. 618]. . .
>
> These terms are . . . misleading, in that the carry-over from the pre-hypnotic transference relationships are not the essence

of the hypnotic state itself any more than the *"Tagesrest"* is the essence of the dream. In hypnosis, the residual stresses derived from recent experiences (here, this is the hypnotist) are subjected to the influence of the familiar mechanisms of condensation, substitution, etc., as in the so-called "dream work," and in both states these mechanisms provide an avenue of access to earlier material. However, if the hypnotic state could be produced without the use of any personal pre-hypnotic maneuvers, the hypnotic subject's thought content would then arise solely out of the depths of his own personality [p. 618].

In their conclusions, they state:

In the hypnotic process, mechanisms are at work identical with those seen in the dream (such as transference, displacement, condensation, etc.). Much has been made of these in the literature; but they are not the essence either of the process or of the state itself [p. 621].

Nevertheless, as we have said, Kubie and Margolin (145) seem to ascribe enormous importance to the relationship between hypnotist and subject, for they believe that in the hypnotic process there is a fusion between hypnotist and subject, and in the hypnotic state an incorporated image of the hypnotist. In fact, they say that hypnosis represents "an experimental reproduction of a natural elemental process" —growing up.

. . . the induction phase parallels the sensori-motor relationships of the infant to the outside world during the earliest phase of infancy, during which the parents play in the psychology of the infant a role almost identical to that of the hypnotist in the mental life of the subject [p. 620]. . .
. . . the final phase in the hypnotic process, which occurs with the full development of the hypnotic state, parallels precisely that phase in the development of the infant's Ego in which its boundaries gradually expand, with the retention of parental images as unconscious incorporated components of the developing Ego of the infant. The incorporated image of the hypnotist plays the same role in the hypnotic subject as

does the incorporated and unconscious image of the parental figure in the child or adult [p. 621].

Kubie and Margolin seem to argue on the one hand that the relationship with the hypnotist is crucial and on the other hand that transference is an incidental phenomenon in hypnosis. We believe there are several reasons for this: in equating the hypnotist with the notion of a sensory field, they ascribe a great deal of importance to him, but, apparently, only as a sensorimotor phenomenon. But more important, we believe, is that they apparently consider that the hypnotic state can be produced without a relationship to a hypnotist. They account for the importance of the hypnotist as a sort of accident of the manner in which hypnosis is ordinarily produced—that is to say, by a person.

It is a major thesis of this book that the relationship with the hypnotist *is* of the essence of hypnosis, and that when procedures are carried out which are in significant ways similar to the induction manipulations which we have described—but do not involve human contact (for example, the experiments of Bexton et al.)—the resulting phenomena bear important similarities to hypnosis, but are yet different from it.

An amplification of the transference theory of hypnosis was made by the present authors, with Knight, in their paper on spontaneous fluctuations in the depth of hypnosis (28). Evidence was offered to show—as would have been expected from psychoanalytic theory—that hypnosis appeared to express both oedipal and preoedipal wishes, both libidinal and aggressive. As described earlier, it was further pointed out that in addition to offering gratification of such wishes, hypnosis could be employed as a defense against them.[2] Freud's insistence on the aim-inhibition of the drive in hypnosis may similarly be understood as implying a defensive aspect. A

[2] The defensive use of hypnosis has implications not only for hypnosis as transference, but also as altered state.

further contribution to hypnosis as a defense was made by
Fliess (73), who demonstrated that a shift to a hypnosislike
state on the part of an analysand could be in the service of
defense—he called it "evasion." This demonstration is likewise a link to the view which finds similarities between hypnosis and analysis as induced regressions.

We earlier referred to Fisher's (72) study of dreams following suggestions to dream made to patients in analysis.
From the point of view of transference, he concludes that
being given a suggestion means being impregnated (and hence
is related to oedipal wishes), usually conceived in pregenital
terms (he found both oral and anal fantasies), and that the
patient reacts by producing dreams which express pregnancy
and childbirth wishes, again in pregenital terms. "The suggestion itself takes on an erotic meaning, becomes in fantasy
an impregnating substance, and its acceptance by the patient
is experienced as an unconscious gratification. The carrying
out of the suggestion, namely, the producing and bringing
of the dream, likewise takes on an erotic meaning, i.e., the
producing of a baby" (p. 424). Suggestions were accepted or
rejected in relation to the degree of anxiety or gratification
attending incorporation or expulsion fantasies. It must be
pointed out that we can accept Fisher's description as applying to hypnosis only if we agree that a state of "suggestibility"
and hypnosis are the same.

Fisher seems to oscillate in his paper from recognizing the
diversity of psychosexual material obtained to attempting to
compress his data into the thesis that suggestion has the
specific meaning of impregnation. Nevertheless, as Fisher
points out, his results "give substance to the erotic tie that
Freud mentioned as the essence of suggestion" (p. 424).

It must be pointed out that there is a distinction between
the transference meaning of being given and acting on a suggestion, and the transference meaning of the state of hypersuggestibility, and that both of these are distinct from the

state of hypersuggestibility which has a structure with its own formal characteristics and modes of function.

## Hypnosis as an "Altered State"

We remarked earlier that psychoanalytic discussions of hypnosis do not explicitly differentiate hypnosis as an altered state from hypnosis as a transference phenomenon. We do make that distinction, however, and now turn to a review of the development and present status of the psychoanalytic theory of hypnosis as an altered state.

It will not be necessary to repeat how just as the phenomena of induction bespeak a regressive moment, so do the phenomena of the state give evidence of a regressed state.

Some remarks by Freud as far back as *The Interpretation of Dreams* (76) are perhaps the best introduction to a discussion of the psychoanalytic conception of hypnosis as a regressed state. In discussing the state of mind which is necessary for a dream interpretation, he says:

> This involves some psychological preparation of the patient. We must aim at bringing about two changes in him: an increase in the attention he pays to his own psychical perceptions, and the elimination of the criticism by which he normally sifts the thoughts that occur to him. In order that he may be able to concentrate his attention on his self-observation, it is an advantage for him to lie in a restful attitude and shut his eyes [this was still a remnant of hypnosis]. It is necessary to insist explicitly on his renouncing all criticism of the thoughts that he perceives. . .
>
> I have noticed in my psycho-analytical work that the whole frame of mind of a man who is reflecting is totally different from that of a man who is observing his own psychical processes. In reflection there is one more psychical activity at work than in the most attentive self-observation. . . In both cases attention must be concentrated, but the man who is reflecting is also exercising his *critical* faculty. . . The self-observer on the other hand need only take the trouble to suppress his critical

faculty. If he succeeds in doing that, innumerable ideas come into his consciousness of which he could otherwise never have got hold. . . *What is in question, evidently, is the establishment of a psychical state which, in its distribution of psychical energy (that is, of mobile attention), bears some analogy to the state before falling asleep—and no doubt also to hypnosis* [italics ours]. As we fall asleep, "involuntary ideas" emerge, owing to the relaxation of a certain deliberate (and no doubt also critical) activity which we allow to influence the course of our ideas while we are awake. (We usually attribute this relaxation to "fatigue".) As the involuntary ideas emerge, they change into visual and acoustic images. . . [pp. 101-102].

The "visual and acoustic images" clearly indicate a shift toward primary-process functioning. We have already stressed in Chapter 2 how the thought processes in the hypnotic state have the earmarks of primary-process organization.

It was in the study of the dream that Freud first discovered the primary process. An important line of evidence for the primary-process organization of thinking during the hypnotic state is the fact that dreams can be readily produced in the hypnotic subject—though not every hypnotic "dream" should be regarded as the same as a night dream (20).[3]

Further evidence for the reorganization of the thought process in the hypnotic state is the manipulability of various aspects of thought organization, such as memory, attitudes, opinions, etc. The phenomena of hypnotic hypermnesia and posthypnotic amnesia are probably the best known, but one of the ever fascinating aspects of hypnosis is the extent to which it may be employed to alter a subject's views and beliefs and to induce ideas at considerable variance to his usual ones. We believe these phenomena are indicative of the dependence of these aspects of thought organization on the emotional relationship to the hypnotist, and are therefore evidence that in the hypnotic state thought moves away from relative autonomy to a greater dependence on emotion and

[3] We shall return to this subject in our discussion of hypnosis and sleep.

drive organization. Generalizing from Rapaport's concept of two types of memory organization (184), we suggest that with hypnotic regression there takes place a shift from the conceptual organization of thought toward the drive organization of thought.

In our presentation of the motility changes in the established state, we quoted Freud to the effect that the dreamer's unconscious impulses are "harmless" because they cannot bring about any motor activity, and moreover that the two conditions under which such unconscious impulses do have access to motility are psychosis and spontaneous somnambulism (76, p. 510). Here Freud seems to make the motor paralysis the proximal cause of the appearance of primitive impulse. This is analogous to the argument that primary-process thinking in dreams is a result of defensive distortion. Neither of these propositions is correct. Primary-process functioning is a form of functioning which depends on a regressed state of the ego. Motor paralysis in sleep is a characteristic of this regressed state as is the fact that primary-process thinking is not transformed into secondary-process thinking. The primary-process mechanisms may be secondarily employed as defensive devices to elude the "censor," but the defensive purpose is not the cause of their appearance.[4]

Similarly in hypnosis, the appearance of primary-process thought is an accompaniment of the regressed ego state. Why the motor apparatus can become accessible to the ego in hypnosis we have yet to discuss.

It was not until *Group Psychology and the Analysis of the Ego* (88) that Freud offered a structural description—what we would call a description as an "altered state"—of hypnosis. He concluded: "Hypnosis resembles being in love in being limited to these two persons, but it is based entirely on

---

[4] It is not clear whether this use should be regarded as "secondary," or whether eluding censorship and cognitive means appropriate to a particular ego state are not two different ways of looking at the same thing.

sexual impulsions that are inhibited in their aims, and puts the object in the place of the ego ideal" (p. 143).[5]

It was this structural view which led Freud to rule out identification as playing a role in hypnosis: "The group multiplies this process; it agrees with hypnosis in the nature of the instincts which hold it together, and in the replacement of the ego ideal by the object; but to this it adds identification with other individuals, which was perhaps originally made possible by their having the same relation to the object" (88, p. 143). Since he felt that identification involved a change in the ego, and since he felt that in hypnosis the change took place in the ego ideal, he denied to identification a role in hypnosis. This point also has bearing on the transference theory of hypnosis.[6]

In discussing neurosis in the same chapter, Freud makes a further distinction between hypnosis and being in love, and here states, concerning the hypnotic state: "To this extent it [neurosis] resembles hypnosis and group formation in having the character of a regression, which is absent from being in love" (88, p. 143).

Rado (176) restated this thesis by saying that in hypnosis a parasitic double of the superego is erected.[7]

Jones (123) developed somewhat further Freud's idea of the object taking the place of the ego ideal by attempting to detail the mechanism by which this occurs. In essence, his explanation rests on what he considers to be the increased narcissism of the ego, resulting from its fusion with the narcissistic elements of the ego ideal. The latter he derives from two sources, (a) that part of the narcissism represented by the overestimation of the parent which is actually a derivative of

[5] In this work the ego ideal was for Freud synonymous with what he later labeled the superego. The term ego ideal has lately been redefined in other ways (Annie Reich, 191, 192), but these differ somewhat from Freud's own earlier, more complex differentiations in the ego, and definitions of the ego ideal in "On Narcissism: an Introduction" (80).

[6] See p. 140 ff.

[7] Freud introduced the notion of a parasitic double of the *ego* in his discussion of traumatic war neuroses (85).

the ego's primary narcissism, and (b) that part of the primary narcissism which has become attached to the ideal ego, another constituent of the ego ideal (see Schilder, 204). The unification of these forms of narcissism in the ego as a result of the regressive dissolution of the differentiation between ego and ego ideal results in a suspension of the critical faculties of the ego ideal, so that "ego-syntonic ideas are able to follow unchecked the pleasure-pain principle in accordance with the primitive belief in the omnipotence of thought" (123, p. 288). The condition for all this Jones finds in the repression of allo-erotic impulses (cf. with Freud's insistence that sexuality in hypnosis is aim-inhibited rather than autoerotic as Jones considers it to be) by a regression of the libido in the direction of autoerotism, which results in a further reinforcement of the ego's narcissism.

In effect, then, Jones was describing the hypnotic state as one of regression in the ego—to a more narcissistic and autoerotic organization—and specifying one aspect of the ego-ideal (superego) regression as suspension of its criticizing faculty. Altogether, his view is expressed more in intrapsychic terminology than was Freud's. He concerns himself much more with structural alterations within the psyche than with the relationships with the object, whereas Freud dealt with both in his formula that the "object takes the place of the ego ideal."

Fenichel explicitly added ego functions to Rado's formulation concerning superego functions in his explanation of hypnosis (64). "The hypnotist takes over the function of the patient's superego, and even some of the functions of the patient's very ego 'as a temporary, parasitical double of the superego'" (p. 563).

Actually, it is clear that Freud would have agreed with this view, since in *Group Psychology and the Analysis of the Ego* (88) he stated: "The fact that the ego experiences in a dream-like way whatever he [the hypnotist] may request or assert reminds us that we omitted to mention among the functions

of the ego ideal the business of testing the reality of things"
(p. 114). By 1923 (88, p. 114 [footnote added in 1923]; 90),
however, he concluded that the function of testing the reality
of things should be ascribed not to the superego but to the
ego, a view which he felt would fit in with "what we know of
the relations of the ego to the world of perception . . ." (90,
p. 34).

We may point out that Freud failed to follow through
some of the consequences of this revision for his distinction
between identification and hypnosis and being in love. In
identification he said that the object is put in place of the
ego; in hypnosis (and love) the object is put in the place of
the ego ideal. This distinction resulted in Freud's failing to
emphasize the role of identification in hypnosis, though he
did ask whether identification and object cathexis could coexist (88, p. 114). It was Schilder who remedied this deficiency
in hypnotic theory, as we pointed out in our discussion of
the transference theory of hypnosis.

Schilder and Kauders undertook a much more elaborate
dissection, from the structural point of view, of the ego in the
hypnotic state, and we will present their theory here as it is
discussed in "A Textbook of Hypnosis" (208).[8]

Schilder's and Kauders' argument is that a suggestive rapport exists between subject and hypnotist which is controlled
by this "more central" portion of the personality, and that
the psychic depth of hypnosis (to be distinguished from the
depth in terms of suggestibility, the usual criterion of depth)
depends on which portions of the personality pertain to the
rapport and which to the "central ego," in other words, how
much of the "central ego" has really accepted the hypnotic

---

[8] Schilder's terminology is to some extent his own. He speaks of a "more
central" portion of the total personality, apparently identifies this with the
controlling personality, and identifies this in turn with the "ego ideal."
Finally he has an "ideal ego," and in Goals and Desires of Man (204) says:
"It would also be simpler to use the terms ego ideal and ideal ego inter-
changeably as I have done, since the ideals a person has about himself, the
way he wishes to be, is indeed an integral part of the superego" (pp. 226-
227)

relationship. They state that this may range from simulation and play-acting to "complete submission."[9]

The further complexities of the view of Schilder and Kauders as to the constituents of the ego in the hypnotic state result from their view of the relation of sleep to hypnosis: they regard the hypnotized person as in varying degrees of sleep, and further believe that if he is not at all asleep, he is not in hypnosis but in a state of "waking suggestion." We will defer further discussion of their views to our chapter on the relationship between hypnosis and sleep.

In our own early paper, "Alterations in the State of the Ego in Hypnosis" (27), summarized in Chapter 2, we enumerated the regressive *phenomena* which occur in the hypnotic state, but we did not see the generally regressive nature of the total hypnotic process. One of us (100) in 1948 suggested that in hypnosis there occurs a weakening of the defensive and synthetic functions and also proposed a principle of selective alteration in these functions as differentiating between regressed states induced by drugs and by hypnosis. Fisher in 1953 renamed this principle "differential regression," and proposed expanding it to explain "differences in depth of hypnosis as well as variations in the characteristics of different states of regression" (72, p. 433). He pointed out that Hartmann and Schilder (116), who, with the help of drugs, had hypnotized ten out of fourteen paretics, were able to show increased suggestibility in the spheres of judgment, thinking, and sensory phenomena (hallucinations) but with the absence of somnolence, amnesia, or motor phenomena. They explained their results in this pioneering study in selective regression as due to the interference with repressive processes caused by a damaged ego structure and the loss of motives for forgetting.

---

[9] This insistence that during hypnosis there persist evidences of the normal waking ego is one to which we have ourselves referred in our description of the phenomena. We will return to it in our own later theoretical discussion of the hypnotic state as a regression in the service of the ego.

Fisher adds that in suggestibility there are regressive changes in the id, ego, superego, and object relations, but that these are of a temporary character and "anchored in specific types of interpersonal relationships" (72, p. 429). The conclusions he draws, however, as to the state of the ego in accepting or responding to the suggestions appear to us somewhat contradictory. On the one hand, because he found oral fantasies in suggestibility, he concluded that suggestibility is associated with a regression from the kind of judgment exercised by the reality ego to that exercised by the pleasure ego (93). On the other hand, because he found anal fantasies, he related his views to Fenichel's argument that after the child renounces his belief in his own omnipotence he considers the adult who has now become an independent object to be omnipotent and tries by introjection to share this omnipotence (64), and concluded that the ego in suggestion is at a stage where there is already consideration for the object.

Fisher emphasizes that both analysis and hypnosis are induced regressed states, quoting the earlier statements to this effect of Macalpine, Nunberg, and Gill, and suggests that this regression is only partial.

For our own extension of the psychoanalytic theory of the established state as an altered state we take as our empirical base what we regard as a crucial difference between the induction and the state of hypnosis—the capacity for the return of apparently normal functioning.

In Chapter 2 we described how a hypnotized subject can seem to be functioning so normally that it is difficult if not impossible for an experienced hypnotist to tell that the subject is in hypnosis: the situation becomes clear only when certain kinds of pressure and stress are applied. But even though we propose to use this phenomenon as an empirical base for our theorizing, we must point out that some necessary evidence remains to be gathered and some perplexing questions arise.

Can we be certain that normal functioning is impossible

during the induction phase? Has anyone tried to test for normal or apparently normal sensorimotor functioning and thinking while hypnosis is being induced? The very asking of the question conjures up a peculiar and paradoxical picture to anyone who has worked with hypnosis, since to test for normal functioning seems to be contrary to the whole aim of induction. Surely such interventions could only halt the induction. Reasonable though such a conclusion seems, experiments will have to be devised to test whether it is in fact true.

And the return of apparently normal functioning during the state? Can this occur spontaneously, or does it have to be induced, and is it therefore only a very interesting but artificial phenomenon and not to be used as the "natural" base for distinguishing induction and state? The apparently normally functioning subject has to be made so by the hypnotist; it is necessary to demonstrate to the subject that he can, on suggestion, behave as though he were in a normal state. We have described how the subject who is left to his own devices in the hypnotic state sinks into a kind of lethargy, awaiting instructions.

We would propose to resolve this issue as follows. Induction requires the restriction of the functioning of the sensorimotor apparatuses and of thinking as well as of the subject's control of these functions. The state, however, is compatible with the subject's control of these functions at the behest of the hypnotist. Whether the subject in the state will spontaneously regain control of his functions will depend in general on his preconceptions of the nature of hypnosis, and especially on the apparent clues to the nature of hypnosis which he is furnished by the manner in which the hypnotist carries out induction. For example, if the hypnotist employs a sleeping technique, we suspect that the subject is less likely spontaneously to regain control of functioning than if the hypnotist had employed the so-called waking technique (223). But this too will have to be empirically studied.

It is also probable that people vary in the degree to which they will spontaneously regain normal functioning. White has pointed out that hypnotic subjects seem divisible into lethargic and alert types, and he believes he has found personality correlates to these types, the lethargic ones being more negativistic and anxious, and the alert types being more affiliative (227). Specific events in the subject's life history may determine whether or not a particular function can be disrupted during induction or restored during the state. This may be the explanation of unexpected and idiosyncratic responses to certain hypnotic suggestions on the part of otherwise good subjects. Ehrenreich has reported an instance in which a subject refused to accept a suggestion to clasp her hands; later exploration revealed fair evidence that this was a result of anxiety aroused by a specific early trauma (51).

One of us earlier proposed that difficulties in producing specific changes (e.g., perceptual or motor) in certain hypnotic subjects may be due to the fact that these autonomous apparatuses had once been regressively invaded by instinctual energy, and that the threatened revival of such regression by the hypnosis was warded off by a defensive maneuver (72, p. 432). Fisher has expressed the same point by suggesting that the attempt to manipulate any function may run into specific fantasy systems and the anxiety connected with them (72).

Kubie and Margolin find the distinguishing characteristic of the difference between the induction phase and the established state in the same set of phenomena we are here discussing. That they refer to the same phenomenon which we call "regaining control of the apparatuses" is seen in the following quotation:

> . . . the hypnotic state differs basically from the process of induction in that once he is fully hypnotized the subject need not remain silent, inert, and apart. If appropriate words from the hypnotist engender corresponding purposes in the subject, he will walk around, converse intelligently, and in general make

it evident that his sensori-motor horizons have re-expanded, seemingly to their pre-hypnotic limits [145, p. 618].

As we have mentioned, their explanation is in terms of ego boundaries: "The shift to the fully developed final phase of the hypnotic state involves . . . a partial re-expansion of the Ego boundaries . . ." (p. 621).

We leave the matter here, but will take it up again in our general theoretical statement in which we will once again deal with hypnosis as an altered state. We would like to emphasize again, however, that the psychoanalytic theory of hypnosis fails to distinguish between induction and state.

But there has been an important structural concept introduced into ego psychology by Rapaport (184) which we believe is applicable to our discussion of hypnosis as an altered state. By way of his studies of thought organization and various forms of consciousness, Rapaport came to propose that there are quasi-stable organizations of the psychic apparatus which are different from each other on a number of parameters, of which he specified four: (1) kind of reflective awareness; (2) changes in, including absence of, voluntariness; (3) changes in thought organization; and (4) cathectic changes underlying these three. Rapaport himself has distinguished and exemplified a number of what he terms "states of consciousness," such as waking, dream, reverie, hypnagogic, the states of consciousness of general paresis and of Korsakow psychosis (179, 184), and, together with Gill, the first and second stages of fugue (183, p. 197).

Hypnosis is clearly another example of an altered state of consciousness. To take up Rapaport's criteria of such a state: (1) A specific kind of reflective awareness. In Chapter 2 we described changes in self-awareness in hypnosis as seen in loss of self-consciousness, literalness, and humorlessness. (2) Changes in voluntariness. We have described these as alterations of motility in hypnosis. (3) Changes in thought organization. The shift to primary-process thinking in hypnosis has been one of our prominent themes. (4) Cathectic changes underlying these three. We will try to describe some of these for hypnosis in our later discussion of the metapsychology of the hypnotic state from the economic point of view. As an altered state, then, hypnosis can be described in terms of Rapaport's concept of states of consciousness. But in our discussions of hypnosis we have used the expressions "states of altered ego-functioning" and sometimes "ego states"; sometimes for the sake of brevity we refer to a changed "ego state" simply as an "altered state." We must discuss the difference between Rapaport's terminology and ours.

He uses the term "states of consciousness" for several reasons: first, his empirical base lies in subjectively apprehended differing kinds of consciousness; secondly, he is attempting to use the term "consciousness" not merely as an index or an epiphenomenon, but rather as a variously organized structure with dynamics, economics, genetics, and an adaptive role of its own.[10] It is for these reasons, we believe, that he appears to regard these various states as levels of organization of consciousness, and speaks of the use which "consciousness" makes of the tools of thought, i.e., the selection of such tools which states of consciousness have at their disposal.

To various "ego states" there are coordinate various "states of consciousness." An ego state includes not only a form of consciousness, but particular defensive and controlling as well as other organizations. The transitional symptoms which occur both on going into and coming out of hypnosis bespeak the fact that the ego state is changing from one form to another.

Rapaport has demonstrated that the various states of consciousness are not discretely isolated organizations, but exist on a continuum, gradually shading from one to another (179). Empirical evidence shows nevertheless that there are various relatively stable and relatively unstable organizations. As will

[10] This view of consciousness as a structure (or apparatus) we will discuss further in Chapter 5.

have been clear from our preceding discussions, we believe a decisive difference between the induction period and the established state is that the former is relatively unstable, the latter relatively stable. We will pursue this distinction in Chapter 5.

## Persistence of Over-all Ego Structure

In this section we will review the psychoanalytic concept of regression in the service of the ego, introduced by Kris (137), show that there are hypnotic phenomena which indicate that hypnosis *is* such a regression, and summarize some of the general differences on a phenomenal level between regression proper and regression in the service of the ego. Our metapsychological discussion of regression in the service of the ego we reserve for Chapter 5.

We have described a number of phenomena which reflect the persistence of the usual psychic organization in some fashion even during the hypnotic state. We have called these phenomena evidences of a reality-oriented relationship between hypnotist and subject, and of retention by the subject of some control of the sensorimotor apparatus and mental functioning. We spoke of gross evidence such as the occasional instance in which the status of the hypnotist plays a role in hypnotizability, or more subtle evidence, like avoidance of an obstacle for which a negative hallucination has been created. We also mentioned evidences of current orientation during a hypnotically induced "chronological regression," and the limits on the antisocial behavior which a subject can be induced to carry out by hypnotic suggestion.

These persisting evidences of the usual ego-functioning will be more gross or subtle depending on the skill and time which have been devoted to the development of some special hypnotic phenomena. For example, if age regression is crudely and rapidly carried out, evidences of current orientation will be gross and obvious. But with time and skill, these will become more subtle and difficult to discern, to the extent that there are even those who regard complete revivification (total reinstatement of a psychic state) to be possible, in contrast to regression. As one of us earlier pointed out (100), total revivification is not possible, as shown, if by nothing else, by the fact that the subject will return to current orientation on a prearranged signal. A good subject for whom such a signal has not been prearranged may seem not to know what the hypnotist is talking about when he speaks to him in his capacity of hypnotist and suggests return to current orientation, but this is just bad technique.[11] It is magic to suppose that the current orientation is "ablated," as the expression has it (55, 146). In fact, it is one of our major constructs that hypnosis is characterized as a particular kind of regression in that the usual organization of the psyche is *not* ablated.[12] Evidences of the persistence of the normal psychic organization have been noted by all the prominent investigators of hypnosis. Freud said:

> It is noticeable that, even when there is complete suggestive compliance in other respects, the moral conscience of the person hypnotized may show resistance. But this may be due to the fact that in hypnosis as it is usually practiced, some knowledge may be retained that what is happening is only a game, an untrue reproduction of another situation of far more importance to life [88, p. 116; see also p. 127].

Schilder (208) also says a good deal about the persistence of normal ego functions: "In other words, all the regressions mentioned above are only partial regressions, whereas a considerable portion of the personality maintains its normal relations with the outside world" (p. 96). This is also the meaning of his remark that "This fact [reservations which the subject makes for himself in hypnosis] deprives hypnosis of the pro-

---

[11] There is an example of this in *The Search for Bridey Murphy* (16).

[12] Nor is it "ablated" in regression proper, even though regression proper is often discussed as though it represented a complete return to an earlier state. We will discuss this later in more detail.

found seriousness which distinguishes every truly great passion. 'Hypnosis is but a timid attempt to return to chaos; it lacks the great, free, unconditional surrender' " (p. 99).

In the following we will try to show that these persisting evidences of normal ego-functioning enable us to classify hypnosis as a regression in the service of the ego, one of the two classes of regression which have been described—regression proper and regression in the service of the ego.

Fisher (71), referring to Sterba's article (215) on the separation of the analysand's ego into an observing and an experiencing portion, suggested that analysis be considered a regression in the service of the ego (an idea which one of us had also proposed in an unpublished paper), but does not explicitly thus characterize hypnosis.

A recent paper by Bellak independently introduces the idea of hypnosis as a regression in the service of the ego, though Bellak prefers to call hypnosis "a special case of the self-excluding function of the ego" (14).

Sarbin (201) has introduced a role-taking theory of hypnosis which can also be characterized as a "regression in the service of the ego" theory, though he does not use that terminology. His special emphasis is on the degree to which various kinds of role-taking behavior, among which he includes hypnosis as a special case, displaces the usual psychic organization.

The concept of "regression in the service of the ego" we owe largely to Kris, who took Freud's explanation of wit (78) as his point of departure. Freud offered the formula, "A preconscious thought is left for a moment to unconscious elaboration and the results are forthwith grasped by the conscious perception" (78, p. 750). In 1936 Kris described regression in the service of the ego as follows: "The ego enrolls the primary process in its service and makes use of it for its purposes" (137, p. 177). In 1949 he stated more elaborately: "The general assumption says that under certain conditions the ego regulates its own capacity to regression, that the organizing functions of the ego include the function of voluntary and temporary withdrawal of cathexis . . . in order later to regain improved control" (136, p. 488).

The systematic position of the concept "regression in the service of the ego" as related to other basic psychoanalytic propositions concerning the relationship between primitive instinctual impulses and id-functioning on the one hand, and derived motivational impulses and ego-functioning on the other hand, is by no means clear. More specifically, the relationships between this concept, sublimation, and neutralization are little understood. The fact that both sublimation and regression in the service of the ego are so frequently discussed in connection with problems of creativity may mean that they are more closely related to each other than either is to neutralization. In a noteworthy passage, Freud describes a process he leaves unnamed but which could be regarded as either regression in the service of the ego or as sublimation.

> Co-operation between a preconscious and an unconscious impulse, even when the latter is intensely repressed, may come about if there is a situation in which the unconscious impulse can act in the same sense as one of the dominant trends. The repression is removed in this instance, and the repressed activity is admitted as a reinforcement of the one intended by the ego. The unconscious becomes ego-syntonic in respect of this single conjunction without any change taking place in its repression apart from this. In this co-operation the influence of the *Ucs.* is unmistakable: the reinforced tendencies reveal themselves as being nevertheless different from the normal; they make specially perfect functioning possible, and they manifest a resistance in the face of opposition which is similar to that offered, for instance, by obsessional symptoms [83, pp. 194-195].

We do not propose to attempt anything so ambitious as a discussion of the relationships between regression in the service of the ego, sublimation, and neutralization, but will try only to clarify the relationship between regression proper and regression in the service of the ego. Much remains to be done in this area. For example, Kris's own writing reveals some lack of clarity in these two concepts. In "On Preconscious Mental Mechanisms" (136, p. 487) he includes sleep and psychosis under regression proper. Later in the same essay (p. 488) sleep is described as an example of the ego's ability to regulate its own capacity to regress, other examples being the creative process and sexual functioning. Thus in the first instance Kris includes sleep under the conditions of ego weakness, while in the second sleep is included in a grouping showing ego strength and contrasted with the ego weakness inferred from the inability of obsessional characters to suspend ego control. We know that ego weakness often precludes sleep; on the other hand, some instances of ego weakness result in hypersomnia. Which of these is regression in the service of the ego? May sleep sometimes be a dethronement of the ego and sometimes be in the service of the ego, and must we therefore define its use in terms of a more total context rather than simply calling it one or the other?

It could be proposed that *all* regression must be considered to be in the service of the ego. It could be argued, for example, that a psychotic regression is an adaptation—regressive to be sure, yet an adaptation, enforced by frustration or some other cause; that since adaptation is an ego function, even such a regression must be viewed as in the service of the ego. Again, regression in an obsessional neurosis, which enables the individual to avoid a yet deeper regression, to psychosis for example, would also deserve to be called a regression in the service of the ego. Where then are we to draw the line? That there is a difference between the regression involved in making a joke and that in a florid psychosis seems perfectly clear, but how are we to define this difference systematically?

As an introduction to our later discussion of the metapsychology of hypnosis as a regression in the service of the ego, we will discuss the descriptive features of a regression in the service of the ego and try to show how hypnosis fits into this description (see Schafer, 202).

It must first be pointed out that there is a very close connection between the individual ego structure and the different kinds of regression. The capacity for the two kinds of regression changes as an ego becomes freer from rigid defensive maneuvers and can more flexibly and adaptively use techniques of control rather than defense: regression in the service of the ego becomes more possible, regression proper less so. This kind of distinction is often but not very helpfully discussed in terms of ego strength and ego weakness. The capacity to joke we know is often revived by a successful analysis in people who before could not remember jokes, let alone tell them. Freer sexual activity is of course one of the most common results of successful analysis, and blocking in free sexual functioning is one of the commonest inhibitions suffered by a "weak" ego. Here we have an explanation for differences in hypnotizability, comparing extreme groups (though not individuals within a particular group): the lesser hypnotizability of psychiatric patients as against normal subjects, for example. This criterion may also help to explain the relatively greater hypnotizability of hysterics among psychiatric patients as compared with other categories of illness. It is generally conceded that, of all psychiatric disorders, hysteria is by and large the syndrome least incompatible with relatively good ego strength. Empirical work needs to be done to determine whether among hysterics those with the greater ego strength are the more readily hypnotizable, though the factor of ego strength is certainly not the only one which determines the issue.[13]

Studies on individual fluctuations in hypnotizability concomitant with changes in ego state would also be pertinent in this connection. We can further point out that the capacity for regression in the service of the ego will vary with the

[13] For a discussion of the cathectic dynamics of the hysteric in hypnosis, see pp. 217-218.

amount of stress under which an ego is laboring. Under relaxed circumstances a person may be able to use humor, which may be impossible when he is feeling tense and anxious. But the situation is quite complex. There are also people who joke only under the stimulus of a certain degree of anxiety or of threatened depression.

A regression in the service of the ego is time-limited. It has a distinct beginning and end, and is not a condition which might indefinitely persist. Hypnosis is also relatively limited in time, has a distinct beginning and end, and is limited to the specific situation of the actual interpersonal relationship with the hypnotist.

We can restate this first consideration from a somewhat different point of view by saying that the regression must end abruptly, with a particular psychic act, so that the psychological functioning is, at a stroke, as it were, restored to its *status quo ante*. The regression must not only be reversible, but its reversal is a sudden, total reinstatement and not a slow and gradual reconstruction. A psychosis which has been successfully weathered may be said to have been a regression which was reversed, but the manner of reversal was a slow reconstruction, and not the sudden, total reinstatement of the previous ego state, which is possible in hypnosis, for example, by the hypnotist's simply giving a signal.

Under proper conditions, a regression in the service of the ego may be terminated by the person himself, unaided. In hypnosis, for example, if a suggestion is made which conflicts too strongly with the subject's moral sense, he may abruptly and without—or even against—the hypnotist's instructions break out of the trance and be restored to his usual self. This kind of restoration, even in circumstances of peril, is unusual in a regression proper. This is not to say that environmental conditions may not play a role in determining the depth of regression in regression proper. It is well known, for example, that hospitalization may result in a sudden, sharp increase in the degree of regression in a person who is psychiatrically ill, and that, on the other hand, a regression may be temporarily overcome when environmental demand rises.

A corollary of the preceding point is that regression in the service of the ego occurs only in the presence of specific "safe" external conditions. The ego appraises these conditions before embarking on the regression. Joking will not occur if it is inappropriate. Sleep will be foregone for surprisingly long periods of time if an emergency situation demands that the person remain awake. Creative work can go on only under quite unusual circumstances if more immediate and pressing demands of self-preservation arise. Regression proper does not wait for propitious external circumstances, but on the contrary is characterized precisely by the fact that the behavior is such as would be regarded as inappropriate and inexpedient by the person prior to the regression. Or it may occur despite his recognition that it is inappropriate and inexpedient. Hypnosis will occur only when the ego judges the external situation to be a safe one.

Having spoken of the fact that in regression in the service of the ego the person voluntarily establishes the conditions for regression, what can we say of the voluntary or involuntary quality of the regressive activity itself? We can define this only by the subjective sense of being active or being receptive and passive. As Kris has pointed out, the experience of passive reception is especially common in states of inspiration (135). This experience is surely to be attributed to the role played by id forces. A similar feeling of helpless compulsion is common in regression proper. Since in regression in the service of the ego the subjective experience may or may not be one of passivity, we must admit that the criterion of the subjective sense of activity or passivity will not differentiate the two kinds of regression; but the subjective sense of voluntarily undertaking the activity can. To at least some extent, people can learn the conditions in which they can create, for example, and actively seek out such conditions. In the wider context, then, regression in the service of the ego is active.

We are here in agreement with Rapaport, who has dealt with the difference between the two kinds of regression in a paper on activity and passivity (187).

In regression proper the ego is helplessly inundated. In regression in the service of the ego, it initiates, lends itself to, and uses regressive mental activity for its own purposes. Hypnosis is a situation which is often specifically sought by the individual, as, for example, when it is used in psychotherapy or as an anesthetic. We will later discuss the activity-passivity balance in hypnosis as a way of characterizing it metapsychologically.

It does not seem possible to differentiate between the two kinds of regression in terms of how widely or totally they encompass the person. A regression in the service of the ego may be sweeping, as in a creative spell or deep somnambulism. The same may be true of a regression proper, which may totally inundate the personality, as in an acute and florid psychotic break, or it may be more specific and localized, as in particular phobias and in the more chronic states of severe regression—an ambulatory schizophrenia, for example.

Another way of stating this last point is to say that the apparent maintenance of many areas of psychic functioning will not—descriptively, at any rate—allow us to distinguish between the two kinds of regression. We have described how the sensorimotor apparatuses and thinking may seem severely impaired in hypnosis, but also that there are hypnotic states in which the apparatuses function apparently unimpaired. And the same thing can be said for regression proper. This accounts for the fact that a searching clinical interview may fail to turn up evidences of thought disorder which are clear on projective psychological tests.

To summarize these considerations: a regression in the service of the ego is

1. more likely to occur as the ego grows more adaptive and less likely to occur as the ego grows less adaptive;

2. marked by a definite beginning and end;

3. reversible, with a sudden and total reinstatement of the usual organization of the psyche;

4. terminable under certain emergency conditions by the person unaided;

5. one which occurs only when the person judges the circumstances to be safe;

6. one which is voluntarily sought by the individual and is—relative to a regression proper—active rather than passive.

And the two kinds of regression cannot be distinguished by

1. how totally they engulf the personality, or otherwise expressed, by

2. the degree to which autonomous apparatuses continue to function.

We must point out that what we have been describing is a model of the two kinds of regression, from which there are actually many deviations. A regression in the service of the ego may tend toward some of the characteristics of a regression proper. In hypnosis, for example, the subject may not feel sure the hypnosis has terminated; the condition may be reversed only gradually and after a more or less prolonged period of reorganization; the subject may be unable to resist a suggestion, once he is in the hypnotic state, even if the suggestion conflicts with his conscious wish or values; the subject may fall into hypnosis on the proper signal even if he has cogent reasons for not wishing to do so at that particular time; he may fall into the hypnotic state apparently compulsively and spontaneously,[14] or, as his ego grows more adaptive through psychotherapy, for example, he may become less and less willing to respond to, and less and less even susceptible to, the induction of hypnosis.

On the other hand, a regression proper may tend toward some of the characteristics of a regression in the service of the ego. The regression may appear in sudden "spells," and disappear equally abruptly (e.g., a tantrum). When such a spell

[14] See pp. 66-70.

s over, the ego may seem to be restored to what it was before. We have already remarked that external circumstances can result in the deepening or inhibition of regression proper. In this sense it may appear only when the individual considers the external circumstances safe. The person, knowing that he is subject to episodes of regression proper, may try to keep his circumstances such that the regression will not prove too damaging; and in movement toward an ultimately more adaptive ego structure there may occur episodes of regression not previously experienced, e.g., acting out in the course of psychoanalysis.

# 5

# THE METAPSYCHOLOGY OF REGRESSION AND HYPNOSIS[1]

In this chapter we will attempt to formulate a metapsychological theory of hypnosis as a regression. If there existed an integrated account of the metapsychology of regression itself, we would have only to relate the special theory of hypnosis as a regression to the general theory of regression. There is no such general theory and we shall not attempt to offer one here, though in our presentation of the metapsychology of hypnosis we will occasionally remark on a more general metapsychological theory of regression.

A general theory of regression would have to distinguish between regression proper and regression in the service of the ego. Since we regard hypnosis as a regression in the service of the ego, we shall occasionally have to distinguish the metapsychology of regression proper from regression in the service of the ego.

Our metapsychological treatment of hypnosis as a regression rests on the familiar concept of relative autonomy of the ego from the id, the much less familiar concept of relative autonomy of the ego from the environment (189), and the relationship between these two autonomies. Before we can specifically discuss hypnosis, therefore, we shall have to make a wide detour for a general treatment of autonomy.

[1] We wish to thank Dr. George Klein for his thoughtful criticism of and helpful suggestions concerning this chapter.

## The Concept of Autonomy

The central advance in the theory of psychoanalytic psychology in the last two decades has been the concept of relative autonomy (Hartmann, Rapaport) which has begun to free psychoanalytic theory from its unduly tight motivational, i.e., instinct, lacing. Formerly all motivations, conflict solutions, and defenses were seen as not only arising from, but also as functionally still completely directed by, primitive id strivings. The concept of relative autonomy argues that though strivings, conflict solutions, and defenses may actually derive from primitive id impulses, these constellations develop a relative autonomy and can operate without direct dependence on id strivings. The derived constellations become structuralized in the personality, and indeed the structural point of view is the foundation of the concept of relative autonomy. Two kinds of autonomy have been distinguished. The one we have just sketched is usually referred to as secondary autonomy, the adjective "secondary" denoting that these relatively autonomous functions and structures were originally derived from id strivings. The concept of primarily autonomous structures designates those elements of the psychic apparatus which are not derived from id strivings. The main examples of such primarily autonomous functions are the ego apparatuses, such as memory, perception, and motility. It is now recognized that these ego apparatuses are primary givens in the same sense in which id impulses are, and enter into the development and functioning of the psychic apparatus as independent variables.[2]

We have been describing autonomy as autonomy of the ego from the id, but the concept of relative autonomy must be systematically broadened so that it includes other relative autonomies. One can conceptualize relative autonomy intra-

---

[2] The concept "conflict-free" cuts across primary and secondary autonomy, since both primarily and secondarily autonomous functions and structures may be conflict-free.

systemically, for example, that a particular form of ego activity pursues a path relatively independent of other ego activities. One can conceive of intersystemic autonomy of the ego not only from the id but from the superego as well, and of autonomy between one of the psychic institutions and external reality. To say this is only to state familiar considerations more systematically. A certain balance between any particular relative autonomy and its opposite—we might call it dependency or influenceability—is apparently necessary for adaptive functioning, but varies in degree for various relative autonomies. The relative autonomy of id* and superego from external reality is normally much greater than that of the ego from external reality. As between the ego and the external world, if the ego were blown aside by every gust of change, it could hardly be a stable functioning apparatus, but if it were rigidly resistant to influence by external changes, however powerful, its adaptability would likewise be seriously impaired.

Despite the fact that relative autonomy of ego from id[3] has received much more attention in the psychoanalytic literature than any other, we believe that relative autonomy of the ego from external environment is equally important.

RELATIVE AUTONOMY FROM THE ENVIRONMENT

Relative autonomy of the ego from the external environment has been systematically discussed only by Rapaport

* For a correction of this terminology, see p. 176.

[3] We follow Rapaport (189) in speaking here and throughout this chapter of relative autonomy of the ego from the "id." The ego comprises various kinds of structures and functions. Certainly two major classes are means structures and motivations. Employing the concept "id" in the sense of the congeries of basic drives, we mean by relative autonomy of the ego that both means structures and motivations are relatively autonomous from basic drive. It is also true that means structures are relatively autonomous from derived motivations as well as from basic drive. But we retain the designation "relative autonomy from id" rather than "from motivation" because we wish to include the idea of relative autonomy of ego motivations from basic drive. There are clearly many complex questions here, but a further discussion would carry us away from our present purpose. We want to indicate that we are not unaware of the sloppiness in thinking which the concept "id" often seems to invite.

(189). The concept was described—though not so named—by Hartmann in his *Ego Psychology and the Problem of Adaptation* (114) in terms of "internalization" and the creation of an "inner world." This inner world he calls "one of the ego's regulating factors" (p. 57). He regards the human intellect as the high point in the evolution of this process of internalization, and then expresses what we will call relative autonomy from the environment in the following way: "Causal thinking (in relation to perception of space and time), the creation and use of means-end relations, and particularly the turning of thinking back upon the self, liberate the individual from being compelled to react to the immediate stimulus" (p. 60). Thus, just as the ego is not enslaved to the immediate drive demand, so is it not enslaved to the immediate external conditions.

The ego is therefore not simply a mediator between id and environment and the slave of both; it is a structure with energies at its disposal and as such it has autonomy from—that is to say, can pit forces against—the id on the one hand and the environment on the other.

Any fruitful application of the concept of relative autonomy from the environment would require an analysis and systematization of the concept "environment" (115). Here we can touch on only a few main points. We must distinguish between the space-time environment and the social environment, that is, between the world of objects in the usual sense of physical objects and the world of objects in the psychoanalytic sense of other human beings. It seems clear that of the two, the space-time environment is the "simpler"; an environment that is differentiated in social terms is necessarily also differentiated in space-time terms, whereas an environment may be differentiated in space-time terms but not in social terms. We will later ask whether one can distinguish two kinds of relative autonomy from the environment, one from the space-time and the other from the social.

Besides this differentiation into two kinds of environment,

we must also distinguish between the environment as an external system of forces and the environment as it is intra-psychically represented. Relative autonomy from the environment is possible only when external reality and its internal representation are more or less congruent. These two environments usually are congruent, since the normal human being does come to know reality more or less "as it really is," though in saying this, we do not intend to minimize the actively selective role the organism plays in perception. In extreme situations, however, this veridical framework can be over-thrown in favor of a restructuring of reality in conformity with drive, and relative autonomy from the environment will be impossible, since the ego must have a fairly good represen-tation of reality if it is to deal with it. When the ego does not have a good representation of reality, it may be said to be ignoring reality, a situation of reality obliviousness rather than autonomy. In fact it may be that such a state of obliviousness comes about as the result of a sharp decrement in relative autonomy. As the ego loses its ability to pit forces against the environment it may resort to a psychotic denial of reality.

An immediate response to a noxious stimulus does not necessarily mean loss of autonomy from the environment; such a response may be the most adaptive one. Immediate response would have the significance of loss of autonomy only if it could be demonstrated that the ego had lost its capacity to choose not to respond immediately.

There are limits set to relative autonomy from the en-vironment by the nature of the environment. The organism can ignore external reality—whether it knows the reality or is oblivious to it—only up to a point, beyond which reality will make itself felt. A man on a hunger strike will eventually die. Psychotic denial of the death of a loved one does not undo the reality of the death. Needless to say, it is also not possible for the environment to force an individual to do what "it is not in him to do." If a child does not have the capacity to read, no amount of urging will make him read. And if a man cannot love or fight or surrender, exhortation will not make him do so.

A concept which is corollary to relative autonomy from the environment, and one which will bulk large in our future considerations, is automatization. This concept was first given a clear and detailed statement by Hartmann in *Ego Psychology and the Problem of Adaptation* (114):

> The ego uses somatic apparatuses to execute actions. I will discuss first the motor apparatuses. In adults they are organized for certain achievements. In well-established achievements they function automatically: the integration of the somatic systems involved in the action is automatized, and so is the integration of the individual psychological acts involved in it. With increasing exercise of the action its intermediate steps disappear from consciousness. To explain this Kretschmer proposed a law of "formular abbreviation."[4]. . . Not only motor behavior, but perception and thinking, too, show *automatization*. Exercise automatizes methods of problem-solving just as much as it does walking, speaking, or writing. . . Observations of automatized functions, and of some other phenomena as well, warn us that the conception of a thoroughly flexible ego is an illusion; yet normally even well-established actions and methods of thinking are not completely rigid. Besides the adaptedness implicit in their use, automatized activities have a certain leeway (of varying latitude) for adaptation to the momentary situation [pp. 87-88].

Later he makes the point which we wish to stress especially:

> Actually both flexibility and automatization are necessary to and characteristic of the ego; purposive achievements depend on some functions taking a flexible, others an automatized form, and still others combining these two forms in various proportions. The ego must also be able to encompass automatized functions in its adaptation processes [p. 92].

---

[4] We will return to this concept in our discussion of the disappearance of the phenomena of the induction stage.

Hartmann's automatizations are those of the apparatuses: perception, motility, and thinking. Automatized apparatuses execute impulses from all levels of the impulse hierarchy; in other words, automatizations are closely related to autonomy. The automatized apparatuses are not only the means by which relatively autonomous motivations are expressed; their formation is a safeguard for the maintenance of the relative autonomy. On the other hand, as Hartmann points out, both flexibility and automatization are necessary for normal functioning. Automatization can interfere with relative autonomy if it means the loss of the capacity to adapt to changing conditions. Thus de-automatization of automatized functions is a part of normal functioning. In what follows we shall show how de-automatization plays a role in the induction of hypnosis.

## THE DECREASE OF RELATIVE AUTONOMY

Though there are many important and interesting problems in how the ego develops its relative autonomy, our principal concern here is with hypnosis, and for hypnosis the issue is that of how relative autonomy can be decreased. In this section we will discuss this issue in general terms preparatory to our later, more specific discussion of hypnosis.

In order to discuss this problem we shall have to distinguish between relative autonomy, obliviousness, and loss of information or input.

The condition of loss of information or of input is not relative autonomy, even though under such circumstances the influence of id or environment on the ego may appear to diminish. We speak of relative autonomy only when the ego is getting information from id or environment, but is not enslaved in the sense that it does not have to respond immediately and in terms of the stimulus, whether from outside or inside.

As we mentioned earlier, relative autonomy must also be distinguished from obliviousness. Relative autonomy from the environment does not mean that the environment is disregarded, but that the environment does not determine in detail the course of events regarding action upon, or perception of, the environment. The normally functioning ego, as described above, must be able to abandon an automatization if environmental circumstances make a more specific and flexible adjustment desirable. Analogously, relative autonomy from the id does not mean obliviousness to motivational urges, but the capacity to assess them and, if necessary, to abandon habitual inhibition or facilitation of discharge. If the ego is oblivious to the id or environmental situation, even though the input is "available," we do not speak of relative autonomy.

Interpersonal perception—that is, the evaluation and understanding of the meaning of interpersonal actions—is probably much more subject to falsification by drive than is the impersonal space-time environment. The primarily autonomous apparatuses of the ego are concerned in the perception of the latter, but there is no similar primarily autonomous apparatus for the former. (This is not to deny that the newborn has an apparatus for socialization [Erikson's concept of mutuality]; but this apparatus is not autonomous from drive in the sense in which are the apparatuses of memory, perception, motility, and the thresholds.)

We make these distinctions because we feel that theoretical discussion would be much obscured if loss of input or obliviousness to id or environment were called increased autonomy. It is true that disregard of id or environment by the ego may appear to be an increase in autonomy, but it is not an increase of *relative* autonomy; it is rather a movement toward total isolation, quite a different thing. In fact, as we shall soon show, when id or environment is disregarded, the id dominates the ego if the environment is disregarded, while the ego comes to be dominated by the environment if the id is disregarded. To forestall confusion, then, we shall speak of increased autonomy only when we mean increased autonomy in an ego which both has access to input and is not oblivious to this input.

A further distinction must be made between decrease of autonomy from id or environment and domination of ego by id or environment. That agency from which autonomy is decreased is not necessarily the agency which dominates; and again autonomy may be decreased from both id and environment, leaving one still to ask which of the two comes to dominate the ego. We shall exemplify various possibilities in discussing the relationship between the two autonomies.

It will be noted that we speak only of the ego as having autonomy. We do not say of either id or environment that it becomes autonomous when it dominates the ego. Autonomy is the name for that relative independence which the growing and maturing ego attains from the id on the one hand and the environment on the other. It is not properly applicable to the id even though the id, like the ego, is an intrapsychic system, because the independence of the id can be only an early normal stage of development or the result of a regression, and not the result of growth and maturation. Nor is it properly applicable to the environment, not only because the environment is an extraorganismic set of forces, but also because domination by the environment can also come about only either as an early normal stage of development or as the result of a regression, and not as a result of the individual's progressive growth and maturation.

It will be useful to have general terms to describe the environmental or motivational situation, since it may or may not be exerting strong pressure on the ego. We will refer to the internal situation as "urge" and to the environmental situation by Murray's term "press" (170).

There are two major ways in which a decrease of relative autonomy may be brought about. These are limitation of input and strong press or urge.

Limitation of input is that situation in which the influx of stimuli to the ego from id or environment is decreased. The decrease may be absolute, as for example in the experiments by Lilly (155) in which the subject is immersed in water, or those by Bexton et al. (17), in which touch, sound, and hearing are significantly reduced. The decrease may be a result of monotony, because the mechanism of sensory adaptation makes monotony equivalent to diminution. This may be called "blocking the channels of intake"; on a level higher than that of purely sensory input, blocking the channels is exemplified by stimuli which give little information. The decreased input may result from decreased motor activity toward the environment, since this cuts down the feedback from activity and thus reduces information or input.

Diminished input from the id is possible only when internal barriers to the reception of stimuli from within are erected, in short, when there exists some form of repression, or more generally, countercathexis. This is likely to be a more or less static condition and is less subject to experimental manipulation than is input from the environment.

We will defer our description of what happens when there is diminution of input until we come to the relationship of the two autonomies, because a change in autonomy from either id or environment is often so closely followed by a change in the other.

The other general way in which autonomy may be diminished is by urge or press becoming strong, since it becomes more difficult for the ego to take distance from and not be compelled to make an immediate response to such a force. A strong social press may range all the way from "keeping up with the Joneses" to brain-washing. A strong nonsocial press may be pressure to attend carefully and for a prolonged period to a space-time stimulus, for instance, driving along a superhighway, flying a plane in close formation, or attending vigilantly to a radar screen while watching for an incoming signal.

A relatively lesser diminution of stimuli from the nonsocial environment can coincide with a relatively greater diminution of social stimuli, as, for example, in solitary confinement.

A strong urge means an increased impulse, however brought about, whether by a process of maturation, as for example puberty, or as a result of the presentation of a particular external object.

Now that we have proposed that diminished input and increased press or urge are two conditions which lead to decreased autonomy, we further suggest that de-automatization is a condition which opens the way for a change in relative autonomy, either an increase or a decrease. De-automatization is an undoing of the automatizations of apparatuses—both means and goal structures—directed toward the environment. De-automatization is, as it were, a shake-up which can be followed by an advance or a retreat in the level of organization.

De-automatization of the apparatuses requires interference with their functioning but is probably not brought about directly by diminished input or increased urge or press. Some manipulation of the attention directed toward the functioning of an apparatus is necessary if it is to be de-automatized, and while such a manipulation of attention may result from diminished input or increased urge or press, these two conditions need not lead to changes in the distribution of attention; and, on the other hand, manipulations of attention with resulting de-automatization may be brought about by means other than these two conditions.

If de-automatization has been brought about as a secondary result of diminished input or increased press or urge and these latter two conditions persist, there will be a decrease of relative autonomy, but if these two conditions either were not originally present or do not persist, an increase in relative autonomy may result, though it need not. For example, strong environmental pressure may forcibly direct attention to a habitual value pattern which then becomes de-automatized. If the pressure continues there may result the substitution of a new value pattern, perhaps even less relatively autonomous than was the old. But if the pressure relaxes, there may result a generally broadened perspective on the issue involved, with an increase in relative autonomy.

## THE RELATIONSHIP BETWEEN THE TWO AUTONOMIES

We must ask whether the autonomies of the ego from the id and from the environment are symmetrical, and whether decrease in one is necessarily followed by decrease in the other.

There are reasons to believe that the relationship is not symmetrical, despite the fact that organism and environment must not be viewed as sharply separable, but rather as an organism-environmental matrix. The assumption of asymmetry follows from consideration of the well-established psychoanalytic proposition which differentiates drive from external stimulus: while drive is constant and inescapable, external stimulus is discontinuous and can be avoided by flight (81). Both autonomies are relative, but the range of relative autonomy from the id is generally more circumscribed than the range of relative autonomy from the environment. Related to this asymmetry is the relative inflexibility of the aim of an instinct as compared with its object.

We must also ask whether decreases of relative autonomy from id and environment always take place together: does one inevitably lead to the other or may they vary independently? The asymmetry of which we have spoken seems to provide a partial answer. The proposition suggests itself that since relative autonomy from the id is the more vulnerable and must be decreased first, the environment will, under circumstances of decrease of autonomy from both sufficient to "dethrone" the ego, be recast in the image of the id forces which gained ascendancy first. But to attribute this leading role to the id without reservation would be to fall into the old fallacy of underestimating external reality. The autonomy of the ego relative to id and external environment is dependent not only on the strength of the ego, not only on the strength of the instincts, but on the "strength" of the environment too. Certain environmental conditions are far more insistent than others. Relative autonomy from the environment is a function of the environment as well as of the ego.

A complexity thus appears in the relationship of the two relative autonomies. In a situation of overwhelming environmental "press," relative autonomy from the environment may be decreased even though there has been no decrease of autonomy from the id. But if the decrease from the environment goes so far that the environment comes to dominate the ego, there will necessarily be a decrease of relative autonomy from the id too, and the motivational pattern will be structured according to the environmental situation (keeping up with the Jonses), and not the environmental pattern according to the motivational press ("wishful thinking").

We will now review what happens when loss of information occurs alone and when it occurs in combination with strong press or urge. If information from the outside world is lost and there is no external press, the result is a restructuring of the external world by idiosyncratic id motivations. The sensory deprivation experiments reported by Bexton et al. are an excellent demonstration of this situation. When the loss of information is from within and there is no strong urge, the result will be behavior determined by the motivation arising from the countercathexis which led to the loss of information from within. This motivation may be primarily derived either from drive or from environmental conditions. The loss of information from outside with a strong environmental press is likely to lead to conformity with this press—a conformity which finally structures the motivational pattern. The famous confessions of the Russian trials seem to be an example of such a situation (19, 134, 168). If there is loss of information from inside, but a strong internal urge, the result may be a condition such as the first stage of fugue, with the environment restructured according to the dominant motivational urge. (It will be noted that loss of information of both environment and the internal state means a loss of all information except as there exists press from outside or imperious urge from inside. In such circumstances it is no longer possible to compare various environmental configurations with one another, or to weigh and balance various and even conflicting motivations.)

Let us review these last considerations in the light of the question of the relationship of the two autonomies. We suggested that when with the loss of autonomy the id comes to dominate the ego, whether because of loss of information from the outside or because of strong urge, the environment is restructured by motivation; when the environment comes to dominate the ego, whether because of loss of information from within or because of strong press, the motivations are restructured by the environment. But a restructuring of either environment or motivation by the other means that there is a decrease of autonomy from the one which is restructured too. In other words, when the ego is dominated by the id, autonomy is also decreased from the environment, and when the ego is dominated by the environment, autonomy is also decreased from the id. In both cases then, the loss of one relative autonomy leads to the decrease of the other. The schizophrenic, for example, who is essentially dominated by the id, may show such a phenomenon as command automatism while the thoroughly brain-washed prisoner who is essentially dominated by the environment may nevertheless show general evidences of an increased emotional lability, albeit in the service of the goals instilled from without. If there is loss of input but no press or urge, the dominating agency becomes the one from which input is coming. But when there is great press or urge, the dominating agency is likely to be the one from which the press or urge comes.

It should also be noted that when as a result of great urge or press either id or environment restructures the other, this also leads to a relative obliviousness to the other, with of course a resulting blocking off of input or information from the other. Furthermore, a great press or urge also leads to a loss of any other input from the same side from which it comes, because the press or urge utilizes all available attention. In other words, great urge or press leads to diminished input from both id and environment except for the urge or press itself.

To summarize: in the normal functioning of the ego, the environmental input is the ultimate safeguard of autonomy from the id, while the id input is the ultimate safeguard of autonomy from the environment.

We must make clear, however, that neither the loss of environmental information nor great environmental press will necessarily lead to decreased autonomy from the environment. Though Bexton et al. say that "the maintenance of normal intelligent adaptive behavior probably requires a continually varied sensory input" (17), this is true only within limits. To disregard these limits is to value too cheaply the structure of the ego. Only some of their subjects showed regressive phenomena; those who resisted the effects of loss of information from the environment did not show evidences of decreased autonomy from the id. If we believe that constant input is necessary to maintain ego-functioning, then we are viewing the ego merely as a mediator between id and environment instead of as a cohesive structure in its own right, and approach the "seething cauldron" concept (177) of psychic functioning. But if we take seriously the ego as a structure, with genuine relative autonomy, we will recognize that it is not so immediately at the mercy of the environment (or the id).

But the examples we have so far offered of what happens when loss of information occurs alone or when it occurs in combination with strong press or urge could all be covered by the hypothesis that relative autonomy from the id and from the environment are parallel and reciprocal phenomena. We have yet to demonstrate the asymmetry which it seemed to us we would expect on theoretical grounds.

We believe that two phenomena demonstrate that this asymmetry exists and has very real consequences.

The first is that when there is a loss of input from the environment, evidences of decreased autonomy from the id appear much more quickly than do evidences of decreased autonomy from the environment when there is a loss of input from the id. In the experiments of Bexton et al. (17), for example, evidences of decreased autonomy from the id appear quickly. But in repression, unless there is some strong external press, the environment is likely to be seen in id terms rather than impulse in environmental terms. Only in obsessive-compulsive extremes, when action initiated from within is paralyzed, may the environment appear to dominate behavior.

Related to this evidence of asymmetry is another. There can be domination by the id with obliviousness to the environment to the point of hallucination (restructuring of the environment in id terms); but asymmetrically, domination by the environment will not be with obliviousness to the id, but will harmonize with id demands. (When we come to the transference aspect of hypnosis we will be able to show how hypnosis exemplifies this proposition.) In other words, if the ego surrenders to the id, its mode of surrender will be much less dictated by the nature of the environment than will its mode of surrender be dictated by the nature of the id if it surrenders to the environment.

Our last major consideration on the relationship between the two autonomies—one which is intimately related to the asymmetry of id and environment—is that an interpersonal relationship constitutes an environmental force which at the same time is an expression of an id urge. In fact, it is just because of this that surrender to the environment can come to harmonize with an id demand. Our point here is a corollary of the whole series of concepts expressed in various forms by both Hartmann and Erikson as the preadaptedness of drive to environment by way of the object of the drive. These concepts have recently been analyzed and compared by Rapaport (188).[5]

## Regression and the Loss of Autonomy

We now turn to the metapsychology of regression proper and regression in the service of the ego. Our considerations in the previous section seem to us to be a basis for renaming the phenomenon of regression; we would like to call it loss of autonomy, since it seems to us that this is just what regression is, and because the new name would enable us to distinguish more readily between decreased autonomy from the id and decreased autonomy from the environment.[6]

We believe that instances of regression proper can be divided into those in which the loss of autonomy is followed by domination by the id and those in which it is followed by

[5] Before leaving the problem of the relationship between the two autonomies, we would like to make a brief comment on the question of choice and freedom. We are referring to choice as a concept, not as a subjective belief. People acting under extreme compulsion may believe they are freely choosing, and people acting freely may insist they are compelled. As far as the philosophical doctrine of free will is concerned, we simply affirm the postulate of psychic determinism, rule out any *deus ex machina*, and define choice as a psychological concept. Choice is possible when the ego is relatively autonomous, both from id and environment. The ego can select both from a number of potential motivational urges and from a number of environmental possibilities. A shift in either id demand or environmental press is rapidly and flexibly responded to. The ego takes both the potential motivational urges and the existing environmental configurations into account in determining on a particular behavior. When a motivational urge becomes so strong that the ego has to seek its discharge no matter how unpropitious the environmental circumstances, or when an environmental press becomes so demanding that the ego has to conform to it no matter how undesirable it is from the point of view of the motivational patterns, choice is lost. The fluid interplay in which both organismic demands and environmental press are rapidly and flexibly attuned to each other with feedback on each other yields the familiar synthesis referred to as the organismic-environmental matrix. The function of choosing itself becomes an apparatus which we call the will. This apparatus shows differing degrees and types of development from person to person (225). As we will note later (p. 187), a structure or apparatus itself gives rise to motivations and serves the function of a saving of energy.

[6] Regressed states then have varying degrees of autonomy. States of fixation or arrest could be thought of as conditions of incompletely developed or retarded autonomy.

domination by the environment. Schizophrenia is an example of domination by the id, while the results of brain-washing and the confessions at the Russian trials are examples of domination by the environment.

We believe that regression in the service of the ego can be divided into decrease of autonomy from the id and from the environment. Examples of decrease of autonomy from the id are dream, artistic creativity, scientific creativity in which the investigator is led by a "hunch," and humor; examples of decrease of autonomy from the environment are scientific creativity in which the investigator is led by the "material," and the established hypnotic state (we hope later to show that in the induction phase of hypnosis the regression in the service of the ego has not yet been established).

We suggested earlier that the so-called "highway hypnosis" (39), or effects seen in observers intently watching a radar screen on which for long periods of time nothing happens but where attention must remain vigilant, are examples of a de-differentiated external environment with a strong press of an impersonal type resulting in a loss of autonomy with domination of the ego by the external impersonal press. It will, of course, have to be demonstrated that these are not simply drowsy states.

We have called a regression in the service of the ego a decrease of autonomy. Yet from another point of view the capacity for regression in the service of the ego may clearly be seen as a regressive adaptation which increases the relative autonomy of the ego. As we will later show, this paradox is resolved by recognizing that the loss of autonomy is by a subsystem of the ego whereas the increase of autonomy is by the over-all ego.

## The Metapsychology of Hypnotic Induction

A discussion of the metapsychology of the loss of autonomy must first deal with the dynamics of the initiation of such loss. We must distinguish sharply the dynamics involved in the movement toward regression from the dynamics of a regressed state itself.

A regressive movement can be initiated in any one of a number of ways. We shall not discuss the general ways in which regression can be initiated except to state that we see them as divided into three main classes: (1) an increase in strength of instinctual impulse; (2) a change in the apparatuses available to the ego for adaptive functioning; and (3) an alteration in the external situation.

It will be recalled that earlier we listed the two major ways in which a decrease of relative autonomy could be initiated as loss of input and strong press or urge. Loss of external input and strong press would be classified under "an alteration in the external situation"; strong urge would fall in the class of "an increase in strength of instinctual impulse"; a change in intake from either id or environment could result from "a change in the apparatuses available to the ego for adaptive functioning." The most general classification, then, would be into changes in id, ego, or environment. The first move in the initiation of hypnotic induction is a change in the environment—the behavior of the hypnotist—but changes in id and ego soon follow.

We will now draw together the implications of the preceding general discussions for a theory of the induction phase of hypnosis. We must emphasize that here we are dealing only with the initiation of regression by attack on the ego apparatuses. We will later present our view of how it is initiated by way of the interpersonal relationship.

We believe that the manipulations of the hypnotist can all be looked upon as an attempt to disrupt the ego's control of its apparatuses. This seems reasonably clear as regards the perceptual and motor apparatuses, but not so clear concerning the various apparatuses relating to thought.[7]

[7] The apparatuses are usually listed as motor, sensory, and memory, with Rapaport adding thresholds, but these are only the primarily autonomous apparatuses. In speaking of "apparatuses relating to thought" we are considering those which are secondarily autonomous too.

We earlier suggested that de-automatization is brought about by manipulations of attention, whether directly or as a secondary result of diminished input or increased press or urge. We believe that during induction the hypnotist, by directing the subject's conscious attention to automatized apparatuses, attempts to de-automatize them. The act of de-automatization expends attention energy formerly available for other uses, and even fresh accessions of attention may be necessary, for with de-automatization an act becomes difficult to perform. In other words, the energy which, as Hartmann has pointed out, is saved by automatization is now once again required as a result of the de-automatization. When attention is absorbed in this way, it is no longer available for sensory or motor exploration of the outside world. A secondary effect of de-automatization, then, will be diminished input. Since we have already seen that diminished input can secondarily lead to de-automatization, we now see that these two conditions reciprocally act to augment each other.

It has been suggested (182) that the energy saved through automatization is available for the synthetic function of the ego, since this energy becomes available as hypercathexis, and it is by means of such hypercathexis that the synthetic function takes place. To the extent that the "saved" energy is lost again as a result of de-automatization, the synthetic function will suffer, the result will be a more primitive variety of synthetic function (since some variety of synthetic function is always present), and thus the way has been paved for the re-establishment of a more regressed state of the psyche.

In dissociation, a formerly integrated movement, perceptual act, or mental activity is split up into its component parts, or made to function as an independent unit instead of as a tool in the service of the integrated ego. We have already described one of the hypnotist's activities as directed toward a dissociation in which parts of the body develop an "independent" functioning. It seems to us that the aspect of dissociation which is a decomposition is to be subsumed under de-automatization (and as we shall later show, function as an independent unit results from the establishment of a new automatization). The advantage of the concept of de-automatization is that it carries the rich connotations of the concepts of primary and secondary autonomy (the ontogenesis of automatization).[8] We are suggesting that dissociation, de-automatization, and interference with the synthetic function of the ego are all different ways of conceptualizing the same phenomenon.

We must introduce here the concept of consciousness as an apparatus of the ego. We mean of course consciousness as it operates in the secondary process where it is brought about by attention cathexis and not as in the primary process in which drive cathexis is responsible for the quality consciousness (180). The concept is not new; it is Freud's, and has been spelled out and clarified by Rapaport (181, 185). Freud called consciousness a "superordinate sense organ," which makes it quite clear that he considered it an ego apparatus. The term "consciousness" is used both for the apparatus and for the result of the functioning of this apparatus as it employs attention cathexes. Consciousness seems to be equivalent to attention, since "attention" may likewise be used to designate an apparatus or the result of the functioning of that apparatus. The conception of attention or consciousness as an apparatus enables us to state that in the induction of hypnosis the ego's control of its apparatuses of motility, perception, and attention is attacked.

To turn now to the other two major factors which can precipitate a decrease of autonomy—loss of information and strong press or urge:

---

[8] We may incidentally note that here is perhaps the germ of truth in Janet's (122) conception of dissociation being due to an "enfeeblement" of psychic energy, since there is a relation between dissociation and interference with the synthetic function.

In the induction of hypnosis the hypnotist deprives the subject of information about the environment, and exerts a strong pressure on the subject to behave in the manner in which he directs. We might expect to see a decrease of autonomy from the environment during induction, but what we actually see seem to be derivatives of the id. The spontaneous outbursts of affect, the accessibility of motility to previously repressed urges, the appearance of ideational representations of such urges in consciousness, the evidence of archaic ego states in the alterations of body image and sensation, and the depersonalization phenomena—fragmentary though these manifestations are—appear to be previously repressed material now released, indicative of a weakening of the relative autonomy of the ego from the id. These phenomena are evidences that the synthetic function of the ego is interfered with. We see in these phenomena one of the evidences of the asymmetry of the relative autonomies. Even in this process which will go on to domination by the environment, there first or more obviously appear evidences of decrease of autonomy from the id.

In hypnotic induction, the hypnotist attempts to bring about a dedifferentiation of the space-time environment and exerts a strong environmental press. Since the same kind of phenomena appear as do in the experiments of Bexton et al. (17), we can assume that the environmental press is not responsible. But the press *is* responsible for the fact that the situation moves on to what will become the established hypnotic state with the loss of autonomy resulting in domination by the environment. The phenomena during the induction period are not only those of decreased autonomy from the id, but also those of beginning suggestibility and compliance to the hypnotist which will become more fully developed in the established hypnotic state.

In this induction period, the subject is in a more favorable position than the subjects of Bexton et al., who were perforce deprived of various stimuli. The potential hypnotic subject need only refuse to obey the hypnotist. He can walk around and look around if he decides to do so—and many subjects do just that, however much they may protest their wish to be hypnotized. In short, if hypnosis is to occur, the ego must accede, meaning that it must select from among its potential motivational patterns one which will conform to the external press. Here we encounter the second consideration we advanced in our discussion of the asymmetry of the two autonomies: with domination by the environment there cannot be obliviousness to the id, but a harmonizing motivational pattern must be found. For hypnosis to be possible, a particular kind of motivational pattern must be accessible to the ego in the particular individual.

As we see it, then, the sequence of events is this: when the hypnotist begins his manipulations, several forces are set in motion. There is a strong environmental press; the search for an appropriate motivational pattern begins, and the usual functioning of the autonomous apparatuses begins to be interfered with. Now the usual synthesis of ego-functioning is not in command, nor has the new synthesis, the established hypnotic state, as yet been formed. This interim period—the induction period—is characterized by evidences of a fragmentation of the ego synthesis, or what we might call fragmentary ego syntheses. We have already discussed the similarity of the phenomena during the induction phase to those produced by Bexton et al., in whose experiments there was an absence of information from the outside, no strong environmental press, and no strong internal drive. Since these phenomena indicate decreased autonomy from the id, one would have to conclude that, though during induction the external press is great, it has been only partially accepted by the ego, and indeed this still partial acceptance can be considered indicative of the induction phase rather than of the established hypnotic state.

The fact that the external press has been accepted even though only partially is what would make it oversimple to view the induction phase as simply a loss of autonomy with domination by the id. As we have indicated, the ego must accede, and searches for a motivational pattern which will correspond to the environmental press. But the established state itself we do regard as a loss of autonomy with domination of the ego by the social environment—specifically by the hypnotist.

We have already discussed the stress which we lay on an important phenomenal difference between the induction phase and the established state: the fact that in the established state the subject is potentially capable to varying degrees of apparently regaining control of the use of his apparatuses. As the apparatuses come under the control of the ego in the established state there takes place a reversal of whatever de-automatization has occurred in the induction phase, that is, a re-automatization.

But now the question becomes: under the control of what kind of ego? We introduce here one of our central proposals for a theory of hypnosis: that in hypnosis a subsystem is set up within the ego. This subsystem is a regressed system which is in the service of the over-all ego; it has control of some or all of the apparatuses, and to the extent that it has control, those apparatuses which were de-automatized are now re-automatized. It is this subsystem alone which is under the control of the hypnotist, and it is by virtue of this control that the hypnotist can control and direct the apparatuses. The over-all ego also maintains a relationship with the hypnotist, the nonhypnotic reality-oriented relationship. The over-all ego relinquishes control of the subsystem to the hypnotist only temporarily and tentatively. It is the fact that this relinquishment of control is only provisional to which we pointed when we earlier described evidences of persisting control of the apparatuses by the ego during the hypnotic state; the over-all ego can yield control of the subsystem to the hypnotist but can at any time take it back. We will attempt a more detailed analysis of this subsystem when we discuss the metapsychology of the hypnotic state.

We do not believe that a regression in the service of the ego has already been established in the induction phase. The organization of the subsystem within the ego is an achievement of the synthetic function of the ego; it is an organized structure. During induction, this structure has not yet been built. And now we can also state more concisely the difference between a regression proper and a regression in the service of the ego, though we again emphasize that this difference is a matter of degree and is a function not only of the manifest phenomena but also of the kind of ego in which the phenomena are taking place. In a regression proper it is the over-all ego which has changed, has suffered a degree of decreased autonomy from id and environment. In a regression in the service of the ego a subsystem within the ego has been formed and it is this subsystem which shows in varying degrees diminished autonomy from the id and from the environment.[9]

It is this distinction between the two kinds of regression which enables us to describe the differences between certain phenomena characteristic of each, superficially similar but vastly different in their actual dynamics. There are many phenomena in the hypnotic state which look like id manifestations—the capacity for hallucinations, the access to repressed material, for example—yet are very different from what is seen in a regression proper, a schizophrenia, for example. Admitting that we run the risk of taking a too reified and manikinlike view of the subsystem, we would say that these id-like phenomena are produced by way of the subsystem rather than the system, that it is the subsystem which can hallucinate, which can recall previously repressed traumatic material. This would be a formulation analogous to the one

[9] To say that the induction phase is a regression proper and the established state is a regression in the service of the ego would make too sharp a cleavage between induction phase and established state.

we made about the apparatuses; in the established state the subsystem controls both the apparatuses and the gateway to the repressed to varying degrees. That the access to the repressed is integrated with the subsystem but not with the over-all system is seen in the phenomenon of posthypnotic amnesia—admittedly relatively infrequent without suggestion, though more common when hypnosis is used in therapy: that the repressed material gained in the hypnotic state is ordinarily not accessible to the ego after the hypnotic state is terminated.

We suggest instead the following formulation: we spoke of the established state as a loss of autonomy with domination of the ego by the environment. We have earlier suggested that when the ego is dominated by either id or environment there is also a diminution of autonomy from the other. The phenomena we have been describing illustrate this principle. With the subsystem's domination by the environment there also occurs a decrease of autonomy from the id, shown by the increased access which the subsystem has to the id.

Throughout our discussion we have described the induction phase as brief and unstable and the established state as more enduring and stable. This difference between instability and stability is related to the fact that in the induction phase there is a regressive movement which necessitates interference with the ego apparatuses, while in the established state there may be a return of control of the apparatuses to a new and different regulation by a subsystem of the ego. We may ask whether this is a difference which can be more widely generalized. Are the unstable states those which do not, the stable those which do have access to the apparatuses? Do we have other criteria to determine whether a state is unstable or stable? Or is the distinction rather that the relationship to the apparatuses must be decisively settled for a state to be stable, whether it is so settled that these are or are not accessible to the ego? Is the dream state a relatively stable one then, which does not have access to the motor or perceptual apparatuses? Or is the sleep state the one we should speak of as stable and is the dream state actually unstable?

Whatever the answers to these questions, there can be no doubt that transitional states of upheaval with disturbance of accessibility to the apparatuses differ in important ways from the stable states with accessibility to the apparatuses. In the chaos of an acute schizophrenia, for example, the disturbance may be so severe that even some of the most ancient, firmly structuralized anticipations and tools of syntax are no longer freely at the disposal of the ego. After the process "settles," even if the disease remains as malignant as before, these structures once again become re-automatized if they have been de-automatized, and come under the dominion of the ego, a reconstituted ego in which the synthetic function has again stabilized, albeit at a new and lower level. It is also well known that a sign of chronicity in schizophrenia is the apparently unaltered functioning of the apparatuses under the hegemony of the ego. Here are seen such phenomena as the thought disorders which are revealed only on psychological testing, after a searching clinical interview has failed to turn them up. With the guideposts of a structured conversation, the apparatuses function with sufficient automaticity, despite the altered ego structure, that the disturbance cannot be seen.

In a somewhat analogous sense the over-all ego is more involved in the regressive process during the induction phase of hypnosis than it is during the established state. Chaos and disorganization are characteristic of the induction phase; during the established state, stability has been restored. The regression is of the subsystem which now has hegemony over the apparatuses. The over-all ego remains "quietly" in the background, maintaining the reality orientation which it has never really relinquished.

## A Synthesis of the Two Kinds of Regression Initiation— Altered State and Transference

We must now integrate into the preceding description of the development and establishment of the hypnotic state its usual description as a transference phenomenon, by which is meant that the hypnotized subject engages in regressive interpersonal relationships. The external press is toward regression. The hypnotist declares himself possessed of great powers and proposes that the subject submit to these. If the subject can find an available regressive motivational pattern with which to respond to this press toward regression, hypnosis proceeds.

To recapitulate and organize some of our central theses: hypnosis is a condition of loss of autonomy with domination of a subsystem of the ego by a part of the social environment. Hypnosis is characterized by the fact that the subject is in a regressed state and engages in regressive interpersonal relationships. Hypnosis is therefore both an altered state and a transference relationship. The normal ego maintains relative autonomy from drives from within and the environment from without. There are two major ways in which this autonomy can be disrupted. An attack on the apparatuses is an attack on the ego state. An attack by way of offering a regressive interpersonal relationship is simultaneously an attack from the outside—the social environment—and an attack from within through the opportunity to regress offered to the drives, which are always to a greater or lesser extent seeking such an opportunity. With the success of the attack on one of the two fronts there is a repercussion on the other. And, as we have already emphasized, regressed state and transference are inextricably linked.

Early in our work we considered regarding the transference as a regression in the id and the regressed state as a regression in the ego, but came to see that this would be incorrect. Apart from the fact that transference manifestations, like any other behavior, are mediated by way of the ego, we believe, as we shall discuss in our metapsychology of the state of regression, that only in regression proper are id, ego, and super-ego all altered. In regression in the service of the ego the subsystem is simultaneously the altered state and the agency which engages in altered interpersonal relationships. As we earlier remarked, we also considered at one time regarding the induction as a loss of autonomy followed by domination by the id and the established state as a loss of autonomy followed by domination of the ego by the external environment. There is some truth to this conception, but it is also somewhat in error. During induction there are evidences of decrease of autonomy from both id and environment, though the evidences of decrease from the id may be more spectacular, partly because of the asymmetry of autonomy from id and environment; and in the established state, though the domination of the ego is by the external environment, there is also the concealed decrease of autonomy from the id by way of the regressive motivational pattern which must be activated to make possible the domination by the social environment.

We are perhaps in a better position now to evaluate the relative importance of the two avenues of approach, the manipulation of the apparatuses and the invitation to a regressed interpersonal relationship. We remember the opposing views—Freud's, that the manipulations are mere technical devices, and the view exemplified by Kubie and Margolin, that the hypnotist is a kind of adventitious factor.

There is one phenomenon which at first seems to bespeak the correctness of Freud's view—namely that there are people in whom hypnosis can be brought about quickly and simply by the invitation to regress, without any manipulation of the apparatuses. These are people in whom there must already exist the subsystem in the ego, ready to be triggered into action. Clearly the regressed interpersonal relationship is the *sine qua non*. Once it is established, the regressed state is inevitable. But on the other hand, despite beginning disruption of the functioning of the apparatuses, the process may fail to go on to the development of hypnosis.

If one could be convinced that the skill with which the hypnotist carries out his manipulations could significantly influence the outcome, the view that the manipulations cannot be simply passed off as a smoke screen would be strengthened. It must be admitted that we have given short shrift in this book to any differential introduced by the skill of the hypnotist. There is, however, a strong current of such belief in some present-day practicing hypnotists. There are a number of instances attested to by hypnotists of an especially skilled and experienced hypnotist succeeding where they had failed. We have made a number of attempts to see whether other experienced hypnotists could succeed in subjects with whom we had failed, but we have been unable to persuade ourselves that we have actually seen such successes. But this is clearly an area open to subjective bias, and one which could be illuminated only by careful empirical work. It would be expected that hypnotists would wish to claim a premium by virtue of their skill and experience. It is possible that the master-apprentice relationship which still exists in the realm of the acquisition of hypnotic skills is an evidence of that aspect of the psychology of the hypnotist to which we referred as his identification with his subject.

It is probable that in any particular instance of hypnotizability, the more important is the manipulation of the apparatuses, the less important is the establishment of a transference, and vice versa. Success in inducing hypnosis in refractory instances by the use of the newer and more potent techniques of manipulating the apparatuses will be required before it is possible to establish solidly the view that such manipulation does indeed play an important role in inducing hypnosis in at least some instances. And in such work it will be important to design experiments with controls for the transference effects of these manipulations.

In either case, whether emphasis is placed on transference or on manipulation of the apparatuses, as long as one sees hypnosis as a regression in the ego, one will look for the explanation of hypnotizability in ego factors—something like ego weakness or a susceptibility to regression, however this would be assessed. Regression in the service of the ego, as we have shown, is evidence rather of a "strong," not a "weak" ego, or probably more correctly, it is evidence of an ego which has the capacity to regress in part while the depth and duration of regression are controlled by the ego as a whole. This is an intrasystemic view of the ego, dealing as it does with the manner in which the synthetic force of the ego can build a total unity which includes a regressed subsystem.

With a predominantly transference point of view of hypnosis, the explanation of hypnotizability will naturally be sought in the motivational patterns of the subject. In *Hypnotherapy* (25) we suggested that there may be nothing specific about the hypnotic state, but that it represents an altered state only in the sense of an as yet incompletely defined specific constellation of the strivings of the subject. We would now disapprove of our original statement on the grounds of its implications about the transference aspects of hypnosis, because it implies that they are the same from person to person. We do not have enough evidence for such a view, and do not know whether it is true. We believe that the psychodynamics of various hypnotizable people—at least as far as "strivings" are concerned—may be significantly different, and that hypnotizability may rather be the result of the balance which is struck between the various opposing forces. This balance results in the development of a particular structured state and kind of interpersonal relationship. The ease with which this structure can be brought into play will vary widely even among those who possess it.

Here we wish to turn to another statement we have made

earlier, and try to restate it in more formal terms more consistent with our present views of the nature of hypnosis. We
have previously suggested that in a psychotherapy employing
hypnosis there are at least two kinds of transference involved
—the transference underlying hypnotizability and then the
usual kinds of transference manifestations seen in any psychotherapy. In terms of our description of hypnosis as a regression in the service of the ego, with a regressed subsystem
in the persisting over-all ego structure, we would suggest that
the transference underlying the hypnosis is the constellation
of strivings within the subsystem, while the "usual transferences" are, together with the current reality interaction,
the manifestations of the "persisting ego" relationship with
the hypnotist.

## Structuralization of the Process of Loss of Autonomy

We turn now to the issue of the disappearance of the phenomena of the induction phase. Whatever question may be
raised about whether or not the phenomena of the induction
period disappear, there is no question that the induction
period shortens in time. The progressive rapidity with which
the hypnotic subject learns to go into hypnosis is frequently
explained as a conditioned reflex. We cannot here embark
on a discussion of conditioning or habit formation, but our
point of view is unsympathetic to such an explanation.

Kubie and Margolin propose a somewhat more dynamic
explanation than habit formation for the disappearance of
the induction phenomena:

> That in any individual who has been hypnotized repeatedly,
> the hypnotic state can be induced almost instantly by the mere
> presence of the hypnotist is not surprising, because the hypnotic
> reaction become a complex conditioned unit in the total ego
> Gestalt, an organized ego fragment into which the individual
> can be thrown in a flash, just as the patient with a specific
> phobia can be thrown into a panic by the appropriate danger
> signal [145, p. 617].

In psychodynamic terms it might be assumed that the subject is ordinarily afraid of hypnosis but that as his fear lessens with increased familiarity, he struggles less against its establishment, and therefore enters it more easily.

But for our explanation, we will take our point of departure from Rapaport's remarks on the use of the concept of automatization to explain much of what is ordinarily explained as conditioning and habit formation (178, 184). We suggest that it is the automatization of the process of going into hypnosis which is responsible for the disappearance of the induction phenomena.

Various fragmentary ego syntheses are seen in the induction period. We may now view these as indications of the struggle which goes on while the ego searches for a motivational pattern which will conform to the external press. To say that the established state has become automatized means that this previously *ad hoc* correspondence of motivational pattern and external press has become organized into an ego structure. Therefore, the struggle need not be repeated again and again, and the evidences of the struggle—the induction-phase phenomena—fall away. The relative rapidity with which hypnosis can be induced, if the subject is one who will respond successfully, suggests that the elements which will become organized into the subsystem—the intra-ego structure —must be readily available.

We apply the concepts of autonomization and automatization (114) to the change in the induction phase as the neophyte becomes experienced. Autonomization and automatization are concepts which have not been distinguished in the psychoanalytic literature, and we too believe they are best used synonymously. But the phenomenon we mentioned previously, called by Kretschmer "formular abbreviation," should be distinguished from these. Both autonomization and automatization refer to the same phenomenon—structure formation. Autonomization stresses the relative independence from drive and environment; automatization stresses the triggering of the structure into action by external or internal stimulus. Formular abbreviation, on the other hand, is a process, not a state: it refers to the dropping out of awareness of many details of a process as that process becomes structuralized. With the dropping out of awareness of details, attention cathexes are saved and become available to the ego for other uses. Formular abbreviation is thus a descriptive term referring to a phenomenon accompanying structure formation.

It is the process of going into hypnosis which becomes formularly abbreviated, not the established state. That the phenomena of the induction period may still persist despite their dropping out of consciousness is suggested by the evidence indicating that a certain time must elapse in each separate induction before the established state is actually well established, however experienced the subject may be. An effort to produce certain hypnotic phenomena immediately after the signal has been given for an experienced subject to go into hypnosis *may* fail. We suggest that despite the establishment of an automatization, there may persist in the preconscious or unconscious a potentiality for the revival of the dynamic interaction on deeper levels of the motivational hierarchy which had earlier led to the first and *ad hoc* appearance of this later automatized structure.[10] Such a view would be consistent with the general theory of *relative* autonomy; in fact, without such a view it would be difficult to explain the de-automatization of what has become automatized. A similar view is implied by Isakower (120) in his discussion of the phenomena which some people occasionally experience while falling asleep. He implies that when these phenomena are not present in consciousness in these people they persist preconsciously or unconsciously, and are presumably preconsciously or unconsciously present in all people while they are falling asleep.

[10] One has to beware of falling into the "seething cauldron" view with such a hypothesis. Compare Freud on whether when a drive produces derivatives, the drive cathexes are all transferred to the derivatives (94, footnote pp. 82-83).

## The Metapsychology of the Hypnotic State

We proceed now to a more detailed consideration of the metapsychology of the established state of hypnosis. Rapaport and Gill have argued elsewhere (190) that a metapsychological discussion must include five points of view: structural, dynamic, economic, genetic, and adaptive. Although we shall not review here the arguments they present, we will organize our discussion of the metapsychology of the hypnotic state under these five points of view.

### THE STRUCTURAL POINT OF VIEW

We have already said that our descriptive differentiation of the two kinds of regression suggests that, structurally, in regression in the service of the ego the usual ego structure persists, but that at the same time a subsystem which has regressive characteristics is formed in the ego. It is also possible in a regression proper for a subsystem within the ego to develop subsequently. But in regression proper the ego within which the subsystem forms is itself an ego which shows regressive features, whereas in regression in the service of the ego the usual ego persists, perhaps even strengthened by the development of the subsystem.

In our description of the metapsychology of the established state, we shall have to deal with the over-all system and the subsystem and with the relationships between the two. The description of the regressed subsystem as such will in many ways parallel what would be the description of a regression proper, except as the subsystem always operates under the domination, whether actual or potential, of the total ego.

We must first characterize the structural relationship of this subsystem to the psychic organization. Fisher has suggested that in hypnosis (72) there is regression in all three psychic systems—ego, superego, and id. We would seriously question this; we believe rather that this is a description of the state of affairs in regression proper, and that it describes, as a matter of fact, one of the major differences between regression proper and regression in the service of the ego. We believe that in hypnosis there exists an *intra-ego structure* which has access to regressed id and superego derivatives. There are significant relationships between this problem and the problem of the concept of the self, which is now being discussed more frequently in the literature. The subsystem is like a subsidiary self. Hartmann, followed by Jacobson (121), employs the concept of the self as a supraordinate one and argues that the opposite of object is self and not ego. He further implies that self-cathexes are found in id, ego, and superego (113). Rapaport (186) believes that this use of the concept self leads to theoretical difficulties, and proposes instead a definition of self as a "function of the ego selectively representing the total personality, and which as such has conscious and unconscious aspects." He suggests further that this "ego subsystem—the self—is 'responsible' for (representative of, reflective of) the ego's intersystemic relationships—among others."

In a similar fashion we are arguing that the subsystem which is established in the ego during hypnosis selectively represents the total personality—and thus has id, ego, and superego aspects. The superego components of the subsystem are derived not only from the subject's superego but also include incorporated aspects of the hypnotist—the so-called parasitic double of the superego (176).

We speak of id and superego derivatives rather than simply id and superego because we are dealing with the same problem with which any consideration of id, ego, and superego relationships must deal. Id and superego never act directly. What we actually know of them we know through the interaction of their derivatives in the ego. The phenomena of the induction phase, for example, which we earlier described as fragments of archaic ego states, are remnants of earlier stable ego syntheses formed as a result of the interaction of id, ego, and superego components.

One of the central structural issues in the relation between the over-all ego and the subsystem is one already discussed—the degree to which the structures de-automatized during induction become re-automatized under the hegemony of the subsystem. To the extent to which this occurs they are of course an essential part of its structure and account for the apparently normal functioning during the established state.

We turn then to the metapsychology of regression proper from the structural point of view. First the intersystemic aspects: the id, ego, and superego relationships alter, and earlier structural organizations and relationships are reinstated. Granting that the demarcation of these psychic institutions is only relative, in regression there takes place a partial dissolution of these boundaries and the lines of division become less distinct. Superego and id invade ego, the ego losing some of the territory it has wrested from these two, and withdrawing into earlier ego positions. Clinically this is perceived as the coexistence of savage self-condemnation and frank instinctual urges.

More systematically expressed, in regression proper the relative autonomy of the ego breaks down, but the ego becomes reconstituted and is again relatively autonomous, though now in a regressed and earlier form. In addition to our previous description of the ego as relatively autonomous from id and environment, we must add that it is relatively autonomous from the superego.

In hypnosis the situation is quite different from the one just described for regression proper. The id and superego derivatives which interact with ego structures in the subsystem are regressed, but the id and superego themselves are not regressed as they are in regression proper. Applying our principle of differential regression (which should actually be named differential access, since it refers not to regressed id and superego but to access to id and superego derivatives), there may be different types of intersystemic relationships in various hypnotic subsystems; some subjects may show marked alterations in ego-superego relationships, but little change in id-ego relationships, or the opposite may be true. Some of these differences may account for some of the conflicting results obtained from experiments on the production of anti-social behavior in hypnosis (21, 231).

Intrasystemic structural alterations occur in all three systems in regression proper, while in hypnosis they occur only in the ego and in the subsidiary ego, the subsystem. The general concept to be described for the subsystem is a loss of established structure or of yet another kind of relative autonomy—intrasystemic relative autonomy. Structures within the several systems in regression proper, and in the components of the subsystem in regression in the service of the ego, may be differentially affected: for example, ego apparatuses may be variously influenced by the hypnotist, depending, in Fisher's terms, on various fantasy systems, and in ours, on their history as autonomous structures. The same considerations apply to secondarily as to primarily autonomous structures. Secondarily autonomous structures in the ego are likely to lose their autonomy and consequently to function more directly in relationship to instinctual energies. (This last point clearly involves the economic point of view.)

We shall not discuss here intrasystemic structural alterations in superego and id. While these topics would need to be taken up in a metapsychology of regression proper, they are not germane to a discussion of the hypnotic state because id and superego, we argue, are not structurally altered in hypnosis.

## THE DYNAMIC POINT OF VIEW

We have already mentioned that a sharp distinction must be made between the dynamics involved in the movement toward regression and the dynamics of the regressed state itself. To discuss the dynamics of the established state of hypnosis requires a further distinction between the dynamics of the subsystem and the dynamics of the relationship between subsystem and over-all ego.

The dynamics of a regressed state can only be described as a more primitive kind of mental functioning in comparison to that of the state before regression. How primitive the functioning will be depends on the degree of regression. The description of the dynamics of the subsystem in hypnosis and of the dynamics of regression proper will differ therefore only in terms of the degree of regression which has occurred. The dynamics of psychic functioning in general can be described as follows: forces bent on discharge interact with inhibiting and channeling forces (in other terminology, defensive and controlling forces). Primitive mental dynamics are characterized by urgency of drive discharge, a relatively direct clash of discharge-bent force and inhibiting force, and relative paucity and inflexibility of channeling forces. More mature mental dynamics are characterized by delay of discharge, and by subtle, complex, and flexible channeling of discharge instead of direct inhibition.

A more global way of dichotomizing mental dynamics is into primary and secondary processes, and in general we may say that the dynamics of a regressed mental state show a movement toward primary-process functioning and away from secondary-process functioning. Freud's view of the relationship between primary- and secondary-process functioning as a central one in regression is seen in the following quotation: "Unconscious [primary] processes only become cognizable by us under the conditions of dreaming and of neurosis—that is to say, when processes of the higher, *Pcs.*, system are set back to an earlier stage by being lowered (by regression)" (83, p. 187). The characteristics of the primary and secondary processes will not be detailed here. In intersystemic terms the difference in dynamics may be characterized by saying that in more primitive functioning, superego and id forces may join or clash directly without being buffered by higher-level ego organizations, while in more mature functioning many and flexible controlling ego forces bring the id and superego motivations to an adaptive discharge. Evidence of diminished integration of superego and ego is seen in the increased ease with which the superego can be "bribed."

A regressive change massive enough to alter the intersystemic dynamics will surely involve intrasystemic dynamic changes too. Altered ego-functioning is shown by: (1) shift to more primitive defensive mechanisms; (2) greater preponderance of discharge by affect processes as against intellectual processes; (3) movement from action to less adaptive discharge patterns; (4) movement toward dedifferentiation. In general, these changes may be viewed as impairments of various signal functions in favor of uncontrolled defensive and executive functions. We have already described these changes in ego-functioning as characteristic of the functioning of the subsystem in the established state (27).

Here again, as under the structural point of view, we shall not discuss changes in intrasystemic dynamics of superego and id, since we do not have propositions to suggest which are peculiar to hypnosis. But the question of intrasystemic dynamic changes does lead us to Freud's only explicit formulation of the metapsychology of regression: "The metapsychological explanation of regression I have thought to find in an instinct defusion, in the segregation of the erotic components, which with the onset of the genital phase were joined to the destructive cathexes of the sadistic phase" (94, p. 46). Of course, instinct fusion and defusion refer not only to conditions within the id, but to derivatives of libidinal and aggressive drives throughout the psychic apparatus (98).

Again, because so far as we can see there are no issues specific to hypnosis involved, we shall not enter the complex issues of defusion, deneutralization, and sublimation, though a systematic treatment of regression would have to deal with them.

The dynamic relationship between the over-all ego and the

intra-ego subsystem may be one of conflict or cooperation. If the conflict is of any severity, the over-all ego re-establishes its hegemony and the hypnosis is interrupted. If the relationship is one of cooperation, the hypnosis persists and the over-all ego may progressively "lend" its functions to the subsystem for automatized functioning under the aegis of the subsystem.

## THE ADAPTIVE POINT OF VIEW

In our general discussion of autonomy we have described how the ego gains a measure of autonomy from the external environment. The ego can henceforth engage in experimental action in thought by way of small cathectic displacements among intrapsychic representations of the environment, instead of acting on the actual external environment by way of large energy displacements (76).

With the regression in hypnosis the subsystem reverts to earlier forms of relationship with the environment, forms both more magical and more dependent on the environment. We emphasize the subsystem here because, as we have said, the over-all ego system remains in its usual adaptive relationship to the hypnotist. In fact, it is this maintenance of the usual adaptive relationship (together with the altered one by way of the subsystem) which constitutes an essential distinguishing feature of the hypnotic state.[11]

It must be pointed out, however, that a regressed state is not simply less adaptive, since each stage of development is an integrated one and constitutes an adaptation. In fact, a regression may be looked upon as an effort to increase adaptation: when the organism meets environmental stress with which it cannot cope—to which it cannot adapt—it regresses to an earlier adaptive organization, as though in the hope of magically reinstating the earlier form of organism-environment interrelationship. But since the environment is likely to

[11] For purposes of clarity we are here and elsewhere making the distinction between subsystem and "over-all" ego somewhat too sharp.

resist this effort at magical manipulation, the regressed state actually turns out to be maladapted.

In hypnosis, however, the environment (the hypnotist) has encouraged the regression, and the adaptation required is to him. Thus the development of the subsystem, which is the means by which this relationship with the hypnotist and his specific demands is established, is itself an adaptive achievement. It is of the kind which Hartmann (114, p. 36) has called a regressive adaptation—in contrast to a progressive adaptation—and which he specifically links to Kris's regression in the service of the ego. The spontaneous fluctuations in the hypnotic state which we have described represent shifts in defense and adaptation.

In regression there is a reversal of the normal developmental progression involving the intrapsychic representation of the external world, both personal and impersonal. We may call this reversal reprojection or exteriorization. In so far as the superego is built up around the incorporation of an external object, a massive reversal of this intrapsychic incorporation may be conceptualized as exteriorization of a whole psychic institution. The description of hypnosis as characterized by the development of a parasitic double of the superego makes use of such a conception (176). Again this must be recognized as the statement of the extreme form of a model, since in normal development the superego never becomes completely autonomous from external objects, nor is its complete exteriorization possible.

But in addition to such massive shifts, there can be exteriorization on a broad continuum, ranging from larger to smaller "segments" of psychic structure. Such exteriorization may be not only of superego components but of ego functions too. We have already discussed examples of the exteriorization of such smaller "segments" of ego-functioning in describing the varying degrees to which the apparatuses come under the hegemony of the subsystem. Here we are proposing that the extent to which they do is a measure of the extent to which they are exteriorized, of the extent to which they have become drawn into the altered adaptive relationship between subject (via the subsystem) and outside world (here the hypnotist). We have also commented on the differing ease of exteriorization of various structures, depending upon the fantasies with which they are linked or on the history of their development of autonomy. Another important factor determining the ease of exteriorization is the closeness of the function or structure to the "central core" of personality.[12]

We have described the adaptive point of view as involving for hypnosis the assumption of both ego and superego functions by the hypnotist and in this sense the relative and partial exteriorization of these functions. A parallel process occurs for the id, giving rise to the realm of phenomena ordinarily called "projection." This may take place with massive segments of instinctual urges, such as the whole range of aggressive impulses, or with the more delimited and specific impulses, such as homosexual urges.

In addition to the reversal of internalization by exteriorization, we must discuss the relation between the psychic institutions and the environment in terms of the sharpness of definition between the internal and external worlds. Just as before we have spoken of a blurring of the boundaries between the id, ego, and superego, so must we speak now of blurring of boundaries between self and not-self. Earlier in psychoanalytic theory this was usually discussed as the problem of ego boundaries (61). But, in accord with our earlier remarks on the concept of self, we would speak instead of the boundaries between one intra-ego structure—the self—and another—the representation of the outside world. Clarification of the meaning of regressive alterations of self-outside boundaries would follow from a clearer knowledge of the genesis of these boundaries. The accepted psychoanalytic

[12] Schilder discussed a related problem in describing two kinds of depth of hypnosis—the usual phenomenal one and one dependent on "genuine" involvement in the hypnosis (208).

view is that originally all is self and that the self progressively detaches the external world from itself. "The ego feeling we are aware of now is thus only a shrunken vestige of a far more extensive feeling—a feeling which embraced the universe and expressed an inseparable connection of the ego with the external world" (95, p. 13). This description seems to be in terms of exteriorization (that is to say, that the self progressively detaches *from itself* the external world) and forces us to ask whether it is contradictory to our view of development as a progressive internalization. Actually, these two points of view can be reconciled by the hypothesis that from the beginning, just as id and ego are undifferentiated, so are self and outside representations undifferentiated. From the point of view of the self, progressive differentiation results in a loss of what becomes outside world. From the point of view of the outside world, progressive differentiation results in a loss of what becomes self. Freud's statement that object loss is a precondition for the development of reality testing is actually a statement of an aspect of this differentiation, since the object has to be not immediately available for the self-object unity to begin to break up (93, p. 184; also 90).

We have already discussed the importance which Kubie and Margolin ascribe to contraction and expansion of ego boundaries in their differentiation between the induction phase and the established state. Freud described an "oceanic feeling" as related to a dedifferentiation of the self-object demarcation and suggested that this oceanic feeling may have "connections . . . with many obscure modifications of mental life, such as trance and ecstasy" (95, p. 22).

## THE GENETIC POINT OF VIEW

The most widespread genetic theory of the hypnotic state is of course that it is a regressive revival of earlier child-parent relationships.

The genetic point of view is especially important in a discussion of regression, since a regression is a reversion to earlier states. A central question is: to what degree can an earlier state of the psyche be reinstated? Discussions of "revivification" as against "regression" in hypnosis deal with a related issue, though, as we pointed out earlier, the concept "regression" in such discussions is somewhat different from that which we use throughout this book.[13]

Freud discussed the revival of earlier states of mind in *Civilization and Its Discontents* (95), where he concludes, "We can only be sure that it is more the rule than the exception for the past to survive in the mind" (p. 20), though by this he certainly does not imply that it can be revived in its old form.

In *The Problem of Anxiety* (94) he discusses this problem specifically for the id, and, as we have already mentioned, suggests that there may be the complete transfer of the cathexis of the original wish to its lineal descendants. But even this would leave the "third possibility that in the course of the neurosis the wish was reactivated through regression, so out of accord with the present may it be" (p. 83).

From the metapsychological point of view a regressed state cannot be considered equivalent to an earlier stage of developmental organization: despite the fact that there are important similarities, there are also important differences, resulting from the development subsequent to the stage to which there is regression. It would seem obvious that no stage of psychic development could ever be reinstated point for point. The ego apparatuses to which the stabilized regressed state has access differ in both structure and function from those to which it originally had access. The subsystem in hypnosis may in some respects resemble early parent-child relationships, but the automatized apparatuses which it may come to control are very different from what they were during childhood.

---

[13] We believe that a hypnotic "regression" approaches "revivification" to the extent to which there has been an adequate development of the subsystem with thoroughgoing synthesis of its various elements, but that revivification in the sense of the complete restoration of an earlier state is a fiction.

Earlier psychoanalytic thinking was inclined to view regression too schematically as a reinstatement of earlier developmental stages, but, as Hartmann said,

> Differentiation progresses not only by the creation of new apparatuses to master new demands and new tasks, but also and mainly by new apparatuses taking over, on a higher level, functions which were originally performed by more primitive means . . . when superordinate apparatuses are blocked or disordered, no pure form of a previous developmental stage emerges [114, p. 50].

We have alluded to the fact that later stages of mental development cannot be looked upon as more adapted than earlier stages, since every stage is an adaptation. In a similar sense, the synthetic function of the ego is not something which simply synthesizes more and more elements of psychic structure in the course of development, but functions in every stage of development and achieves some kind of a total unity or integration at each stage. Hypnosis, once the established state has been stabilized, is not less of a unity but rather a different kind of unity.

## THE ECONOMIC POINT OF VIEW

Kris (136) has given the most complete description of the metapsychology of the economics of regression in the service of the ego. He suggests that in the inspirational phase of creativity (regression in the service of the ego), countercathexes are withdrawn from their use in repression and added to the speed, force, or intensity with which preconscious thoughts are formed. He contrasts this to the elaborational phase of creativity in which the countercathectic barrier may be reinforced and cathexis directed to other ego functions such as reality testing, formulation, communication, etc. In further discussing shifts of cathexis in ego-functioning he points to a shift between perception and preconscious thought, suggesting that the one operates at the expense of the other. In effect, he proposes three kinds of ego function —repression, preconscious thinking, and reality testing, including perception. In regression in the service of the ego, cathexes are withdrawn both from repression and reality testing and used for preconscious thinking. In the elaborational phase repression and reality testing are the preferred functions and preconscious thinking suffers. In all of these considerations we speak in relative terms; cathexes do not totally shift from one function to another.

Using Kris's formulation as our point of departure, we would like to suggest several additions to clarify and sharpen the differences between regression proper and regression in the service of the ego, and between several kinds of regression in the service of the ego. First, we have proposed the subsystem as a structural concept. Whether or not a subsystem is established in all forms of regression in the service of the ego, we do not doubt its existence in hypnosis. Not only the apparatuses (and this would include much which for Kris would be preconscious thinking), but also the "higher" ego functions of reality testing, formulation, communication, etc., can, to a greater or lesser degree, as we have pointed out, come under the dominion of the subsystem. Second, as regards the cathexis of the higher functions, Kris speaks only of the withdrawal of cathexes from these functions. It may be true that in a regression in the service of the ego characterized by inspiration, cathexis may be withdrawn from these functions; still, they can remain cathected in hypnosis. Third, because the over-all system remains in effect, it must to some extent retain cathexis. To maintain itself and to prevent the "recapture" of the apparatuses and higher functions by the over-all ego, the subsystem will have to expend some energy in the countercathexis of these remaining cathexes in the over-all system.

Actually, the retention of cathexis by the over-all ego in the hypnotic regression (and the consequent necessity for countercathexis) is a central feature in what makes hypnosis possible. The organism is assured, as it were, that the over-all ego is in only temporary abeyance. To speak anthropomorphically, the over-all ego must be sufficiently secure in its ultimate mastery to permit an apparent loss of control.

Fourth, we suggest that in regression *proper*, not only are cathexes withdrawn from "higher functions," but that some structures are "dissolved" so that the defensive and controlling functions which they exercise with relatively small quantities of hypercathexes must now be carried out in a fluid struggle employing greater quantities of cathexes at a lower "potential." In regression in the service of the ego, cathexes are only partially withdrawn, and partially they remain, so that countercathexes must be erected against them by the subsystem, and structure is not dissolved. (We are again speaking of the poles of processes which exist on a continuum.)

We may speculate about the way in which the cathexes are deployed in the two main kinds of regression. In regression proper, the cathexes withdrawn from higher functions are employed to guard against even deeper regression. A new over-all ego comes into being, not a subsystem within the usual ego integration. (Again, this distinction is a matter of degree.) In regression in the service of the ego, the countercathexes withdrawn from their use in withholding the repressed material, now permitted to emerge, may be employed as countercathexes against higher functions, or against the over-all ego.

To summarize, in regression proper, cathexes are withdrawn from higher functions and distributed among ego functions, a larger share than before going to defense. In regression in the service of the ego, cathexes are withdrawn from defense and employed in the building of a subsystem whose maintenance requires a countercathexis of some of the cathexes retained in the over-all ego.

It is probable that in the functioning of the subsystem, synthetic achievements on this "lower" level require greater quantities of energy, though on a lower potential. We may further suggest that unconscious energies no longer counter-cathected by defensive energies likewise contribute to the enhancement of preconscious thinking in the manner in which, to quote Freud, "the unconscious becomes ego-syntonic" and the result is that "they make specially perfect functioning possible, and they manifest a resistance in the face of opposition" (83, p. 195)—in other words, are strongly cathected.

We turn again to Freud in *The Interpretation of Dreams*: his remarks on the state of mind required for dream interpretation—which he regards as akin to the hypnotic state of mind—describe the withdrawal of energy from one function (defense?) and its use for another.

> In the state used for the analysis of dreams and pathological ideas, the patient purposely and deliberately abandons this activity ["a certain deliberate (and no doubt also critical) activity which we allow to influence the course of our ideas while we are awake"], and employs the psychical energy thus saved (or a portion of it) in attentively following the involuntary thoughts which now emerge, and which—and here the situation differs from that of falling asleep—retain the character of ideas. *In this way the "involuntary" ideas are transformed into "voluntary" ones* [76, p. 102].

It becomes clear now why the capacity for regression in the service of the ego is the mark of a "strong" ego. Only the "strong" ego can allow the emergence of the repressed without having to erect a countercathexis against an upsurge of even more deeply repressed contents, and have available countercathexes to employ against higher functions. One more consideration, following Kris, suggests itself. The transiency, reversibility, and employment of countercathexes against higher functions in regression in the service of the ego suggest that the cathexes employed in these operations are largely neutralized, whereas those employed against even deeper regression in regression proper are rather deneutralized cathexes, whether libidinized or aggressivized. These cathexes are the ones which come from "dissolved" structure. Just as structure formation involves neutralization and the availability of hypercathexes, so does structure dissolution involve deneutralization and the loss of available hypercathexes.

This economic description makes more understandable the clinical fact of the higher incidence of hypnotizability in the normal as against the neurotic. In the neurotic with precarious defenses, the countercathectic energies holding down the primitive instinctual impulses cannot be spared to be used as countercathexis against the over-all ego or for the building of the subsystem. However, as we have mentioned, there are instances in which hypnosis is possible despite severe psychiatric illness. These pose crucial problems for the theory just stated, but we offer these suggestions: First, it may be that these are instances in which countercathexis against primitive instinctual drives is loosely held and easily yielded. Second, it may be that in such instances the amount of countercathectic energies necessary to hold the over-all ego in abeyance is less.

This economic view likewise enables us to advance a hypothesis for the metapsychological description of the greater hypnotizability of hysterics as against obsessional neurotics. Granted that we are schematizing, we follow Freud (94) in finding repression the major mechanism of defense in hysterics, and isolation and undoing the major mechanisms in obsessional neurosis. It is probable that the forms of countercathectic energy distribution in hysteria are different from the forms in obsessional neurosis. To speak in terms of an analogy, in hysteria the energy distributions are ranged along a front, with a well-defined no-man's land between ego and id. In the obsessional neurosis the warfare is more of the guerrilla type, with deep invasions of each force into the other's territory and islands of the enemy within each country. We are only stating here in another form the phenomena described as the manifestations of the synthetic function of the ego, the erotization of thinking, and the conversion of a defense into a gratification as, in a general way, they characterize the obsessional neurosis in contradistinction to hysteria. We speculate that these different ways of deploying counter-cathexis make massive cathectic shifts more possible in hysteria than in the obsessional neurosis, and thus account for the greater ease of hypnotizability in hysteria.

These economic explanations of problems of hypnotizability are not intended to minimize the role of transference factors in explaining hypnotizability. Again we stress that both altered state and transference factors must be considered.

It should be pointed out once again that regression proper and regression in the service of the ego are not as sharply dichotomous as is implied in some of this discussion. Not only are there transitional and complex mixed states, but also what began as a regression in the service of the ego may get out of hand, as it were, and become much closer to a regression proper. We have already discussed such changes as clinical phenomena observed in hypnosis.

NOTE: Too late for inclusion of more than this note, we realized that Edward Glover's theory of ego nuclei (see his paper "The Concept of Dissociation." *Int. J. Psa.*, 24:7-13, 1943, reprinted in Glover, E.: *On the Early Development of Mind*. New York: International Universities Press, 1956) provides a genetic underpinning for the kind of subsystem in the ego which we have postulated in our discussion of the metapsychology of hypnosis from the structural point of view.

*Part II*

Part II

# HYPNOSIS, SLEEP, SOMNAMBULISM, AND DREAM

Hypnosis has long been regarded as a variety of sleep by many investigators. The reasons seem clear enough. The hypnotized subject, particularly during induction and especially if hypnosis has been induced by sleep suggestions, looks like someone at least partially asleep. The hypnotic subject is said to be in a trance. Even if he talks and walks about, even if he has his eyes open, he usually seems like a somnambulist, a sleepwalker. But it is also true, as we have discussed, that the hypnotic subject in the established state has the potential for appearing—unless he is "pushed" too hard—like someone in an ordinary waking state of consciousness. We will divide our discussion into a first section on EEG evidence and hypnosis; a second on the relation between sleep and the induction of hypnosis; a third on hypnosis, sleep, and somnambulism; and a fourth on the metapsychology of hypnosis, sleep, and dream, with special emphasis on the metapsychology of the hypnotic dream.

## EEG Evidence

Despite the apparent relationship between hypnosis and sleep, the findings of most physiological studies of hypnosis link it more to the waking than to the sleeping state (105). With the development of the electroencephalograph and the demonstration that the EEG of sleep is markedly different from the EEG of waking, a new tool was at hand to decide, and hypnosis was quickly ranked among the waking states by those who studied the problem (222).

Barker and Burgwin (7) demonstrated that sleep waves could be produced in hypnosis by the suggestion of ordinary sleep, though their finding has been contested by True and Stephenson (220). Barker and Burgwin differentiated between hypnotic suggestibility and hypnotic sleep, the latter, they say, being sleep superimposed upon the hypnotic state.

It has been questioned by many whether *any* kind of difference between the electroencephalogram of the waking state and of hypnosis can be found, even with various kinds of hypnotic suggestion.

An early investigation by Loomis, Harvey, and Hobart (159) reported persistence of alpha waves during eyes open with the suggestion of hypnotic blindness (ordinarily the alpha waves disappear when the eyes are opened). But Lundholm and Löwenbach (160) were unable to confirm this finding. Barker and Burgwin did report inhibition of alpha rhythm in the presence of visual hallucinations.

A recent investigation (210), however, does report some changes in the EEG on certain suggestions. Positive and negative findings (with suitable controls) were these: (1) Nine out of eleven subjects showed the suppression of alpha waves during visual hallucinations with eyes closed. (2) Five subjects showed during hypnotic visual hallucinations a special kind of wave called a lambda wave which is associated with attending to vision. (3) Five subjects showed minimal or absent lambda waves during hypnotic blindness. (4) No persistence of alpha waves during hypnotic blindness with eyes open could be demonstrated. (5) There were minimal changes in the photic response during hypnosis. (6) There were no consistent changes in the EEG with the suggestion of anesthesia in hypnosis. (7) There were no changes in the wicket rhythm, a type of wave associated with movement, in hypnotically induced movements of a phantom hand. (8)

Sleep was produced in seven subjects as far as spindles and v-waves in some. No subject showed k-complexes. (9) Automatic frequency analysis showed no change in the "resting" hypnotic state as compared with the waking state. In one subject during regression to the age of three, there was a shift to a record resembling drowsiness or light sleep. (10) Hypnotic regression in five subjects showed no change. (11) Hypnotic activation techniques in genuine epilepsy showed no changes in the EEG, nor any recall of pertinent material in connection with seizures. (12) Patients with hysterical seizures showed spells with hypnotic activation techniques, but no changes in the EEG. These investigators confirmed an earlier finding that amnesia holds for genuine epilepsy but that the events of psychogenic seizures can be recalled (216).

It seems likely, then, that EEG changes can be produced by suggestion in the hypnotic state.

Our own study on the EEG in hypnosis was carried out prior to the study by Schwarz, Bickford, and Rasmussen, just described. We set up a joint study when an opportunity presented itself to work in collaboration with Drs. Chester Darrow and Charles Henry[1] of The Institute for Juvenile Research in Chicago. Using a college population as volunteer subjects, we selected by means of group hypnotizability sessions twenty-two students, nine of whom were very poor and sixteen excellent hypnotic subjects. We obtained simultaneous records of the following: electroencephalogram, blood pressure, respiratory rate and depth, galvanic skin response, electrocardiogram, and eyelid muscle movement. Continuous recording in the normal waking state and in hypnosis, running for several hours or even longer, enabled us also to study the transitional periods on going into and coming out of hypnosis, and in a few instances we obtained records of the subject's normal sleeping state as well. In addition, we tried a number of motor and sensory suggestions, both unilateral and bilateral, but were unable to see any clear-cut

[1] Dr. Henry is now at the Institute of Living, Hartford, Connecticut.

changes in the EEG record by gross inspection. We did not attempt to demonstrate changes as a result of these suggestions by frequency analysis or statistical techniques. Our main findings in the broadest terms were two: first, that hypnosis is definitely not a variety of "sleep," i.e., electroencephalographic patterns in a wide variety of hypnotic states and in physiological sleep are clearly distinguishable from each other; second, that hypnosis and *alert* waking states do not appear to be identical, i.e., EEG in-phase correspondence between occipital and motor areas during respiratory expiration is statistically higher in hypnosis than in the alert waking state. With the use of a sleep-waking index obtained from alpha and delta measurements, hypnosis can be differentiated from sleep *and from alert waking conditions*, but not from low alpha, low voltage nonhypnotic states, such as relaxed and/or drowsy states. While the question whether or not the differentiation from the alert waking state was a statistical artifact does not seem unequivocally decided, we do not feel qualified to form a judgment independent from our collaborators of the physiological data gathered during the course of these investigations.

One of the difficulties we ran up against and which we did not satisfactorily solve was that of the continua of states and spontaneously shifting states which occurred. It became clear that we could not assume that a relaxed and an alert waking state were necessarily the same electroencephalographically. The prolonged periods in the experimental procedures, often with relatively little stimulation, meant that the subject was likely to become relaxed, whether in or out of hypnosis. There were also spontaneous tendencies to drowse, again whether in or out of hypnosis. The drowsy EEG differs from the alert EEG, but we did not know whether we could equate relaxation with drowsiness, either in hypnosis or in the waking state. We attempted to find out, by inquiring whether our awake subject was relaxed or drowsy or alert. And we attempted to control the hypnotic state by deliberately suggesting periods of alertness and periods of relaxation. It will be seen that three dichotomies are involved: awake-asleep; hypnotic-nonhypnotic; and relaxed-alert. To what extent they overlap, and how to be sure in an experimental setup that one is dealing with one or another, are essentially unsolved problems.

It is clear that hypnosis is not the same as deep sleep. But this should not be surprising, since the hypnotic subject engages in a kind of mental activity and sometimes physical activity which does not ordinarily occur in deep sleep.

But since mental and physical activity can occur in a sleeper who is dreaming, as in somnambulism, we must ask whether the hypnotic state may be similar to the dream state physiologically, and what are the EEG findings in dreams. Recent experiments promise to shed some light on this question. Aserinsky and Kleitman (4) reported the occurrence of periods of rapid, jerky, conjugate eye movements during sleep, and an association of these movements with dreaming. The association was established by awakening the sleeper both during such periods of eye movements and during control periods of quiescence of the eyes, and asking whether he had been dreaming. Subsequent studies by Dement (49, 49a) and Dement and Kleitman (50) showed a cycle of the EEG pattern during sleep and the association of these eye movements during only certain phases of the cycle. In all instances (eighteen)

. . . as the subject fell asleep, the brain waves progressively increased in amplitude and decreased in frequency for approximately 40 minutes and then a change in the opposite direction began. At about 60 minutes after the onset of sleep, the EEG was characterized by low voltage fast activity. This persisted for 5 to 20 minutes, and then a progressive increase in voltage and decrease in frequency was again observed. This cycle repeated itself over and over through the night. The periods of low voltage fast activity became progressively longer with each cycle and the periods of high voltage low activity became shorter, with the maximum amplitude and frequency also decreasing. Discrete periods of rapid eye movements were observed during the periods of low voltage fast activity and at no other times [49].

The dream EEG, then, does not show the high voltage low frequency waves ordinarily associated with sleep.

On the other hand, it is also true that in certain circumstances alpha activity can be seen in the sleeper. Blake and Gerard describe the appearance of 10 per second or faster rhythms immediately following a movement or a disturbing stimulus in sleep (18). Adrian reported that sensory stimulation can cause a return of the alpha waves without necessarily arousing the sleeper (3).

So far, then, the EEG findings allow us to say with certainty only that hypnosis is not deep sleep. We do not have the right to say that hypnosis is the same as the ordinary waking state: first, there is some evidence—shaky, it is true—that the EEG of hypnosis will be shown to differ from the EEG of the alert waking state; and second, an individual who seems to be asleep may show EEG patterns ordinarily associated with wakefulness (the changes during stimulation of the sleeper who does not awake, and during dreaming). As far as the EEG is concerned, it is still possible to call the hypnotized subject a dreamer.*

## Sleep and the Induction of Hypnosis

In spite of the association in the literature between hypnosis and sleep or going to sleep, detailed reports of attempts at hypnotizing while the subject is falling asleep are almost nonexistent. While the literature contains frequent references to the increased ease of inducing hypnosis in a sleeper, reports are either based only on the weight of an authority or are

* A thoughtful study stressing the equivocal nature of the evidence and issues which must be clarified in further investigations appeared too late for inclusion in this summary: Chertok, L., and Kramarz, P., Hypnosis, Sleep, and Electroencephalography. *J. Nerv. Ment. Dis.*, 128:227-238, 1959.

anecdotal. A welcome experimental study of the phenomenon has recently been made by Barber (5, 6).

Barber approached twenty-two subjects asleep in their own rooms during the night. He measured their responses to seven standard tests of suggestibility. Twelve of the subjects remained lightly sleeping—they did not move, did not open their eyes, appeared to be asleep during the experiment, and later either stated that they were at least partly asleep or else had complete amnesia for the experiment. The same subjects were later hypnotized and given the same tests, and later still, given the same tests in the waking state as a control. On the tests of suggestibility, Barber found no difference in the responses of the twelve subjects after hypnotic induction and during the light sleep. Sixty per cent of these subjects were at least as suggestible as people in the third stage of hypnosis on the Davis and Husband Scale (complete amnesia, or follow a simple posthypnotic suggestion), one third as if they were in the second stage of hypnosis, and one subject as if he were in the first. Barber found, then, that at least one third of his original group were good subjects. This figure is higher than the usual 20 per cent figure for good subjects in the normal population, and furthermore was obtained with the sleepers under quite unfavorable conditions—that is, Barber did not try carefully to get into contact with the sleeper, slowly build up and stabilize the contact, and then give the suggestions. He simply came into the room, approached the subject, and gave the suggestions, though the subjects did know beforehand that the experiment was going to be performed. As far as can be judged from Barber's account, he always tested the subjects in the same order: sleep first and then hypnosis. The responses in the two correlated highly. Since he did not test hypnosis first and then sleep, we cannot tell how the results in hypnosis were affected by the procedure during sleep, nor what might have happened had the order of the two procedures been reversed.

Barber interprets his results as showing that the term "hyp-

nosis" has been applied to two quite different phenomena—
increased suggestibility during light sleep and increased suggestibility during the waking state. In effect, he is saying that
those who responded in their sleep were asleep and not in
hypnosis.[2]

## Drugs and Hypnosis

Another approach to the problem of the relation of hypnosis and sleep is the use of drugs to facilitate the induction
of hypnosis. Various kinds of drugs have been employed,
generally those producing a state of somnolence. We ourselves have done some unreported work with intravenous
sodium pentothal and concluded that the drug facilitates
hypnosis only where it would probably have occurred anyway
without the drug. There is, however, fairly widespread agreement among those who have employed such drugs that they
do facilitate the induction of hypnosis. (Some of the experi-
menters speak of the enhancement of suggestibility rather
than of hypnosis, but we shall assume a direct relationship
here.) We refer the reader to the summary in Weitzenhoffer
(222).

Kubie has reviewed the various drugs that are used to induce "hypnagogic states," and regards such states as facilitating the induction of hypnosis (141). The facilitation of
hypnosis by various means may mean simply its facilitation
in instances in which it would have been obtainable in any
case. On the other hand, it could mean that a shift of forces
is brought about by the adjuvant, whether sleep, drugs, or
whatever, which makes the difference between whether hypnosis can be induced or not.

It must be made clear that the altered state which is regarded as facilitating hypnosis should not be confused with
the hypnotic state itself. The inducibility of hypnosis in a

---

[2] A difficult point to interpret is whether the amnesia shown is a posthypnotic amnesia or a postsleep amnesia. Since Barber regards his subjects
as being asleep, one might question his use of a hypnotizability scale to
grade their suggestibility.

state of light sleep does not mean that sleep is a necessary part of hypnosis. And if it were demonstrable, for example, that the administration of certain drugs facilitates hypnosis, this would not mean that the state produced by the drug itself is hypnosis, but rather that the hypnotic state is super-imposed upon the drug state (118). The administrator of the drug may behave in such a way as to produce a hypnotic state without realizing that he is doing so, and in this way he may mistakenly conclude that the drug state is the same as the hypnotic state.[3] Contrariwise, it may be possible to produce an altered state in hypnosis which is not to be confused with hypnosis but which is superimposed upon—and may some-times replace?—the hypnotic state. This may be the explana-tion of the production by suggestion of apparently genuine sleep in hypnosis (7).

## Hypnosis, Sleep, and Somnambulism

We will review some of the major statements on the rela-tionship between hypnosis and sleep before offering our own summary of the problem. The commonality between sleep and hypnosis has been said to reside in the withdrawal from the external environment. Freud, for example, said:

> Now the command to sleep in hypnosis means nothing more nor less than an order to withdraw all interest from the world and to concentrate it on the person of the hypnotist. And it is so understood by the subject; for in this withdrawal of interest from the external world lies the psychological character-istic of sleep, and the kinship between sleep and the state of hypnosis is based on it [88, p. 127].

Schilder and Kauders (208) view the relationship between hypnosis and sleep as a most intimate one. In fact, they say that the hypnotist induces sleep by means of "the suggestive rapport" and that during sleep the rapport is maintained with

[3] Cf. Grinker and Spiegel, Men Under Stress (111).

the "sleep vigil." The sleeper, they say, has a "sleep vigil" and a "sleep ego." But despite the fact that the rapport is maintained only with the sleep vigil, they believe that the sleep ego must be present for the state of hypnosis to exist. As they say: "When the latter [the sleep ego] predominates to an extreme degree, we are confronted with the phenomenon of sleep with suggestibility. . . . where the sleep ego . . . [is] practically nil . . . the person enters a state of waking suggestion" (p. 78). This is similar to Barber's argument. We would formulate the problem as follows: if the rapport is a function of the sleep vigil, and not of the sleep ego, why should the disappearance of the sleep ego result in something called "waking suggestion" rather than hypnosis and the hypnotic state be considered terminated?

The situation is further complicated for Schilder and Kauders in that they find that the sleep ego may include two dream egos, an unconscious one and a preconscious one. If the sleep ego is heavily "infiltrated" by the unconscious dream ego, the suggestive rapport may be almost completely dissolved, but in other instances it may be scarcely affected. Preconscious material (which may be preconscious material other than that of the preconscious dream ego) may also affect the rapport in a similar fashion to unconscious dream material.

They close their discussion, however, with an insistence that "despite its many divisions, the ego maintains its homogeneity" (they postulate an over-all "controlling ego"), and that many of the phenomena ascribed to the ego differentiation mentioned overlap as follows: the two measures of depth of hypnosis—suggestibility and psychic depth—are likely to vary together. If the sleep ego plays a large role, the dream ego is likely to be prominent. If the sleep ego plays a small role, dreamlike and preconscious material will not play much role; and where the dream ego and preconscious material play a large role, the depth of rapport is not likely to be great.

The numerous variables introduced by Schilder and Kauders are, then: (1) psychic depth of hypnosis, (2) suggestibility depth of hypnosis, (3) controlling ego, (4) sleep vigil, (5) sleep ego, (6) unconscious dream ego, (7) preconscious dream ego, and (8) rapport.

A serious and confusing difficulty can be introduced into a discussion of the relationship between hypnosis and sleep if one fails to distinguish between sleep as a state and sleep as a subjective psychological content. A particular person may very well equate hypnosis with sleep, and may feel about hypnosis as he does about the sleep with which he equates it, but this is very different from saying that hypnosis and sleep are objectively related states.

Lewin has made some interesting observations on the meaning of hypnosis as a psychological content equated with sleep. He has proposed that an effort be made to write the metapsychology of the analytic situation from the point of view of sleep and the dream. He derives the analytic situation genetically from the hypnotic situation, as a result of a resistance to being put into hypnosis which he equates with a resistance to going to sleep. A compact was reached, he suggests, in which in return for accepting a state less like sleep, the subject agreed to take more responsibility in free association. Lewin emphasizes that he is not arguing that hypnosis is sleep any more than that anesthesia is sleep, but that the two are psychological equivalents (149).

The patient's fear of hypnosis, he says, may be based on a fear of losing control, a severe loss of inhibition, or on one of the meanings of sleep. Sleep, as Lewin reminds us, may mean death, or the various pregenital varieties of the fear of death or sleep, viz.: being devoured, being poisoned, being suffocated (all oral, be it noted), and fear of afterlife. Being hypnotized, anesthetized, killed, put to sleep, are all equivalents, and all may be represented by lying down on the analyst's couch.

Free association is described by Lewin as a substitute for sleep. "The wish to be put to sleep has been supplanted by the wish to associate freely in the analytic situation" (149, p. 171). Actually, free association has more of the characteristics of a dream than of sleep, and if one wanted to follow this line of reasoning (which to us carries the danger of confusing the psychology of an individual person with reconstructions of the history of the development of psychoanalytic technique), one might say that while the analytic patient wishes to dream, the hypnotic subject wishes to sleep.[4] As Lewin himself points out, and as we quoted earlier, Freud (76, p. 102) equated free association not with sleep, but with the state of mind that precedes sleep and with hypnosis. Here again it may be desirable to make a separation between the induction period and the state itself. The induction period could be equated with going to sleep, and the hypnotic state with being asleep and dreaming.

Lewin has pointed out that the resistive patient may become either too sleepy or too alert for free association. Kanzer also says that "fluctuations in hypnotic state correspond to variations in resistance that occur in the course of free association during analysis" (126, p. 228). We have similarly pointed out that the resistive subject may become too deeply hypnotized (too sleepy?) or too alert (too awake?) to produce the kind of material we want. And we have proposed that in going into too deep a hypnosis the subject may be employing a defense.

Lewin finds that the analyst plays a number of different roles in the analytic situation. He may be day residue for dream; he may be soother; he may be disturber. In the hypnotic situation, the hypnotist plays the same three roles for the subject, but more obviously and actively, since in each hypnosis he puts the subject "to sleep" and terminates the hypnosis by "awakening" him.

Kanzer likewise argues that the hypnotist makes contradictory demands and that the patient is forced to split the

---

[4] Note that this is not the same as saying that the analytic patient *is dreaming* nor that the hypnotic subject *is sleeping*.

hypnotist into two figures—one who is a proponent of the wish to sleep and one who contradicts this wish.

The general proposition into which we may fit our discussion of the possible facilitation of hypnosis by sleep is the following: if the induction of hypnosis is the initiation of a regressive movement, this should presumably be facilitated by other conditions in which a regressive movement has already occurred.[5] Sleep is a regressed state which facilitates the induction of hypnosis. From one point of view it could be said that the standard method of hypnotic induction actually makes use of just this phenomenon, and that hypnosis is induced by a regressive movement of another kind. It could be said that the subject is made drowsy, and this drowsiness is a regressed state which facilitates the induction of hypnosis. This might be considered a short-cut way of stating a good deal of what has already been said about induction in this book. But such a statement would only bypass the issue, for the issue would then become that of how drowsiness facilitates hypnosis and how one goes about producing the state of drowsiness, and the entire question of the methods of inducing regressed states—of interfering with the ego's relative autonomy—would still be before us. Furthermore, it is not a question of drowsiness per se but of the production of drowsiness in the context of a particular interpersonal relationship, and therefore it is correct to speak of hypnotic induction, not of the production of drowsiness.

We argue, then, that an essential part of the hypnotic state is a relationship to an external person, and that in so far as the relationship to such a person exists, a subject is *not* asleep. This is to state the familiar phenomenon that the sleep state allows for a simultaneously persisting relationship to some external object, whether human or not—the mother to her child, the miller to the sound of his wheel. It could

---

[5] But this does not mean that any regressed condition facilitates hypnosis. As we have mentioned, psychiatric illnesses are regressed conditions in which hypnosis is in general more difficult to induce than in the normal person.

be said that hypnosis and sleep are alike in that there is a withdrawal of interest from the external world, but different in that the withdrawal is more complete in sleep than in hypnosis. But even this is a misleading statement: it is not only less complete in hypnosis but selective—that is, in terms of the apparatuses included in the subsystem, a subsystem through which is maintained a transference relationship to the hypnotist, and all under the control of the total ego which maintains a reality relationship to the hypnotist.

In other words, the apparent withdrawal of interest from the external world is true only for the sleeping type of hypnosis in which the apparatuses are for the most part not under the control of the subsystem. This kind of hypnosis resembles sleep, because sleep is characterized by an ego (in this case too a subsystem, but with much more extensive withdrawal of cathexis from the over-all ego than is true in hypnosis) which does not have control of the apparatuses, whether sensory or motor.

The "missing link" is furnished by spontaneous somnambulism.[6] Here a subsystem which has some control of the apparatuses is established in a subject who is clearly asleep— or more correctly, dreaming. The conclusion suggests itself that somnambulism is to be explained as the endogenous development in the ego of a subsystem which, like that of sleep, has no relationship to an outside person and, like that of hypnosis, has some control of the apparatuses. It might be expected that it would be easy to get into hypnotic rapport with a subject in somnambulism. This is not necessarily true, however, since the dynamics of the subsystem and its establishment might be opposed to such control. We do not know of any valid evidence on the subject. Though we have seen a few cases in which a history of somnambulism was associated with good hypnotizability, we do not know how regular this association is.

[6] Somnambulism as used here simply means sleepwalking. In the next chapter we deal with the other phenomena for which the same term is used.

We would interpret Barber's results as showing that the induction of hypnosis had been found to be facilitated by the sleeping state and hence in accord with our hypothesis. Barber divides what is usually called hypnosis into two conditions—sleep suggestibility and waking suggestibility. He has made no effort to distinguish hypnosis from other kinds of waking suggestibility. Schilder and Kauders want to make a distinction between waking suggestibility and hypnosis, and do so by saying that in hypnosis there is a sleep ego as well as a sleep vigil. We want to make a distinction between hypnosis and other kinds of suggestibility too, and do so by saying that there is a subsystem in the ego in hypnosis, but we do not identify this subsystem with the sleep subsystem. Because Schilder and Kauders do identify these two, they had to distinguish a sleep ego and a sleep vigil. We believe that if one does not make the error of regarding the hypnotized person as necessarily being to some degree asleep (and we suggest that Schilder and Kauders introduce the sleep variable because they believe activity of a physiological sleep center plays a basic role in hypnosis), it is enough to postulate two organizations in the ego, the ordinary "controlling organization," and the regressed subsystem organization. The extent to which the subsystem has recruited ego apparatuses would be a measure of the "suggestibility," and the extent to which the over-all ego organization has yielded cathexis to the subsystem would be a measure of the "psychic depth" of the hypnosis.

We pause here for a remark on the relationship between hypnosis and hysteria. In hysteria a subsystem is also established. This subsystem captures control of the apparatuses on an extensive continuum ranging from control of a single limb to the apparent complete submergence of the over-all ego, as in fugue with change of personal identity.[7] In hysteria, in contrast to hypnosis, the subsystem is not under the domination of an external person, but it is often possible for this subsystem to come under the control of an external

[7] See Chapter 7.

person—in other words, we are speaking of the greater hyp-notizability of hysterics as compared with other psychiatric disorders.

We will later discuss specific features of the relationship between increased hypnotizability and fugue states, the trau-matic neuroses, multiple personality, and somnambulism. Here we wish only to say that in a more general sense these states, like sleep, facilitate the induction of hypnosis because they are already regressed states.

## Hypnosis and Dream

We have argued that there is no necessary connection be-tween hypnosis and sleep as states, though they may be sub-jectively closely connected, even equated, for any particular person. It may actually be that the common psychological equivalence of the two states is to some extent responsible for their being so frequently related in psychological theory.

If the hypnotic subject is regarded as partially asleep, does this mean that at least part of his mental activity is dream-ing?[8]

There have been attempts to relate hypnosis to a dream state. Kanzer, for example, says that the hypnotist tends to assume the role of a dream figure of the subject's own crea-tion: ". . . the hypnotist . . . , as focus of contending forces, moves through the sensorium of the patient like a materialized dream." The interplay "lends the proceedings the characteris-tics of the manifest content of a dream" (126, p. 229). But we note that he calls it "manifest content." We could not call the hypnotic subject a dreamer unless we could demonstrate that his mental content actually has the characteristics of a dream. Here we see that the comparison breaks down at

---

[8] We say only "part" of his mental activity because another part of it is the reality relationship with the hypnotist which could be considered analogous to a sleeper retaining contact with an outside object, like the miller with his wheel. Our view is that even if a particular hypnotic subject is also asleep, he maintains two kinds of relationship to the hypnotist, the transference and the reality relationships.

once because despite the fact that we have argued that the thinking of the hypnotic subject moves toward the primary process, we cannot maintain that it shows the characteristics of dream-thinking, if only in that it uses a good deal of verbal thinking (which is not simply day residue) and is not restricted to pictorial thinking.

But we have argued that the ready inducibility of dreams in hypnosis is an indication of the regressive nature of the hypnotic state and we must here pose a number of questions. Why are dreams readily inducible in the hypnotic state? What are the characteristics of hypnotic dreams and what is the mechanism of their production? How do they relate to spontaneous night dreams?

We will be able to discuss these questions better if we review briefly the psychoanalytic theory of dreams.

Sleep is a state of narcissistic withdrawal and dream formation begins with an exception to this withdrawal, the retention of cathexes by some preconscious thought of the preceding day. The first step in dream formation is the reinforcement of these preconscious day residues by the establishment of a connection with repressed material in the unconscious; the second step is the formation of "the preconscious dream-wish . . . which gives expression to the unconscious impulse in the material of the preconscious day's residues" (84, p. 226); the third step is a topographic regression: "The process, begun in the *Pcs.*, and reinforced by the *Ucs.*, pursues a backward course, through the *Ucs.* to perception" (84, p. 227); "When regression has been completed, a number of cathexes are left over in the system *Ucs.*—cathexes of memories of *things*. The primary psychical process is brought to bear on these memories, till, by condensation of them and displacement between their respective cathexes, it has shaped the manifest dream-content" (84, p. 228); this then becomes "conscious as a sense-perception; while this is happening it undergoes secondary revision, to which every perceptual content is subject" (84, p. 229).

The dream is divided into manifest and latent content. Its latent content includes the latent dream thoughts which are preconscious and may include preconscious wishes and the unconscious wish. The dream work is the process by which the cathexes of the memory traces of things are worked on by the primary process to shape the manifest content.

The two major advances in dream theory since Freud have been, in our view, first the more speculative theory of the dream screen advanced by Lewin (150, 152, 153), who argues that every dream takes place on a backdrop which represents the breast and which is a survival of the early relationship between suckling and going to sleep; and second, the more convincingly demonstrated work of Erikson (58) who shows, by a reanalysis of the Irma dream, that the manifest content may be as revealing of the dreamer's ego as is the latent content of the dreamer's id.

To return to our questions about the hypnotic dream: one of us (20) has published an article on dreams in hypnosis.[9] A crucial point of that paper was to show that the suggestion to dream in hypnosis results in a whole range of phenomena —from clearly preconscious productions to productions which are on the surface indistinguishable from spontaneous non-hypnotic dreams. It is the latter of course which require explanation and with which we now deal.

The mechanism of the production of hypnotic dreams has recently been discussed by Fisher (71, 72). He believes it is not difficult to explain the fact that dreams can be suggested and, it will be recalled, he found that they could be successfully suggested to patients in analysis and even to normal subjects in the classroom situation. Since, as Renneker has discussed (195), the ego can gain some control over dreaming, and since certain functions can be turned over to the hypnotist, why not the function of control of dreams, asks Fisher?

In discussing the mechanism of their formation, Rapa-

[9] This article is partially reviewed in Chapter 11.

port (184) points out that hypnotic dreams unite several elements:

a) the content of the suggestion which is objected to by the censorship with a severity that varies with the individual; b) the intention of the subject to carry out the suggestion, which depends upon the relationship to the hypnotist and on the form of suggestion, hence ultimately on personality characteristics determining both; c) a wish of the subject, mobilized by the suggestion or prevailing in the subject generally or temporarily, which in either case depends on the control of wishes (drives), characteristic of the subject's personality. It is likely that a) and b) together are related to c), as day-residues to the dream wish [p. 266].

Fisher proposes that every dream suggestion actually results in two day residues: the content day residue and the transference day residue. The former refers to the content of the suggestion and the latter to the meaning to the subject of being told to dream.

These two actually correspond quite closely to the elements postulated by Rapaport. The content of the suggestion is like Fisher's content day residue, while both the intention of the subject to carry out the suggestion and the wish mobilized in the subject are related to Fisher's transference day residue. The wish mobilized is a function of the meaning to the subject of being told to dream while the intention to carry out the suggestion is a particular example of such a wish in the form of a fairly high-level derivative. By the transference day residue Fisher apparently refers more to the unconscious and infantile roots of what might issue in such a preconscious intention to carry out the suggestion. He would probably therefore see the wish described by Rapaport as including both the transference day residue and "a wish . . . prevailing in the subject generally or temporarily."

Recent unpublished work by Newman, Katz, and Rubenstein (171) indicates that there may be three distinguishable elements in the dream referable to the hypnotic situation—

the two proposed by Fisher and Rapaport which relate to the suggestion, and a representation of the patient's response to elements of the hypnotic situation other than the dream suggestion. A dream, for example, may include, first, use of a suggestion as a content day residue, whether or not it activates in addition a "natural day residue"; second, a transference day residue in Fisher's sense—for example, a pregenital representation of impregnation or birth; and third, some comments on the hypnotic situation. For example, in one subject's dream, a shabby man handing out two opiate pills but keeping eight for himself was a representation with various distortions of the induction of hypnosis by counting to ten.

We have asked about the relation of such suggested dreams to spontaneous nonhypnotic dreams, and to naturally present unconscious wishes. In psychoanalytic theory, the motive power of dreams is an unconscious infantile wish. Rapaport says such a wish is mobilized by the suggestion and prevails in the subject generally or temporarily. Fisher also seems to imply that the suggestion must make contact with a previously existing wish. We would argue, of course, that for a hypnotic dream to have the same structure or significance as a spontaneous dream, a hypnotic suggestion must activate an already present infantile wish. With the multiplicity of infantile wishes always active in everyone, this seems a feasible mechanism.

In hypnosis we must also take account of the influence on dreaming analogous to the influence of the analytic situation on dreaming. Freud said that in analysis the sole motive force for many dreams is an unconscious wish connected with the positive transference. "In many dreams which recall what has been forgotten and repressed, it is impossible to discover any other unconscious wish [other than that connected with the positive transference] to which the motive force for the formation of the dream can be attributed" (91, p. 145).

In a later passage it becomes clear that Freud means here that the appearance of some kinds of repressed material cannot be attributed to a wish from the dreamer's repressed infantile impulses, but to the repetition compulsion, and that the upward force of the repetition compulsion can be assisted by wishes deriving from the positive transference. A similar situation exists in hypnosis. The motive power for some hypnotic dreams may derive not from repressed infantile impulses but from unconscious wishes connected with the positive transference, these wishes serving in a fashion analogous to that which Freud regards as responsible for bringing to light painful, unwished-for, repressed material in some dreams in analysis.

But it would be possible to account for the appearance of unwished-for repressed material as a result of the positive transference alone without invoking the repetition compulsion. In analysis the unconscious wish to please the analyst may become very strong. In the interest of the gratification of this unconscious wish, countercathexes can be withdrawn from painful repressed material. It is probable that the wish to please the analyst draws motive power not only from the unconscious transference, but also from a preconscious wish to please the analyst. But such a preconscious wish could never alone provide the motive power for the dream. The preconscious wish to please the analyst, however, acts like a transference day residue which establishes a link to more primitive unconscious wishes related to the positive transference.[10] It should not be forgotten, however, that Freud suggested that dreams could be roughly classified into those "from above" and those "from below." It is quite possible

[10] "Again, the dream-wish must not be confused with the wishful impulses which may have been present, though they certainly need not necessarily be present, amongst the preconscious (latent) dream-thoughts. If, however, there *were* any such preconscious wishes, the dream-wish associates itself with them, as a most effective reinforcement of them" (84, p. 226). And: "My supposition is that a conscious wish can only become a dream instigator if it succeeds in awakening an unconscious wish with the same tenor and in obtaining reinforcement from it" (76, p. 553).

that a hypnotically suggested dream is ordinarily "from above," a dream in which the preconscious wish manages to establish a connection with an infantile unconscious wish. Except in so far as there may be such a thing as a spontaneous dream in hypnosis, perhaps the hypnotic dream is always a dream "from above" since it is initiated by a suggestion which presumably must first make a connection with a preconscious thought or wish. Possibly all suggested dreams in hypnosis are of that class of dreams whose motive power issues from infantile wishes linked to the positive transference. It seems at least very probable that a suggested dream in hypnosis must derive motive power from an unconscious wish related to the transference, whether it be positive transference or some other facet of transference. This suggestion gains greater cogency if we remind ourselves that though dreaming in hypnosis is regulated by the subsystem within the ego, this subsystem functions under the control of an object in the external environment—the hypnotist.

We must also discuss further the relation of the suggestion to latent dream content and to the dream wish. The suggestion can influence manifest content; any kind of reaction to the suggestion can be latent content; and the suggestion can activate an unconscious wish. As Fisher (72) says, the suggestion influences the dream wish: "One can attempt to activate the unconscious dream wish by offering specific day residues—that is, a certain content which the dream wish can seek out and utilize to gain access to the preconscious" (p. 409). The important point is that the wish to fulfill the suggestion to dream cannot alone be sufficient motive power for a dream, but must link up with a primitive infantile wish. Or at any rate, this mechanism must obtain if it is argued that the mechanism of dream formation in hypnosis is the same as the mechanism of dream formation in a night dream.

In his paper on the metapsychology of the hypnotic dream (126) Kanzer argues that in induced dreams "the voice of the hypnotist takes the place of the day's residues, his ideas shape the latent thoughts, his comments give rise to the dream wish" (p. 229). As would follow from our earlier remarks, we believe this overstates the case. While the hypnotist does play a role in shaping day residue, manifest, and even latent content, the dream wish must arise from the subject's own infantile unconscious.

Having discussed the mechanism of formation of a hypnotic dream, we still have to ask whether the hypnotic state is peculiar in that it makes possible the induction of dreams and if so, in what this peculiarity consists. Is it enough to say that the hypnotic state is a regressed state and hence facilitates the regressive phenomenon—dreaming? What of Fisher's experiment (72) in which dreams were induced in a fair per cent of members of a psychology class and of people in analysis? It must not be forgotten that in the latter two types of experiment the dreams produced were dreamed during a sleep following the suggestion by some hours; in hypnosis too a dream may be suggested to occur the following night, but it may also be suggested to occur immediately after the suggestion during the hypnosis. In a dream occurring during sleep the ordinary mechanisms of dreaming are at work and the experiment demonstrates only that the suggestion can influence the dream, but in hypnosis it seems possible to instigate dreaming itself. It is possible that what happens is that the hypnotic subject goes to sleep and dreams during sleep, then returning to hypnosis. One of our subjects, on being told to dream in hypnosis, would roll over on his side and tell us later that he had been briefly asleep during the hypnosis.

It would seem that even though we deny that a hypnotic subject is necessarily asleep, there must be some relationship between the hypnotic state and the state of a dreamer which makes it possible for a subject to pass readily from one state to the other. We believe that the regressed subsystem of the hypnotic state is akin to the ego system which is active during sleep. We have found the difference in that hypnosis includes a relationship to an external person, potential control of the apparatuses, and the absence of sleep. We point again to the extraordinary interest and importance of the phenomenon of somnambulism as a connecting link. In this remarkable state the ego of a dreamer likewise gains some control of the apparatuses, but he remains asleep. The connection with an external person seems a crucial index of the difference between spontaneous somnambulism and hypnotic somnambulism.

Before leaving the subject of hypnosis, sleep, and dream, we pause for a comment on the relationship between sleep and orality, a topic of long-standing prominence in psychoanalytic theory, which has in recent years been much emphasized by Lewin. In so far as there exists a relationship between hypnosis and sleep—and we mean now not a relationship as objective states but as subjective psychological equivalents—there is probably a relationship between hypnosis and orality, and just as hypnosis is related to sleep, one of Lewin's triad of oral wishes, so is it to the other two, the wish to devour and the wish to be devoured (151). Here we can connect these ideas and our earlier discussion of the unconscious fantasies in the hypnotic relationship, in which we postulated a mutual identification with oral wishes to devour and to be devoured playing a prominent role.

# 7

# FUGUE AND HYPNOSIS

There are several spontaneously occurring states which have for a long time been linked to hypnosis. These are fugue, somnambulism, multiple personality, and more recently, traumatic neurosis. Before proceeding to a discussion of the relationship of these states to one another and to hypnosis, we must indicate why these states should be linked to hypnosis at all. Historically, of course, it has been assumed that the psychology of hypnosis is similar in important ways to the psychology of these states. A clear example is Janet's dictum that hypnosis is an artificial somnambulism (122).

There are two lines of empirical evidence, neither one of which, unfortunately, has been sufficiently exploited, which suggest a relationship between these states and hypnosis. One is that people who have shown or are showing these conditions are more susceptible to hypnotic induction than other segments of the population. The other is the related finding that hypnosis is an effective medium of therapy for people suffering these conditions, indeed that certain quite specific effects are produced when hypnosis is employed in these disorders.

To take up hypnotizability first: it is an accepted belief that people suffering from fugue, multiple personality, traumatic neurosis, and somnambulism are readily hypnotizable. This is to some extent a corollary of the belief that hysterics are hypnotizable, since these conditions are regarded as occurring either predominantly or exclusively in hysterics. But there is also some more direct evidence. The difficulty with much of this evidence is that it consists of reports based on few cases. A study by Abeles and Schilder (1), however, included sixty-three cases of fugue. Hypnosis was attempted in twenty-five. In eight it was "wholly successful and in six partly so." For control figures we must use those of a psychiatric population. It is our experience that, roughly, one out of ten patients can be deeply hypnotized. We must presume that "wholly successful" means successful to the degree of hypnotic somnambulism. Eight out of twenty-five is 30 per cent, a high figure for hypnotic somnambulism. For partial plus deep hypnosis we have a figure of eight plus six, or fourteen out of twenty-five, or about 50 per cent, again very high. There is some evidence from the last war for the hypnotizability of patients with traumatic neuroses. Kartchner and Korner (128) report that they used hypnosis in one third of their cases, indicating hypnotizability of at least one-third.

Rosen and Myers (198) report: "We have seen few patients who could not be hypnotized on first trial within, at the most, a five-minute period, provided that symptoms seemed of the type for which abreaction therapy was indicated as part of the treatment program. Ready suggestibility seems almost characteristic of such patients, whether they show psychotic-like pictures or not, and this is especially true of acute battle casualties with pronounced regressions" (p. 163).

These authors even say that though it was at first impossible to hypnotize soldiers who for medicolegal reasons were hospitalized by order of a court martial, or those completely out of contact because of severe depressions, severe regressions, or confusional states with extreme disorientation, after an initial abreaction brought about by a barbiturate, hypnosis could be used with "most such cases."

Kaufman and Beaton (129) report on the acute combat psychiatric casualties in a similar vein: "On the whole, the vast majority of patients seemed to be easily hypnotized. We knew of only three patients who were not put to sleep in this way. There may have been many more, but generally the technique was surprisingly successful" (p. 4).

A recent study by Kennedy and Neville (130) reports the treatment by hypnosis of thirty-one out of fifty-three cases of sudden loss of memory. The article does not state whether an attempt was made to hypnotize all members of the series, so the per-cent hypnotizability may have been even higher than 60 per cent. The authors note that it was "easy to induce hypnosis if induction is rapid and amnestic somnambulism rather than light hypnosis is the aim."

We have already discussed the relation between hysteria as a diagnostic category and hypnotizability, and the theory of the relationship between hysteria and hypnosis in our discussion of the metapsychology of hypnosis as a regression. The link between the two seems to be the use of repression as the preferred mode of defense. Where repression is the preferred mode of defense, massive shifts of cathexis are possible, and it is such massive shifts which make possible the change in ego state in fugue, allied conditions, and hypnosis. We have elsewhere discussed the problem of the hypnotizability of people other than hysterics. Here we face an added problem: do fugue, somnambulism, multiple personality, and traumatic neurosis occur only in hysterical personalities? The evidence contradicts this assumption. Fugues have been reported in all manner of personality types (99, 167, 214). The incidence of traumatic neurosis in combat is far higher than could possibly be the incidence of hysterical character structures in the soldier population.

It is possible, however, as Fisher has suggested (70), that a fugue state is a hysterical phenomenon, though it occurs in various personality types. Such an explanation takes some of its force from the progressively accepted trend of differentiating between character structure and neurosis or symptom complex, and acceptance of the idea that a symptom complex of one coloring can occur in a character structure of another: for example, hysterical symptoms may be found in hysterical, obsessional, or even schizophrenic people. Such a conclusion is likewise in line with the progressive application of the structural point of view, and with the recognition that the relation of a symptom complex to unconscious dynamics is not necessarily direct and fluid but that a symptom complex may develop a relatively autonomous structure of its own.

To return to our theme: the evidence for the link of fugue and allied states to hypnosis. Our suggestion that the use of hypnosis in these states—in which amnesia plays a central role—results in quite specific effects will be recalled. The issue clearly has to do with amnesia. In so far as the lifting of the amnesia is therapeutically effective, the hypermnesia of the hypnotic state makes it especially useful in these conditions. The problem of the value of such therapy raises issues which were prominent in the cathartic, abreactive period of psychoanalytic practice and theory: "An hysteric suffers from reminiscences" (33, p. 7), which operate unconsciously, and must be transformed into conscious memories before the patient's suffering can cease. In the hypnotic state the memories become available to consciousness. But thereafter, the subject in the nonhypnotic state readily becomes amnesic again for the memories uncovered. The phenomenon is akin to the availability of the memories of one fugue only during another fugue. If we conceive of memory as having both a drive organization and a conceptual organization (184), and if fugue and hypnosis are drive-organized states, the availability of a special class of memory only in fugue and hypnosis would be understandable. It remains only to argue that the drive organizing a fugue state and a hypnotic state is the same in any one individual, or at least that the activation of one drive state makes another more available to consciousness. This point should be considered in the light of our discussion of the question whether or not the dynamics of hypnosis are the same for all people.[1] If our line of reasoning is correct, we can maintain that the dynamics of hypnosis

[1] See p. 136 ff.

are the same for all hypnotizable people only if we maintain
that the dynamics of fugue and allied states are the same for
all people. But since we argued that a fugue may be a relatively autonomous structure appearing in widely differing
personality types, for hypnotizability we need to assume only
the capacity for developing such a structure, and not the
identity of the underlying dynamics of character structure in
all hypnotizable people. We are again led to the conclusion
that hypnotizability need not involve a particular set of psychodynamics, but only a capacity for a particular kind of regression and a particular kind of alteration of distribution of
cathexes related to the defense mechanism of repression.

The fact that fugue and allied states have something in
common has been perceived by others; we only add traumatic neurosis to the usual list.

The first to stress the relationship of these conditions to
each other (and to hypnosis) was Janet (122). He considered
them all forms of somnambulism, the model of which,
"monoideic somnambulism," was the hallucinatory reliving
of a traumatic episode in an altered state of consciousness.
Though in most of his examples the "somnambulism" begins
during the waking state, he cites an occasional one which
begins during sleep. Historically, the term has at least two
other meanings in addition to Janet's usage which we have
just described. Another meaning of somnambulism is sleepwalking, an altered state of consciousness which begins during sleep and, unlike Janet's somnambulism, is not necessarily
a reactivation of a traumatic memory (though this point has
been debated), but may be the enactment of a dream or a
fantasy. We will later elaborate on the significance for these
states of this distinction between memory and fantasy. The
third meaning of somnambulism, a deep hypnosis, in which
hallucinations and amnesias are possible, indicates the relationship of hypnosis to spontaneous somnambulism.

Janet's summary of the "laws of somnambulism" outlines
his conception (122). He presents these laws in the chapter

on fugue, after he has already discussed somnambulism, which explains why in the quotation he speaks of fugue rather than somnambulism, though he refers to both.

> First, during the abnormal state there is a certain idea, a certain system of thoughts that develops to an exaggerated degree. . . . second . . . the other thoughts, relating to the former life, the family, the social position, the personality, appear to be suppressed. . . [Third], during the period considered as normal . . . the recollections of the fugue have vanished. . . [Fourth], at the same time, the thoughts and feelings connected with an idea that predominated during the fugue have disappeared more or less completely. . . Lastly, during the state considered as normal you find the development of the psychological phenomena that were suppressed during the period of the crisis: recollection of the entire existence, perception of all present occurrences, exact notion of personality [pp. 55-57].

According to Janet, the fugue differs from somnambulism in that it involves no hallucinations ("the development of the idea is less intense"), and its central idea is not absolutely isolated as is that of somnambulism ("the mind is not distinctly reduced to a single idea"; the patients can travel, etc.).

> We can make the same remark concerning the state called normal: the oblivion of the fugue is total, but the oblivion of the directive idea and with it the feeling connected with it is by far less distinct, and the restoration of the normal self is much more complete. In short, a fugue lasts much longer than a monoideic somnambulism. It is necessary for a fugue to be able to last so long that the state should approach the normal state, and that the character of somnambulism should be attenuated [pp. 60-61].

Janet refers to the fugue as a transformation by "degradation" of monoideic somnambulism (p. 61), and describes polyideic somnambulism as a transitional form, in which instead of a single idea possessing consciousness, there is a "feeling in its entirety . . . that has separated from general consciousness and that develops in an independent way" (p. 65). (It is such a feeling, too, which he holds accountable for fugue.)

Janet regarded hypnosis as an artificial somnambulism which can be induced only in hysterical individuals, and believed that hypnotizability disappeared as the hysteria was cured. We believe that Janet showed admirable clinical acumen in seeing the relationships of these several conditions. As Rapaport points out in his *Emotions and Memory* (183), in which he discusses these several states from the point of view of memory and finds the connecting link between them that they all show some variety of amnesia, there was a retrogression in clinical understanding from Janet's insights, which, however, have been partially restored in the writings of Fisher.

We believe that observations of the kind reported by Janet can be organized somewhat more effectively by taking, not somnambulism, but the fugue as our model, a model which we will describe as consisting of three stages. Thus, reversing Janet, we regard somnambulism as a "degradation" of the fugue rather than vice versa.

First, however, we must discuss the traumatic neurosis. Janet treats the traumatic neurosis from the point of view of the paralyses to which psychic traumata may lead, but does not integrate it into his conception of somnambulism. The terms trauma and traumatic are used in several senses in present-day psychological writing. "Traumatic neurosis" ordinarily refers to a neurosis brought about by a situation of overwhelming external danger, such as a natural catastrophe or war. In another usage (for example, in Freud's "Analysis Terminable and Interminable," 97), a trauma is an "accidental" psychological influence which comes to bear upon an individual, in contradistinction to the constitutionally determined nature of his instinctual life. Finally, in the clinical and more delimited sense, "trauma" refers to a specific emotional event which results in a particular psychopathological symptom. It was in this sense that the term was used, for example, in Breuer and Freud's *Studies on Hysteria* (33), in the period in which therapy was conceived of as abreaction of a trauma. We will later consider the relationship between traumatic neurosis (especially war neurosis) in the first sense and hypnosis. Here we want to point out that Janet's mono-ideic somnambulism was the reliving of a traumatic event, whereas his fugue was not. In present-day writings, the concepts of somnambulism and fugue are telescoped in that the word "fugue" is applied now to both the reliving of a trau-matic episode, and the fugue, for example, the assumption of a new personality, which is not simply the reliving of a trau-matic event. (One reason for this is that "somnambulism" is now used only for an episode that begins during sleep, not during waking, whereas Janet used "somnambulism" for both.)

Despite the fact that on the level of phenomena it is valu-able to distinguish the reliving of a trauma from the acting out of a fantasy, it is also desirable to keep in mind that both phenomena are derivatives of drive. The trauma activates a repressed drive and the re-enactment of the trauma is a dis-torted expression of the drive, which serves as a defense against the emergence of the drive as such into consciousness. Likewise in a fantasy, a drive gratification appears in con-sciousness in the form of more or less distorted derivatives (see Fisher, 69).

Now to our three-stage model of the fugue. A comparison with Janet's laws of somnambulism will show how close he came to such a conception.

*Stage One.* An individual under severe emotional stress goes into an altered state of consciousness[2] dominated by an intense, relatively unitary drive and affect, or at least by a conscious motive which is a derivative of and condenses a

[2] For a discussion of this concept, see pp. 155-157.

number of primitive strivings. He may or may not lose his personal identity.

*Stage Two.* Stage one is terminated by a massive repressive maneuver in which the individual either returns to his normal state with amnesia for stage one, or, if personal identity was lost in stage one, he goes into a stage two with a reaction to or modification of the loss of personal identity; he may (a) become aware of this loss; (b) change his identity; (c) return to a chronologically earlier period of his identity, a phenomenon equivalent to hypnotic "regression in age."

*Stage Three.* Personal identity returns to its former condition but with amnesia for stages one and two.

To return to the first stage: consciousness is dominated by a more or less unitary impulse which has to be acted upon without delay or inhibition, and by a corresponding intense emotion. The impulse may be murderous, suicidal, a frantic urge to escape an imagined persecutor, or to live out a deeply charged fantasy, such as a prostitution fantasy. The impulse may appear as such in consciousness or in the form of derivatives of varying degrees of distortion. In the case reported by Gill and Rapaport (103), the conscious drive was to find a job, though it was subsequently discovered that for a brief period suicidal impulses of which this need was a derivative had been conscious. Even if a goal appears prosaic, however, the need to pursue it is felt with overwhelming, whole-souled intensity as an overbearing necessity, and all else pales into insignificance. This compelling urge is accompanied by behavior characterized by a subjective sense of automaticity, in so far as there is any reflective awareness remaining.

The imperious quality of the impulse leads to hallucinatory "wish fulfillment," perceptual alterations of external reality to conform to the drive. A would-be murderess mistakes an apartment door for that of the sister she wants to murder (70). A desperately fleeing man sees a stranger in a restaurant as a crazy doctor from a movie who is out to kill him; and this stranger was seen as a condensation of the doctor from a movie and a sailor who had actually recently insulted him (69). The man wanting a job believed himself at work in the hospital, regarding the doctor as his boss, the other patients as fellow employees, and the hum of the ventilating system as arising from the machine at which he was allegedly working (103). Fugues and somnambulism may be arranged on a continuum, depending on the degree to which such distortions of external reality occur. These perceptual alterations cannot be distinguished from the delusions and hallucinations of the more usual psychosis. One might argue that a striking difference is that the former occur transiently in the first stage of a two-stage process and disappear in the second, while the latter are of greater duration and do not occur in a two-stage process. But there are short-lived psychoses and over a longer perspective more usual psychoses are also divisible into stages. It may well be that what are nowadays called brief schizophrenias are actually more closely related to fugues than to the ordinary psychoses. This is especially likely to be true of the "brief schizophrenia" in soldiers in wartime.

The characteristics of the first stage are clearly manifestations of primary-process functioning: an intense drive accompanied by an intense affect, and even distortion of external reality because the internal constellation is so prepotent.

Concerning the first phase, crucial clinical and theoretical issues revolve about its other major characteristic, the loss of personal identity which is intimately interwoven with the issue of awareness of loss of personal identity. The issues are: (a) Is personal identity necessarily lost during the first phase? (b) When is awareness of loss of personal identity present? (c) What is the relation between loss of personal identity and awareness of its loss?

Gill and Rapaport (183) were, we believe, the first to make a systematic distinction between loss of personal identity and awareness of loss of personal identity, and to make this distinction the basis of a biphasic description of fugue (103).

Fisher has questioned whether there is really a loss of personal identity in the first phase, suggesting instead that there is simply a lack of concern about the question of personal identity. It is true that in the first phase there is a lack of concern about personal identity and indeed a general loss of reflective awareness. But this does not mean that personal identity may not actually be lost in the first phase: Gill and Rapaport (103) observed a case in the first phase of fugue who had lost his personal identity, but who on being questioned about the loss was unconcerned about it. This case developed at most a very fleeting phase of awareness of loss of personal identity, and moved almost directly into phase three, to be discussed below, with amnesia for the fugue. Fisher likewise reports a case who, while describing in hypnosis the events of the first phase, stated that he believed if he had been asked who he was, he would not have known. With the general loss of reflective awareness during the first phase there will of necessity be loss of awareness of personal identity, but the latter exists even when the former is not complete, or even, as in the case reported by Gill and Rapaport, when the subject's attention is drawn to his personal identity, demonstrating that the loss of awareness of personal identity is specific.[3]

The model of the two stages is: first stage: drive paramount, primary-process character, loss of reflectiveness generally, loss of awareness of identity specifically; second stage: massive repression of drive, return of reflective awareness, reflective discernment of loss of awareness of identity. As for deviations from the model, it seems possible but doubtful that with sufficient distortion of the drive in stage one there is not necessarily loss of personal identity; it is common for the second stage to be abortive so that the awareness of loss of personal identity is transient. The awareness of loss of personal identity may be resolved not by a restoration of the

[3] The phrase "loss of personal identity" can be understood only as a shorthand way of saying "loss of awareness of personal identity."

original identity but by a change of personal identity or a return to a chronologically earlier period of identity.

Fisher (69) has offered the suggestion that only when the individual is questioned as to his identity does he actually lose it, as if he then realizes that if others do not know who he is, perhaps he need not either, and seizes this way of repressing personal identity and together with it the panic-producing drive and affect.

Not only does such an explanation telescope loss of awareness of personal identity and awareness of loss of personal identity, but it seems to us to overestimate the role of interpersonal communication in initiating fugue, though unquestionably a breakdown in interpersonal communication accompanies the onset of fugue. We do believe it probable, however, that the awareness of loss of personal identity can occur on being questioned and that therefore together with this awareness can come the repression of the drive and the reinstituting of controls, the second phase thus being initiated by the re-establishment of interpersonal communication. As we will discuss later, hypnosis and fugue differ in that in the former a disturbance of interpersonal communication does play an important role in its onset. It has been argued that the second phase of fugue is ushered in by the loss of personal identity and the awareness of this loss. This theory holds that the personal identity and the strivings of the first phase are repressed together. Fisher has explained the loss of personal identity as a denial and "resolution" of the drives activated in stage one. In response to a superego command, the drive of stage one is denied, either by losing or changing personal identity or by regression to a time prior to the emergence of the drive into consciousness. While we accept the hypothesis that the activated drives and the loss of personal identity are psychodynamically related, we would argue on the contrary that the loss of personal identity and the emergence of the strivings occur together in the first phase and that the second phase is ushered in when the strivings are repressed. At that point the individual becomes aware of the loss of personal identity. We would then be left with the original formulation made by Rapaport and Gill that in the full development of the model of the fugue, there is in the first phase a loss of personal identity and with the return of reflective awareness and the repression of the drive of the first phase, there is an awareness of loss of personal identity. Rapaport has proposed (181), and we find his suggestion plausible, that awareness of personal identity is related to a particular balance between drive and drive control; when there is loss of control, awareness of personal identity is lost, as in stage one, and when there is overcontrol it is lost as in stage two.

In stage three, there is a restoration of personal identity, but with amnesia for the impulse, affect, and behavior of stage one, and usually also for the period of awareness of loss or alteration of personal identity of stage two. This is an amnesia which often lifts relatively easily, whether by artificial means or spontaneously. It must also be noted that in subsequent fugues, especially where there has been a change of identity, there may be accessibility of memories of earlier fugues (175).

In his tripartite classification of fugue, Fisher (69) has described fugue with loss of personal identity, fugue with change of personal identity, and retrograde fugue (return to a chronologically earlier period). It will be clear that we have favored a single model and regard Fisher's latter two types as varieties of the second stage of our model.

One form of fugue may change into another. For example, the person with change of personal identity or with retrograde amnesia may have a transitory or more prolonged loss of personal identity and then awareness of such loss before the transition to stage three. He will be likely to have amnesia for both episodes of phase one and both variants of phase two.

Incidentally, it may be noted that multiple personality is simply a variation of the class of change of personal identity and that return to a chronologically earlier identity is a less drastic change of personal identity. In instances such as Miss Beauchamp (175), or *The Three Faces of Eve* (218), where a number of personal identities of differing degrees of complexity and synthesis can readily flip from one into another, it is clear that stage one may become abortive, so that an intense drive is no longer necessary to initiate the "fugue." But the amnesias still hold, or various complex combinations can occur, in which the several personalities do or do not have knowledge of each other. It is generally agreed that many of these complexities are products of hypnotic suggestion. Several subsystems of the kind which we described for hypnosis are formed, structuralized, and can be triggered into action by the appropriate stimulus.

How does sleeping somnambulism fit into our model? The sleeper arises and carries through an act as though he were an automaton. It has been demonstrated that he is acting out a dream (76, 120a, 156, 217). (This is clearly—like hypnosis—another example of an altered ego state in which a subsystem of the ego may gain control of an apparatus.) He is impelled by a relatively unitary drive and affect. He is in our stage one. If he is gently interrupted, he may awaken and have amnesia for what he was doing. He would then be in stage three. He may go back to bed himself and not reach stage three until he spontaneously awakens, when he will have amnesia for stage one. If rudely interrupted, or sometimes spontaneously, he may have a transient period of confusion in which he does not know who or where he is. This would be an abortive form of stage two.

In Janet's mono- and polyideic somnambulisms, the individual interrupts his usual activity and relives an earlier trauma. What distinguishes mono- or polyideic somnambulism from sleeping somnambulism is that the former can begin in either the waking or the sleeping state, and that the intense affect and ideational content is—proximally at least—structured around a memory, not a fantasy. The memory serves as a derivative and distortion of a fantasy. The mono- and poly-ideic somnambulisms are, like sleeping somnambulism, composed of stage one, with or without an abortive stage two, and then stage three with amnesia for stage one and for stage two if there was a stage two. Of course it is possible that a particular instance of sleeping somnambulism may likewise be a re-enactment of a trauma, and thus be a memory in its manifest content. Such a re-enactment of an earlier trauma furnishes us with the link to the traumatic neuroses, but we will discuss them separately in a later section. (Here we should note that the sufferer from a traumatic neurosis may have episodes of somnambulism, originating from either the waking or sleeping state, in which he relives his trauma. The reliving may take the abortive form of a fit or fainting or blackout spell.)

Speaking more generally, the phases of our model are: (a) a strong affect or wish, with a relative narrowing of the field of consciousness under the influence of this affect and wish; (b) a transient disorientation when for internal or external reasons there is an interruption of this state; and (c) a return to a more potentially diversified state with subsidence of the affect, and a tendency toward amnesia for both the affective state and the disorientation.[4]

We will turn now to a comparison between hypnosis and fugue.

We have already characterized hypnosis as occurring in two stages. We could also speak of a stage three, when there is a restoration of the original condition with (often) amnesia for stages one and two. But it would undoubtedly be too facile to regard fugue and hypnosis as analogous stage by stage. Though a comparison does show certain similarities, there are also differences.

First of all, it must be asked whether stages one and two of hypnosis (we are calling the induction phase stage one

---

[4] Startle reaction, dream, and daydream could be conceptualized as abortive forms of, respectively, traumatic neurosis, somnambulism, and fugue.

and the established state stage two) bear the same relationship to one another as stages one and two of our model of fugue. The induction phase seems to be a temporary transitional stage on the way to the established state, and, in fact, hypnosis can occur without any apparent stage one. Is stage one of a fugue merely preparatory and can a fugue occur without it? In part the answer to these questions is yes. Stage one may become aborted in the development of a fugue so that instead of being initiated by a period of emotional stress, the fugue may be precipitated by what almost seems like a signal.[5] In fugues which have become aborted to a fainting spell or blackout, the first stage may be transient and the fainting a variant of the second stage with its massive inhibition. The analogy in hypnotic phenomena is the aborted induction in the experienced subject who goes into hypnosis on a signal.

But we have not described stage one of fugue as a preparation for stage two, but rather stage two as a way of ending and resolving stage one. Can the established hypnotic state be regarded as a resolution of the induction phase? Is the established state one of a massive repression of the phenomena of the induction stage, as stage two of fugue is of stage one of fugue? Stage one of fugue is characterized by an intense affect and drive, acted out in a more or less disguised manner. The same may be true of hypnosis, but in an even more disguised and latent form. The hypnotist initiates a relation in which infantile cravings can be gratified: by beginning his manipulations, he arouses these cravings in the subject. Although this arousal leads to different results than in the fugue, its occurrence nevertheless constitutes an important similarity between the first stage of fugue and the first stage of hypnosis. In fugue there is a more manifest expression of the infantile cravings in stage one, more massive repression and denial in

[5] Fisher gives a good illustration of this in the case of a soldier in whom "anything which forcibly reminded the patient of the *Luftwaffe* was capable of precipitating a fugue" (69, p. 444).

stage two, even to the point of maintaining the loss of personal identity of stage one. In hypnosis there is less manifest expression in stage one, less massive repression in stage two, and gratification continuing in stage two, so that though the two stages bear the same relationship to one another, they are not as starkly contrasted as in fugue.

That the two stages of hypnosis are less opposed to one another may shed some light on the highly fluctuating character of hypnosis in many of its varieties, especially as it is employed in psychotherapy, though we earlier suggested we may have been influenced in so describing hypnosis by the fact that in a psychotherapeutic relationship employing hypnosis, especially when transference material is being discussed, the hypnosis is being constantly "disturbed," since the dynamics of the hypnotic state may hinge on the transference itself. Hypnosis may be a considerably more stable state when employed otherwise, for example, for experimental purposes.

Shifts in the hypnotic state, which we originally discussed as a change in depth to lighter or deeper, would more properly be described as transient movements, now toward stage one, now toward stage two. Since certain kinds of alterations of body image are more highly characteristic of the induction stage than of the established state, an empirical check on this theory would be in terms of the kinds of situations in hypnosis which are marked by a spontaneous appearance or disappearance of these body-image changes—is their appearance accompanied by a more manifest expression of drive?

Recognition that the two stages of hypnosis are similarly related but not as sharply contrasted as the two stages of fugue will enable us to show that some of the differences between fugue and hypnosis are more apparent than real.

We have characterized stage one of fugue as organized around a single overwhelming motivation or one which condenses a number of strivings. In a sense, the same may be said for stage two in that it is a massive repression of impulses for the purpose of defending against this motivation.

We can say the same for hypnosis, and that this is in essence another way of stating the transference aspect of hypnosis. R. W. White has in fact characterized hypnosis as organized around a single striving, the goal being to act like a hypnotized subject, as this is continuously defined by the hypnotist and understood by the subject (226). While the application of psychoanalytic understanding can clarify and specify the dynamics of hypnosis considerably more than this, it remains true that in the hypnotic state a number of unconscious infantile strivings are condensed and fused into a single striving.

At first glance, the difference between the mental content of the fugue and of the hypnosis seems tremendous. The fugue patient is occupied with the stark violence and passion of an "id" wish; the hypnotic subject with the often apparently trivial suggestions of the hypnotist. But we must take care to distinguish between manifest and latent content. The latent content of fugue and hypnosis is the same—powerful infantile strivings. The manifest content of the first stage of fugue is most often a fairly open appearance of the latent content, though sometimes this latent content may be heavily disguised. In the second stage of fugue the manifest content is notably stereotyped and barren. In the induction period of hypnosis, outbursts of affect may reveal the latent content, and the same may occur in the established state.

If we turn to fugue as an altered state we see a number of parallels between the first stage of fugue and the hypnotic state. We have characterized fugue as showing in the first stage violent affect. Hypnosis is ordinarily quiet, but in certain circumstances storms of affect can arise which clearly indicate that the usual quiet of hypnosis is more apparent than real, and that the gulf between hypnosis and the violent affect of stage one of fugue is not so great. If the subject's freedom to respond as he believes he is supposed to in the hypnotic situation is in some way interfered with, the intensity of the conflict and emotion which appear bears witness to the intensity of the drives involved in the hypnotic relationship. One way of interfering is to try to get the subject to analyze his motivations on going into hypnosis, as we have discussed elsewhere.[6] The reluctance and distress which the subject experiences also makes it clear why he is not more fully aware of his needs and their intensity. Other ways of interfering are by various devices which actually prevent the subject from carrying out a suggestion. An example of what can happen is vividly described in the paper by Brickner and Kubie on a "miniature psychotic storm" precipitated in a subject who was prevented from carrying out a posthypnotic suggestion (34).

Another characteristic of the first phase of fugue is that there is an acting on the impulse in an imperious way, which brooks no delay, and indicates the capture of the motor apparatus by primitive impulses. The same is characteristic of hypnosis. We have given examples of the alteration of motor behavior in both induction and the established state. The same kind of compelling action or impulse is characteristic of the manner in which a posthypnotic suggestion is carried out. The behavior, in so far as the subject in fugue is able to reflect, is carried out with a sense of automaticity and lack of ordinary voluntary control. Such conditions may likewise appear spontaneously or be produced in hypnosis. Automatic writing is a characteristic example of such behavior in hypnosis.

Yet another major characteristic of the first stage of fugue is distortion of the perception of the external world in the service of the drives. This characteristic is matched in the delusions and hallucinations producible in the established state at the hypnotist's suggestion, but also appears in the spontaneous space-time and perceptual distortions during induction.

The states of consciousness of the individual in fugue and in hypnosis show important similarities. In both, a unitary striving dominates the mental content and it is this striving

[6] See p. 85 ff.

which is responsible for the narrowing of consciousness in both. A patient of Fisher's stated that in hypnosis he felt much as he had during the first stage of his fugue: he had only one idea in his mind then [to kill Nazis and avenge his parents] and he has only one idea in mind in hypnosis—to do whatever the hypnotist suggests (69, p. 445). We have already discussed this "one-track mindedness" as one indication of the alteration in ego-functioning in general and attention in particular in the hypnotic state. A broad span of consciousness requires a motivational state in which a fairly free play between various and even conflicting motivations is possible. As we have already discussed, this free play is a function of the autonomy of the ego. When a single or condensed striving becomes regnant, the ego has lost some of its autonomy.

An interesting historical note reflects this theme, a note which incidentally should also be remembered in connection with the relationship of hypnosis and sleep. Braid, who coined the word *hypno-sis*, later concluded that he had been mistaken in considering hypnosis a form of sleep, and attempted to change the name of the phenomenon to "monoideism" because it seemed to him that hypnosis was characterized by the presence of a single prevailing idea. We also remember that Janet called his paradigmatic state a monoideic somnambulism.

It is clear that fugue is a regressed state, as is hypnosis; that the alterations in self-awareness, affect display, and motility in the first stage of fugue are evidences of the loss of autonomy with domination by the id, and thus parallel the induction phase in the sense in which induction is properly described by this formula.

Now to the second stage. In the first stage of fugue, as in the induction phase, there is no subsystem in operation. The ego continues in control of its apparatuses, though now in the service of the id. In the second stage of fugue, with awareness of loss of personal identity the situation becomes analogous to the established state, for in this second stage of fugue a subsystem has been built. Since a fugue cannot be terminated at will, we know that the subsystem is not voluntarily under the dominion of the over-all ego, but just as the subsystem in the established state has to maintain itself by a counter-cathexis against the over-all ego, so does this subsystem have to countercathect higher functions—here notably the personal identity. The very fact that such countercathexis has to be exerted demonstrates that the normal, the over-all ego, retains cathexis, as does of course also the clinical fact that the normal ego is suddenly reinstated when the fugue terminates. The preoccupation, impoverishment, and slowing down which have been described in this type of second stage of fugue result from the employment of energy for counter-cathexis of the over-all ego. In both the established state of hypnosis and the second stage of fugue, the subject impresses the observer as preoccupied and impoverished to the degree to which the range of apparatuses to which the subsystem has access is cut down. We may note incidentally that by the suggestion of loss of personal identity an artificial situation analogous to the second stage of fugue can be produced in the established state of hypnosis.

Where there is change of personal identity there too we have a subsystem within the ego, though again not under the control of the over-all ego. In this variant of stage two, there is access to a very broad range of ego apparatuses, or, as it is usually expressed, a person in this kind of fugue seems to the external observer to be functioning quite normally. Where there has been a return to an earlier period of personal identity, the range of access to ego apparatuses is broad, but the blocking out of a period of life results in dislocations so severe that the subject is soon forced to recognize a disparity between his subjective situation and his environment.

The most general way of stating the parallel between stage two of fugue and the established state of hypnosis is that the loss of autonomy is followed by domination by the environment in both. This becomes especially evident in that form of the second stage of the model of fugue which is characterized by awareness of loss of personal identity. In such instances the person helplessly seeks aid from his environment. The dependence on the environment seems to have ceased in changes of personal identity and in returns to an earlier period of personal identity, and in these forms of stage two the individual more closely approaches stage three, and is more like a normal person. The drive and behavior of stage one have succumbed to amnesia and the subject is capable of ordinary intercourse with his environment, though, especially where there has been a return to an earlier period of personal identity, this is subject to some restrictions. But here again the parallel is to those forms of the established state of hypnosis in which, after re-automatization of the apparatuses, the subject appears to be behaving normally and independently.

Now to the third stage. The analogy which immediately strikes one, of course, is that just as in fugue there is amnesia for stages one and two, so after hypnosis too there is sometimes an amnesia for the hypnotic experiences. That amnesia for stages one and two of fugue is a regular occurrence while for hypnosis it is only occasional results from the fact that in fugue repressed material becomes so much more frequently manifest, with the resulting increased need for wholesale rerepression. Posthypnotic amnesia may be spontaneous; or it may come about only when a specific suggestion to this effect has been given; but it may persist even in the face of a suggestion to remember the events of the hypnosis. Schilder and Kauders (208) offer the psychodynamic explanation that the subject forgets the events of the hypnosis because he is embarrassed to have accepted being in such a state.

For a metapsychological explanation, we will employ Rapaport's distinction between a drive organization and a conceptual organization of memory. An earlier form of this distinction is Claparède's (41) conception of the "me-ness" of memory organization, in contrast to an impersonal memory organization. The events of the fugue have occurred in a form of thought organization which is structured around drives, and therefore they succumb to amnesia when the drive organization yields to the conceptual organization. It is possible that the events of the second phase of fugue become amnesized because they too are closely associated with the drive organization, though it must be remembered that they are amnesized less regularly than the events of the first phase, especially if recovery has been achieved through therapeutic techniques rather than spontaneously. It may be that anterograde amnesia plays a role here, the mechanism of which would be akin to that conjectured by Isakower (120) for *déjà vu:* when primary-process mechanisms are working, phenomena subsequent to the arousal of a repressed drive become invested with the same affect pertaining to the drive and are therefore rerepressed together with the drive.

The point made here in terms of drive and conceptual organization of memory may be stated in terms of the synthetic function of the ego, which is integral to the secondary process and to the conceptual organization of experience. Gill (100) has accounted in such terms for spontaneous regression upon the induction of hypnosis: ". . . re-enactment takes place in the present tense not because it is a reproduction of the original experience but because with the weakening of the ego which permits the experience to return to consciousness there is a diminution of the synthetic ego function" (pp. 46-47).

What we suggest then is that during the altered state centered on violently driving impulses and emotion, the synthesizing activities of the ego fall to a lower level and that this is related to the loss of these experiences from consciousness. Apparently it depends on the synthesizing function of the ego to what extent an experience becomes integrated into a conceptual organization of memory instead of being tied in solely with a drive organization—and correspondingly to what extent it is available to consciousness when not pressed upon it as a drive representation.

We have up to now attempted to state the similarities between hypnosis and fugue. Of differences we have discussed only those which we considered to be more apparent than real, though we have mentioned that the subsystem is not under the control of the over-all ego in fugue. We come now to the significant and important differences between the two conditions. Fugue is *generally* initiated and terminated from within, while hypnosis is *generally* initiated and terminated from without. Even more specifically, in hypnosis there is the initiation, precipitation, and termination of a relationship with a real and present person, the hypnotist, whereas there is none such in the fugue. Though he may do so more or less implicitly, the hypnotist must actively awaken the subject's cravings and promise to play a part in their gratification. The borderline instances which seem exceptions to this generalization about the difference between hypnosis and fugue themselves testify to the close relationship between the two states.

Though we have described a fugue as initiated from within, the clinical story of some fugues makes them seem to be initiated from without. Reconstruction of the dynamics of a case, however, makes it clear that the figure from without is only a trigger, seen not as himself but distorted by projection into a figure from an internal drama. When an external figure attempts to come into contact with a person in fugue, this may be "an invitation to murder," in which case the external figure has simply become part of the private world of the fugue—or if communication is really established, the first phase of fugue terminates as we have already described, and awareness of loss of personal identity may appear. A "spontaneous" hypnotic state may seem to be initiated from within, but, as we have already discussed, in such instances there is actually a relationship with a current figure, either a hypnotist or someone who stands in a similar relationship. Where this is not the case, the condition actually begins to resemble a fugue more than hypnosis—a spontaneous re-enactment of the hypnotic relationship engendered from within is no longer hypnosis.

In hypnosis the relationship with the hypnotist persists. With the development of an apparently different state, it may be difficult to tell whether the hypnosis has persisted—whether we are dealing with a state within a state—or whether we should say the hypnosis has terminated. If, for example, there is a spontaneous regression on the induction of hypnosis, the hypnotic state may have ended, and we may be dealing instead with a somnambulism in Janet's sense. Our case of spontaneous regression on the induction of hypnosis illustrates this difficulty (100). As soon as the spontaneous regression set in, the hypnotist apparently lost contact with the subject. When he sensed what was happening, he began to play a role in the regression, but in so doing he stepped out of his hypnotic role and the contact as well as the patient's state were apparently not hypnotic. The hypnotist was perceived as a figure in the patient's private world. Only after the hypnotist had succeeded in being identified as himself in the current situation could the hypnotic situation be said to have been clearly re-established. But how could one be sure that it had not persisted all the time? In an induced hypnotic age regression, where the hypnotist also plays a role in the patient's private world, we do assume that the hypnotic relationship has persisted.

In the termination of hypnosis and fugue the situations with regard to an external person are again to be contrasted. Hypnosis is generally terminated by the hypnotist, though the subject must consent. But again there are exceptions: a previously good subject may refuse to enter hypnosis or the subject may terminate himself, in which case of course hypnosis no longer obtains. Is the subject who refuses to be terminated still in hypnosis? According to this line of reasoning, he probably is not. These various evidences of the limits on the hypnotist's control of the hypnotic situation emphasize again that the over-all ego in hypnosis remains potentially active and in control.

The general initiation of hypnosis by an external person and of fugue from within is expressed in an important difference between induction and the first stage of fugue. In hypnosis there must first be a stage in which the autonomy of the ego is shaken, but in stage one of fugue this has already occurred. This function of the induction stage is in fugue matched by the period of stress prior to its onset.

The natural course of fugue is to terminate spontaneously, whether one refers to passage from first stage to second or from second to third. But again exceptions: it is possible for an external figure to play a role in the passage from first to second, and of course the external figure as therapist may play an important role in passage from second to third.

We have already described how the major similarity between fugue and hypnosis—that stage two of fugue is a resolution by repression of stage one, and the established state is a resolution by repression of the drives aroused during induction —is obscured because the disparity between how manifest are the drives in the initial stage and how latent they are in the succeeding one is greater in fugue than in hypnosis. This difference is also connected with the one just discussed— the relation to an external figure. It is because there is an external figure that the drive in hypnosis may remain hidden, that it may in part be projected to and in part be realistically ascribed to the hypnotist who does actually participate in initiating and carrying on the proceedings.

And the relation with an external person in hypnosis and not in fugue is only a specification of the basic distinction between hypnosis and fugue—that hypnosis is a regression in the service of the ego, while fugue is a regression proper. The over-all ego remains in control, however "quietly," in hypnosis, while it loses control in fugue. The hypnotic subject can voluntarily terminate hypnosis, but the victim of fugue cannot deliberately decide to bring it to a halt. For this reason we say that the subsystem in the second stage of fugue is not under the control of the over-all ego, while in hypnosis it is. But we do have here an illustration of our theoretical statement that a subsystem in the ego can be built in both regression in the service of the ego and regression proper. But surely no structure is "dissolved" in fugue, as we said it sometimes is in regression proper. The over-all ego retains cathexis in fugue and must be countercathected.[7]

To return to our discussion of the economics of the two kinds of regression: though fugue is a regression proper, it is a borderline instance in which structure is not "dissolved" and in which, though the cathexis withdrawn from the over-all ego is greater than is the case in regression in the service of the ego, countercathexis must be deployed against the cathexis persisting in the over-all ego.

[7] See p. 214.

# 8

## TRAUMATIC NEUROSIS AND HYPNOSIS

As we have indicated in the preceding chapter, somnambulism links fugue to traumatic neurosis. In fugue a fantasy is acted out; in traumatic neurosis a traumatic experience is relived, but in somnambulism either may occur.

Using the acute traumatic neurosis of war as our paradigm,[1] we will sketch a model of the traumatic neurosis, and compare it with the stages of fugue and hypnosis.

War gives rise to many kinds of psychiatric casualties. Kardiner (127) made a valiant effort to delineate the specific characteristics of a traumatic neurosis, which in war may of course occur combined with other psychiatric disorders. The history of a trauma, traumatic dreams, startle reactions, and diffuse aggressiveness have long been accepted as essential features of a traumatic neurosis of war. Perhaps the clearest description of the traumatic neuroses of the last war came

---

[1] Freud (85) suggested that the traumatic neurosis of war might have more kinship to the usual transference neurosis than does the usual peacetime traumatic neurosis: "In traumatic and war neuroses the human ego is defending itself from a danger which threatens it from without or which is embodied in a shape assumed by the ego itself. In the transference neuroses of peace the enemy from which the ego is defending itself is actually the libido, whose demands seem to it to be menacing. In both cases the ego is afraid of being damaged—in the latter case by the libido and in the former by external violence. It might, indeed, be said that in the case of the war neuroses, in contrast to the pure traumatic neuroses and in approximation to the transference neuroses, what is feared is nevertheless an internal enemy. The theoretical difficulties standing in the way of a unifying hypothesis of this kind do not seem insuperable: after all, we have a perfect right to describe repression, which lies at the basis of every neurosis, as a reaction to a trauma —as an elementary traumatic neurosis" (p. 210).

from Grinker and Spiegel (111), who called them anxiety states, both severe and mild. Their use of this designation seems unfortunate, however, since it runs the risk of obscuring the traumatic neurosis as a specific disorder.

In battle neurosis there is a prolonged period of extreme tension, with more or less prolonged episodes of hyperalertness. These periods of hyperalertness seem to involve a narrowing of attention because the alertness is to very specific kinds of stimuli, while other stimuli are ignored. For example, a soldier may not realize he has been wounded until the battle which keeps him at high pitch is over. This hyperalert narrowing of consciousness seems to be analogous to narrowing of the range of motivation and attention in the hypnotic state.

But this preliminary period of hyperalertness and narrowing of consciousness is an effort to *prevent* a traumatic neurosis, in accordance with Freud's theory of the stimulus barrier, which holds that attention cathexes are mobilized to reinforce the barrier and prevent its rupture (87).

The stimulus barrier appears to us to play a nonspecific role in the explanation of traumatic neurosis. The neurosis may be precipitated by a rupture of the barrier by a violent, unexpected, massive assault, or by the cumulative exhausting effect of the violence of sounds and sights on the battle field, but in such instances the relationships between the trauma and specific psychological vulnerabilities of the casuality are obscured. In other instances the neurosis is precipitated by an event which has a specific important meaning to the individual, the death of a buddy or witnessing a particular kind of mutilation, for example.

This preliminary period of hyperalertness and narrowing of consciousness in which the individual is functioning in an integrated way to protect himself and attack the enemy is succeeded by the essential ingredient of the first phase of traumatic neurosis—a shift to "unimotivational" activity but now directed not by the ego, but as in the first phase of fugue, by an id drive. Cases of traumatic neurosis may be ranged on a continuum according to the degree to which behavior is controlled by the ego or the id, with the less severe traumatic neurosis never becoming principally id dominated. When an id drive does clearly take over, it may be aggressive, a running amok toward the enemy; defensive, a wild fleeing from the battle field; or more specifically related to a trauma suffered, as for example when a soldier drags the body of a dead buddy a long distance with apparent loss of regard for personal safety. This phase may of course be accompanied by manifest anxiety, mild if the soldier's functioning remains under the domination of his ego, more severe if control is yielded to the id.

The second phase of the traumatic neurosis is a massive amnesia for the trauma, and may be accompanied by a wide range of loss of ego capacities. When this loss is more severe, there may be loss of personal identity and the picture then approximates the second stage of fugue. It may be even more severe than in the usual second stage of fugue so that the individual is in an unresponsive stupor, or it may be restricted to a loss of a specific capacity such as speaking or hearing and thus resemble a conversion hysteria. In milder cases it may be restricted to a loss of self-confidence.

The first stage may be abortive. A sudden explosion, for example, may result in only a transient impulse to flee, succeeded almost at once by a stupor—that is, a second stage.

The third stage is a restoration of function, with amnesia for the traumatic experience. This stage differs from the third stage of fugue in that in traumatic neurosis this stage is characterized by a reliving of the trauma in dreams or in the waking state, in full-fledged fashion, or abortively in fainting spell, blackout, or fit. In fact, stage three is that of the chronic traumatic neurosis. Stages one and two are the acute traumatic neurosis.

The first phase of traumatic neurosis, as we have described it, shows similarity to the first phase of fugue, but to bring this similarity into sharper relief we will have to point out some issues overlooked in those discussions of traumatic neurosis which focus on the external trauma and neglect the reaction to the trauma determined by drives. It is this reaction which makes it understandable that in the disorganized panic state, as in the first stage of fugue, the individual abandons an ego-directed interaction with the external environment, and becomes overwhelmed by a blind, imperious urge to act. The individual differences in reaction to a particular event, i.e., why one person is deeply affected and not another, become understandable, because the traumatic neurosis arises not simply as a result of the overwhelming of the stimulus barrier, but is a function of the individual psychodynamic organization.[2] We see here a bridge between the earlier emphasis in psychoanalysis on the traumatic memory and its later emphasis on the instinctual drive: the external trauma acquires its meaning because of the drive which it awakens. In fact, we propose that the memory of the trauma comes to serve as a derivative of the drive, so that the effort to repress the memory is really a defense against the drive, while conscious preoccupation with the memory serves—among other functions—to prevent a more direct drive representation from rising to consciousness.[3]

Our second stage of traumatic neurosis, then, is clearly related to our second stage of fugue. It is one of massive repression, which may be, though ordinarily it is not, as great as in fugue, as in those cases of traumatic neurosis in which the wild first phase is succeeded by one of catatonialike mute withdrawal.

[2] While the stimulus barrier presumably has important constitutional determinants, the individual's experience must likewise contribute to its nature, but again in a nonspecific way. Barriers to the perception of certain psychological realities are specific instances of denial and not nonspecific effects of a stimulus barrier.

[3] A note by Glover (104) discusses how a memory of a trauma may be held in consciousness to screen an even more traumatic event. Greenson (110) sets the screen function into a broader perspective.

The ordinary mild case of traumatic neurosis differs from fugue in that in traumatic neurosis phases two and three are less sharply contrasted than they are in fugue. The repression is less massive in phase two; in fact, it may even be possible for the soldier to remember some features of the trauma if he tries to do so. Phase three as compared with fugue is a more prolonged restoration of normal functioning with gradual disappearance of the episodes of reliving.

The comparison to hypnosis can be made against the background of our discussion of the relationship of fugue and hypnosis. Phase one of the traumatic neurosis is analogous to the induction phase because both are characterized by the awakening of infantile drives, and phase two of traumatic neurosis and the established state are analogous because both are characterized by the repression of these drives and preoccupation with their distorted derivatives, but the two phases of traumatic neurosis, like those of fugue, are more sharply contrasted than they are in hypnosis. Phase three of traumatic neurosis is again more prolonged and attenuated, in comparison with the analogous posthypnotic state with amnesia, and with stage three of fugue. As in fugue, in phase one of traumatic neurosis the loss of autonomy is followed by domination by the id, while in phase two it is followed by domination of the ego by the environment.

Here we can develop further the problem of hypnotizability in states allied to the hypnotic state. The patient with traumatic neurosis is hypnotizable in phases two and three. He is of course rarely under medical care during phase one. As we noted in our discussion of fugue, we must take care not to confuse induction of a hypnotic state with precipitating a spontaneous reliving of the trauma by the hypnotist's manipulations. On the other hand, the alleged increased hypnotizability of the traumatic neurosis is not merely the precipitation of an abreaction, since abreaction in relationship to a hypnotist can produce therapeutic results whereas a spontaneous abreaction cannot.[4] Further, hypnotizability is also high in the more chronic case of traumatic neurosis in which the hypnotized subject must be urged to remember and relive the trauma.

This distinction again highlights a crucial aspect of the hypnotic situation—the relationship to a hypnotist, i.e., a real figure in the external environment. In other words, the ego is dominated by the environment after autonomy has been lost. In the first stage of fugue, in the first stage of the traumatic neurosis, and in the spontaneous regression, whether or not it was set off by an attempt to induce hypnosis, the loss of autonomy is followed by domination by the id.

But to return to the hypnotizability of the traumatic neurotic. Most interpretations to date have been in terms of psychodynamics. It is said that the individual is so shaken and insecure that he is happy to accept an opportunity, however much magic may seem to be involved, to put himself in the hands of someone who promises to be a powerful protector.

We add a metapsychological explanation. The traumatic neurotic in stage two is attempting by a massive expenditure of countercathexis to hold in repression a traumatic event, or, as we have said, the drive which the traumatic event has activated. When the repressing forces are weakened, as in sleep, the experience may surge into consciousness in the form of the repetitive dream in which the experience is relived. In hypnosis, we have argued, there is an activation of primitive infantile drives and a partial repression of these drives. We suggest then that the traumatic neurotic is hypnotizable because his repressive countercathexes, already occupied with holding the traumatic memory and associated drive in repression, are less available to prevent the activation of infantile

---

[4] Analogously, sodium pentothal can precipitate an abreaction, but therapeutic results are not forthcoming unless the wielder of the syringe simultaneously enters into a psychological relationship with the patient (111, p. 392).

drives toward the hypnotist. We argue further that when the energy which has been employed to hold in repression the traumatic memory becomes shifted to hold in partial repression the now activated infantile drives, this results in releasing the repressed traumatic memory into consciousness. This mechanism appears to us to offer an economic explanation of the recovery of traumatic memories in both our own case material and that of others. It may have a more general application to the recovery of traumatic memories. As we observed in our discussion of fugue, the releasing of this traumatic memory into consciousness may result in its being relived in the present tense instead of appearing as memory images because, with the weakening of the ego which permits the experience to return to consciousness, there is a diminution of the synthetic ego function to the degree that past and present are no longer distinguished (100). We argue then that a state in which a massive repression is being precariously maintained is a state in which hypnosis may be produced. This explanation would hold for the second stage of fugue too. There a massive repression is being precariously maintained, as is attested by the frequent spontaneous lifting of this repression. The hypnotist activates infantile drives. These are the more readily activated because repressive counter-cathexes are fully employed elsewhere. And, as with the traumatic neurotic, when there is a partial repression of these activated drives, there is a lifting of the repression of the personal identity and of phase one, the period in which the impulses of the fugue were in ascendance. It must be noted that often personal identity is recovered when phase one is not. The explanation may be that it is both more difficult and less imperative to maintain the repression of personal identity than of the drives of phase one of fugue.

It is generally easier under hypnosis to recover the traumatic memories of the traumatic neurotic than it is to recover the memory of the drive of phase one of fugue. The mere induction of hypnosis may initiate a spontaneous reliving of the trauma in a traumatic neurosis, but we know of no report in which the induction of hypnosis without any probing resulted in the recovery of the memory of the drive of phase one of fugue. Perhaps the memory of the traumatic event is less strongly repressed than the drive of phase one of fugue. We would conjecture that it might be as difficult to recover the frequently overlooked repressed drive of stage one of traumatic neurosis as the repressed drive of stage one of fugue.

It may also be that there comes into play here a factor which we have not yet mentioned. The "repetition compulsion" has been proposed as an explanation of reliving—which is thus seen as an attempt to master the influx of stimuli which shattered the stimulus barrier. Without necessarily accepting any of the more speculative theories connected with the concept of the repetition compulsion, notably the death instinct, we believe this is a plausible mechanism to account for, as before, a nonspecific factor impelling toward the repetition of the trauma.

How does the traumatic neurosis differ from hypnosis? As with fugue, the regression is spontaneous and not induced. It is not a regression in the service of the ego. And again the question of the relationship with an external figure provides an essential difference.

In both first stage of fugue and first stage of traumatic neurosis there is withdrawal from reality. At first sight hypnosis and traumatic neurosis seem alike in that they are initiated by something from without, and are both different from fugue which begins with the usurping of the psychic apparatus by the drive from within. But we have tried to show that this is a spurious resemblance between traumatic neurosis and hypnosis. While the external trauma initiates the illness, it appears that to a significant extent it has this power because of the drive which it arouses. In hypnosis too the hypnotist arouses infantile cravings, but the expression of these cravings and their continued arousal remains tied to the persisting relationship to the external figure—the hypnotist. In traumatic neurosis the trauma starts the process going, but in hypnosis the activity of the hypnotist remains an intrinsic feature of the process.[5]

---

[5] As an addendum, we would suggest a possible experimental use of traumatic neurosis in relation to hypnotizability. If our thesis is correct, the presence of a traumatic neurosis should increase hypnotizability. It may be possible to produce a miniature traumatic neurosis by subjecting an individual to a series of unexpected, somewhat frightening stimuli, perhaps to a succession of loud noises and bright lights. The parallel to the battle casualty could be made even more complete by having the subject at the same time be forced to attend very carefully to avoid a painful stimulus. Hypnotizability studies carried out directly after such a series of events might well show an increased hypnotizability.

# *9*

## HYPNOSIS AND BRAIN-WASHING

Hypnosis and brain-washing are two conditions in which the widespread loss of autonomy with domination of the ego by the social environment brings into sharp relief the whole problem of ego-environment relationships.

We would like to compare hypnosis and "brain-washing," not only because the two are often vaguely equated, but also because it seems to us that the similarities and differences we can describe will help to illuminate both.[1]

It is not easy to define the limits of what should properly be called brain-washing. We of course do not hold that any attempt to persuade someone of the truth of an ideology is brain-washing. We call it brain-washing only when the techniques described are used in a situation in which the persuader has reality power over the subject, and in practice, of course, the term is not employed until the power reaches a significant magnitude, however difficult that may be to define.[2] We make no effort at a systematic survey of the literature of brain-washing. We must also note at the outset that even if our theoretical explanation of brain-washing approximates a correct one, the brain-washer himself (with

[1] Bruno Bettelheim (personal communication) feels that there is a grave social danger in presenting brain-washing as a mysterious, irresistible force, because such a view of the process may give social sanction and rationalization for many kinds of motives which can hide behind the myth of the supposedly all-powerful technique.

[2] But it must not be forgotten that the reality power is not necessarily grossly in evidence. Compare the cogent remarks of Moloney on how psychoanalysis may be perverted into brain-washing, particularly in the training situation where the analyst has reality power over the candidate (168).

whose motivations we are not here concerned) may employ a very different theoretical structure to explain the effects he produces.

There are several kinds of situation which are lumped together as brain-washing. An effort may be made to inculcate a particular sociopolitical philosophy either in a foreigner or in someone who is already a member of the general culture, either to replace a particular political allegiance or to instill one in someone whose opinions are as yet unformed or only vague. A related situation is the effort to get the subject, whether or not he is an adherent of the political philosophy, to make a confession of misdeeds—a confession which according to usual standards would be a false one. These situations, however, are all variants of a single process and have the same goal, to end up with an individual who is fully subservient to a particular set of beliefs, genuinely convinced of their righteousness, and willing to carry out the instructions of those who rank above him in the administrative hierarchy of this ideology.

Freud considered hypnosis, love, and group psychology so mutually illuminating that he discussed them together (88). These three kinds of phenomena are avenues toward the understanding of the lifelong influence of the social environment on human beings, and illustrate how relative is the ego's autonomy from its environment. In that phase of his theory-building in which he was concerned chiefly with the drive determinants of behavior, Freud often seemed to consider that the human being is essentially totally autonomous or independent from external reality. In *Group Psychology and the Analysis of the Ego* (88) he dispelled this impression, representing the ego's autonomy as relative in relation to social reality.

In discussing the attack on the ego which brings about the regressed state in hypnosis, we especially emphasized two main features, the attack on attention and on the primarily autonomous apparatuses, and the manipulations designed to elicit transference phenomena.

In discussing brain-washing, we shall have to describe not only these same two features but in addition must consider another kind of attack, that on the secondarily autonomous apparatuses, more specifically on that organization within the ego which underlies an individual's values and ideology.

Some recent writings have suggested that brain-washing attacks what Erikson has described as the "ego identity" (59), an important bridge between the psychological and sociological frames of reference. Erikson has related the concept of ego identity to such phenomena as social role, ideology, and sociopolitical beliefs; we shall not enter the complex problems of these relationships here, but will simply refer generally to "values and ideologies." Whatever structure of the personality is the final goal of the brain-washer's attack, it certainly is a higher-order integration, an apparatus of secondary rather than primary autonomy.

## Interference With the Avenues of Intake

Like the hypnotist, the brain-washer too attacks the primarily autonomous apparatuses of perception, weakening them through fatigue, loss of sleep, drugs, starvation, and more directly, preventing their functioning by various forms of isolation, i.e., stimulus deprivation. But in addition, the brain-washer eliminates that constant influx of information which usually supports a person's sociopolitical ideology. We are perhaps never fully aware of how incessantly we are flooded by information which serves as food or fuel for the particular sociopolitical philosophy which we hold. It is shared community property, and all the avenues of public communication as well as countless private interpersonal interactions shore it up. All of this suddenly ceases for the person subjected to brain-washing. He is denied access to publications and deprived of interpersonal interaction with anyone who shares his views.[3] If the brain-washer were willing to argue in the opponent's terms, this would provide some food for the prisoner's ideology, but the brain-washer is not likely to argue except in his own terms. With this removal of social supports for a particular ideology, these structures, if they are to survive within the ego, must do so without any external help.

## Interference With the Apparatuses of Output

The hypnotist prevents the subject from engaging in motor activity. The brain-washer on occasion likewise attacks the primarily autonomous apparatuses of motility. The subject may be imprisoned, even kept in chains, or forced to maintain fixed positions for long periods of time. A coffinlike box in which the prisoner is forced to remain has been described. But in addition and analogously, the brain-washer prevents the subject from "motorically" employing his higher-order apparatuses—from using his ordinary ideology to exert any influence on other people. We are usually unaware of the extent to which we employ our ideologies to influence those with whom we come in contact. Our ideologies have this power because they are shared to various degrees by those with whom we interact, but they are useless against the brain-washer, for he does not give them any credence; in fact, he will not even listen. On the contrary, the extent to which the subject continues to voice his ideology may determine the extent to which he will be punished for maintaining his beliefs. Just as a structure needs an influx of support to main-

---

[3] In less extreme cases, however, a group of like-minded prisoners, who are allowed to communicate to some extent, may mutually provide ideological food for each other. It is difficult to draw a line between brain-washing and various other kinds of forcible indoctrination. See the interesting article in *The New Yorker* magazine (131) on the U. S. Defense Department study of American Korean prisoners of war.

tain its autonomy, so is its autonomy threatened if it cannot be exercised by serving as an effective instrument in action.[4]

## Absorption of Attention

The hypnotist absorbs the attention of the subject by a continuous patter. We have suggested that this process deprives the subject of the free use of attention cathexes. A similar process of course goes on in brain-washing. There is an unending barrage of talk about guilt and the new ideology. The "facts" of the former are incessantly sought and the principles of the latter are constantly dinned into the subject's ears. He is kept so preoccupied by the new ideology that he cannot reflect on his own. He is not left alone but is always in the company of others who are at a more advanced stage of brain-washing or are stooges who attempt to convert him (see Lifton's discussion of "struggling" [154]). It is their job to get him to see the truth. They are strongly motivated, since their own fate depends on their success. It should be noted that their activity results in their own incessant preoccupation with the new ideology: their active attempt to persuade someone else amounts to their "exercising" it, a kind of "exercise" which, as we have pointed out, the old ideology is no longer permitted. A similar technique, bringing the synthetic function of the ego to bear on the new system, is employed when the subject is required to discuss and criticize material presented from the point of view of the new ideology. Thrown off his guard, the subject may eagerly seek flaws in the new ideology, while his teacher will sanctimoniously claim that he encourages free discussion in an

[4] Rapaport has offered some suggestions about the implications for psychotherapeutic technique of the theory of relative autonomy from the environment (189). There is another one here. By refusing to argue with the patient in his own terms (i.e., in terms of his defensive system), the therapist denies food to the patient's defenses and by interpreting them he hopes to prevent their "exercise."

effort to make the ideology a more consistent and ethically desirable system.[5] But the effect is to increase the subject's preoccupation with the new ideology.

How does such preoccupation with the new ideology affect the subject's former ideological structures? Rapaport (189) has suggested that a kind of mutual intrapsychic nourishment of higher structures is one important factor in their normal functioning. It is as though in order to persist they must reinforce each other and thus must have the opportunity to interact. Preoccupation with the new ideology results in the mutual reinforcement of these higher-order structures in terms of the new ideology rather than the old. Apparently these higher-order organizations are not completely structuralized, so the ego, in its synthetic functioning, must constantly expend cathexes not only to maintain their unity but also to countercathect opposing ideas and impulses. Otherwise expressed, they never reach the degree of automatization that lower-order structures do.

## Interference With Attention to Promote De-automatization

As we have described, in the induction of hypnosis the hypnotist diverts attention from distance receptors to the body and focuses attention on its individual parts in an effort to de-automatize the functioning of the primarily autonomous apparatuses. The brain-washer adds to these techniques an effort to bring about the same kind of de-automatization in the higher-order organizations (though, as we said, they are not as completely automatized as the lower-order structures) to promote their replacement by a new organization. An ideology is not only a structure which helps to maintain equilibrium among a number of higher-order structures, it is

[5] Again we may note that the therapist seeks to get his patient to "exercise" new ways of thinking and particularly hopes the patient will find them effective in interaction with other people.

also designed to deal with disturbing affects like guilt, anxiety, and shame. The technique of de-automatization therefore is either to highlight the kinds of inconsistencies in the subject's own ideology which will lead to the development of such affects, or to attempt to produce these affects by other means so that the ideology is demonstrated to be inadequate to cope with them. This method will be the more effective with people who are already predisposed to doubt, and may account for certain instances of the success of brain-washing in religious people whose religion should presumably sustain them against guilt and anxiety. Precisely because their religion is an effort to hold in check grave doubts, these affects may be evoked in such persons by showing them their failure to abide fully by their religious principles. Freud has pointed out that the stricter the superego the greater the guilt (95). It will be difficult for a subject with such a superego to remain uninfluenced by the constant reiteration that he is a guilty man. There is a type of chronically doubting, obsessional person in whom the ideological structure is at once both particularly extensive and erected on a particularly narrow and precarious base, and there may well be a tendency toward such an ideological structuring in all obsessional characters.

De-automatization may be further promoted by bringing into juxtaposition the individual's sociopolitical or religious value system with primitive pregenital material. For example, a devout Christian was exceedingly disturbed by a drawing of Jesus masturbating which his jailor pasted on the excretion bucket in the cell (154).[6] In such circumstances the affects associated with pregenital material, which the subject's ideology protects against, threaten to invade the ideological structure and to bring about the deneutralization of the cathexes which maintain the structure.

[6] The power of such a technique may be judged by the reader asking himself whether he did not feel some measure of revulsion at such an idea.

## Capitalizing on Transference Potentials

Just as the hypnotist attempts to stimulate a regressive process in the subject to increase the likelihood of activating childhood behavior patterns, so does the brain-washer attempt to evoke feelings of helplessness and dependence, which stimulate infantile transference attitudes. The brain-washer is often in a better position than the hypnotist to do this because of his reality power over the subject, but we must not underestimate the power accruing to the hypnotist by the needfulness of the subject, for example when the subject wants to be hypnotized so that he may be freed from mental or physical pain. The brain-washer's victim is forced into helplessness, rage, and fear by the general restriction of his freedom even to the point of being chained; he may not be permitted to carry out even primitive bodily functions with any freedom (the restrictions and degradations heaped on the prisoner in toilet, sex, and sleep behavior are described by Lifton [154]). There are massive attacks on the individual's over-all sense of dignity and individuality. He is stripped of any status which may have contributed to his sense of security and power. Lifton reports that the subject is never called by his name but by a number. A prisoner who protested that he was a doctor was told that he was not a doctor but a spy.

As we indicated in our discussion of hypnosis, many of the actual manipulations influence the primary apparatuses and transference attitudes at the same time. We have already mentioned the generalized nonspecific weakening of the ego in brain-washing by fatigue, loss of sleep, starvation. Any successful attack on the secondary apparatuses will likewise simultaneously provoke transference attitudes, but the manner in which the manipulations of the apparatuses are carried out will determine, in the light of the subject's particular susceptibilities, which manipulations will be most influential in eliciting transference attitudes. Some subjects may react to gentleness and pleading, others to angry browbeating. A maneuver which has especially strong repercussions on the transference is that of capturing control of the apparatuses. We have described how the hypnotist does this by bringing about movements, sensations, and thoughts for which he can claim responsibility. Analogously, the brain-washer sets forth ideas which he knows the subject will accept, but does so in a manner which seems to indicate that he expects the subject to oppose them. Their acceptance is then treated as if it were a victory, resulting in the subject's feeling that he has succumbed. It may be a victory for the brain-washer if he gets the subject to talk at all, and a way he can get a toe hold is by asking questions that the subject feels there is no particular reason for not answering.

Yet another manipulation by the hypnotist directed toward both apparatuses and transference is the technique of confusing the subject, who is then glad to accept directions from the hypnotist. The analogous procedure by the brain-washer is to apply great pressure and then suddenly lift it. The temptation to accept the new point of view rises sharply during the relaxation of the pressure and cessation of punishment. For one thing, there is a positive demonstration that things can be easier. For another, there is an inevitable diminution of opposition once the pressure drops, even though the interrogator was responsible for the pressure in the first place. The technique of obtaining relief in a difficult situation by first increasing the difficulty and then restoring the original level of difficulty is well known.

Brain-washing then, like hypnosis, attempts to bring about the ego's surrender of its autonomy from the external environment. As we have pointed out in our general discussion, when there is diminution of autonomy from the external environment, the ego becomes especially submissive only to certain aspects of the environment, in this instance a particular ideology and the people who rule in its name. To other aspects of the environment, competing ideologies in particular, the ego becomes oblivious. It will be remembered that we pointed out that while such obliviousness may be called "total autonomy," this does not represent an increase of that *relative* autonomy which we have described as optimal for ego-functioning.

This diminution of autonomy from the external environment is accompanied by an analogously selective diminution of autonomy from the id. Various phenomena deriving from relatively primitive instinct and emotionality appear, channeled though they be in their outward expression by the adopted ideology. In our general theoretical discussion we pointed out that the asymmetry of the ego's relation to id and environment means that for autonomy from the environment to be lost, an id pattern—a motivational structure—must be found which conforms to the environment's demand. The skill of the brain-washer or interrogator depends on his skill at suggesting such motivational patterns. If the old Bolshevik can be shown that by confessing to nonexisting crimes he is saving the revolution, that the very ideology he professes must lead him to the conclusion demanded from him (134), the interrogator has won his point, since now there is a motivational pattern to conform to the external press. Indeed, this seems to us to be always the ultimate goal sought in brain-washing: the reorganization of the elements of the existing ideology so that they feed the new and starve the old.

An exceedingly important problem is the dynamics of the individual who is able to resist brain-washing. We may note here that when a differentiated external environment is lost, the ego may attempt to spare itself a loss of autonomy *from the id* by relinquishing control to the superego instead. Rapaport has suggested that this could explain such phenomena as wreck survivors organizing their environment into manifestations of God's will—e.g., the Rickenbacker story (228). It is also possible that this is what takes place when an individual is able to resist attempts at brain-washing. We ordinarily say he is sustained by a value system. But just as we have shown that an ideology can be attacked not only through the ego but also by way of its id and superego components, so must we remember that a sustaining value system, such as consciously held democratic ideals, must likewise be fed from the id and superego as well. This may mean in general that when the ego is threatened with a loss of autonomy with domination by id or environment, it can save itself by surrendering control to the superego instead. This may be the metapsychological explanation of why one can resist totalitarian pressure only by great faith in some other credo.

Having discussed these similarities between hypnosis and brain-washing, we would like to point to some essential differences.

Hypnosis develops rapidly as compared with brain-washing, which may take years to succeed. Of course this may be related to the fact that an unhypnotizable subject is soon given up, but if a man is to be brain-washed or to be brought to a confession, his captor will be set on pursuing his course until he succeeds. If one insisted on working with a subject until he was successfully hypnotized, it might eventually be accomplished too. But even so, hypnosis is clearly a more rapid process than brain-washing. The essential reason for this may be something which lies close to the heart of the matter. Compared to brain-washing, hypnosis is play. Since the hypnotist ordinarily has no reality power over the subject, hypnosis almost always has some element of a game, but the brain-washer may well have the power of life and death over his subject. The goals of the two are likewise vastly different. The hypnotist seeks to evoke a transient state for highly specific purposes. The brain-washer is attempting to change the total life course and outlook of his subject.

We would argue, therefore, that the *successfully* brain-washed has not undergone a regression in the service of the ego but a regression proper. There must be many who are supposedly brain-washed but who have in fact undergone only a regression in the service of the ego, and these must be further distinguished from those who consciously pretend to accept the alien system. Where the subject pretends, the pretense may dynamically resemble the behavior of a "psychopath," or it may simply be a calculated effort to win privileges or to escape punishment. There is probably a con-tinuum of instances from such pretense to the apparently genuine conscious acceptance of the system by the building of a subsystem—the kind of result we would call regression in the service of the ego—an acceptance which, however, breaks down soon after circumstances change. Such a con-tinuum would enable us to account for the varying reactions of the brain-washed once they have been set free. Lifton reports (154) that there are a few who shift orientation almost at once, a few who remain persuaded of the new ideology, and the majority who fall between.

The relative permanence of a change in the ego may be measured by whether or not it will survive a shift in ego organization and/or a marked alteration in the external situa-tion. Hypnosis is terminated by intervening sleep; brain-wash-ing which is a regression in the service of the ego is not, but it is terminated by a marked change in the external situation. Brain-washing which is a regression proper survives both.

It may be felt that in regarding the brain-washed person as in a state of regression we are expressing a value judgment on a totalitarian system. This is not necessarily true. What indicates a state of regression is a rigid adherence to any value system (including the so-called democratic one) in a manner which yields independence of judgment to an external au-thority. Our definition of regression, then, is not in terms of specific ideology, but in terms of the surrender of control to the external environment after autonomy has been lost.

In terms of our description of brain-washing, where shall we class mass phenomena such as the devotion of a nation to a totalitarian leader? We do not call such phenomena brain-washing, even though one might argue that they represent a surrender of control to the environment by an ego which has lost its autonomy, because we believe that in such mass-psychological phenomena, social, economic, and other factors play a role in a way which goes far beyond what we have described as brain-washing, essentially a phenomenon of individual psychology, though it occurs, of course, in a social context.

How about the change which comes over a group, let us say as they are listening to an impassioned address by their leader? Such people are sometimes said to be hypnotized. They show regressive phenomena similar to those revealed by a mob. That Freud regarded the manifestations of hypnosis and mob behavior as somehow related is seen in his calling hypnosis a "group of two." (It must be remembered that Freud used "group" in parts of his *Group Psychology and the Analysis of the Ego* [88] as practically synonymous with "mob.") Does this mean that a group under the sway of a leader is hypnotized? Freud finds the essential difference between a group and hypnosis to be the identification among the members of a group with each other, a proposition which could be generalized to the view that hypnosis is a phenomenon of individual psychology and the group phenomena sometimes called hypnosis are phenomena of social psychology. But a crowd temporarily altered by the impassioned address of a leader may be making its essential identifications with the leader, abetted though these be by identifications which the members of the crowd make with each other. Clearly, there may be such a thing as group hypnosis. Matters of definition are involved too, and there are phenomena which cannot be clearly demarcated as either only individual or social psychological. We realize of course that these labels do not solve the problem and that an adequate elucidation of these issues would require the discussion of important and difficult problems of the relationship between individual and social psychology, but obviously such a discussion would take us beyond the scope of this book.

# *10*

# TRANCE IN BALI[1]

Bateson and Mead's *Balinese Character* (11) attracted our attention to the phenomenon of trance in Bali and its relation to hypnosis. Trance plays a prominent role in Balinese life and obviously fulfills an important function in the culture. The authors themselves call attention to the connection between trance and hypnosis: "The trance itself approximates closely to the phenomenon of hypnosis, and comparison of our trance films and records, and those of Miss Belo, with materials on hypnotic subjects in this country, has revealed no discrepancies, except for the substitution of a formalized situation for the hypnotist" (p. 35).

Bateson and Mead consider interrelationships between trance and other aspects of Balinese culture, but they do not explore the trance-hypnosis-culture relationship. We will attempt to do that by reviewing their data, and will center specifically on the connection between trance and other aspects of the culture to examine whether or not they support the theory of hypnosis advanced in this book.[2]

Bateson and Mead inform us that "trance is a Balinese

[1] We wish to thank Dr. Margaret Mead and Gregory Bateson for their helpful comments and suggestions concerning this chapter.
[2] A trap can lie in such an analysis, of course. If we begin with a theory as to the meaning and nature of the hypnotic trance—as of course we do—we may be selecting only those aspects of Balinese culture which fit into our theory and the connections we make may be unjustified. It is also possible that Bateson and Mead were more aware of the implications of their data for a theory of hypnosis than they make explicit, and that therefore some of their formulations about Balinese personality may themselves have been implicitly based on a theory of hypnosis.

cultural form accessible to most Balinese but occurring in very different proportions in different communities. There are villages where everyone has been a trancer, villages where no one has been in a trance" (p. 35). From this we infer—and later will offer our reasons for this inference—that almost everyone in Bali apparently possesses the *capacity* to go into a trance, but that trance usually occurs only when encouraged by the specific social situation. We assume with Bateson and Mead that the prevalence of trance and its importance in the culture means that the conditions of personality development in the culture favor a personality structure which is hypnotizable. We believe therefore that a study of this personality structure would illuminate some of the features which go to make up hypnotizability as well as the function which trance can serve in the successful adaptation of a personality. Our frame of reference is the bridge between individual and social psychology built by Erik Erikson (56). He has made clear that the organ zones function according to "modes" of which he distinguishes five—incorporative (sucking), incorporative (biting), retentive, eliminative, and intrusive. The modes are the patterns upon which the basic social behavior forms—the "modalities"—are modeled. Every society fosters certain child-rearing practices which act on the modes and facilitate the formation of certain modalities and prohibit that of others. Every society can be characterized in terms of its basic and essential modalities.

Although Balinese society and child-rearing apparently foster the potentiality for trance and provide a social niche for it, we cannot assume that in any other society of similiar structure and personality development trance will necessarily play an organized role in the culture; it may well be that other factors must coexist for a particular kind of culture and personality development to result in the appearance of trance as an organized societal technique.

For a discussion of how Balinese character is related to trance-suggestibility, we must first sketch what Bateson and

Mead suggest is the core of the emotional development of the Balinese, since it is this core which is most closely connected with the manifestations of trance.

> . . . the Balinese baby is subjected to a peculiarity of the mother-child relationship which is apparent when the child is only five or six months old and which becomes steadily more definite as the child grows older. This is a series of broken sequences, of unreached climaxes. The mother continually stimulates the child to show emotion—love or desire, jealousy or anger—only to turn away, to break the thread, as the child, in rising passion, makes a demand for some emotional response on her part. . . . As the child gets older, from about eighteen months on, the teasing, the stimulus to the never realized climax becomes more patterned and more intense. . . For the first two or three years of their lives, children respond to these stimuli, although perhaps the increasing strength of the stimulus may be taken as a measure of the increasing resistance which they are developing. . . Later, the child begins to withdraw. . . And once established, his unresponsiveness will last through life.[3] Most children reach this state by the time they are three or four, vacillating at times, falling into deep sulks or violent tempers, only to resume again their newly acquired imperviousness [pp. 32-33].

The kind of unresponsiveness described results in a character structure in which strong affective display takes place only in very special circumstances such as exaggerated glee in funerals, in theatricals, and in the trance.[4]

The unresponsive withdrawnness of the Balinese is closely connected with another characteristic: a widespread tendency

---

[3] We call attention to the fact that the sequence described is similar to the dynamics of boredom as explained by Fenichel (63).

[4] Mead describes her perplexity at the difficulty in winning the friendship of the Balinese until she "had the opportunity to study the behavior of other Europeans who had come to Bali as they might go to the theatre, and saw how much more easily the Balinese responded to their exaggerated interest than they did to my affection for individual babies. . . I . . . learned to exaggerate and caricature my friendly attitudes until the Balinese could safely accept them as theatrical rather than real" (pp. 31-32).

to abstracted states or dissociations in the course of daily living. We regard these states as abortive forms of trance, and since they are universally present among the Balinese, they form an important line of evidence for our inference that almost all Balinese have the *capacity* to go into trance.

Bateson and Mead describe as characteristic of the Balinese sudden and frequent lapses into an abstracted state in which they seem temporarily out of contact:

> An obverse of the Balinese love of crowded scenes is their habit of withdrawal into vacancy—letting themselves suddenly slip into a state of mind where they are, for the moment, no longer subject to the impact of inter-personal relations. This withdrawal occurs in a large variety of contexts, but is perhaps especially common in parent-child and teacher-pupil relationships, and following some definite activity of work or play. The face of mother or child, or both, will become vacant immediately after unusually active play; or the face of an artist will be similarly unresponsive after he has just finished a carving [p. 68].

It is to be noted that this withdrawal into vacancy is described as the counterpoint of the Balinese love of crowds ("*rame*"). "In the most rapt crowds, when the clowns are performing some fascinating new version of an absolutely reliable joke, one can still see face after face which contains no response to the outside world" (p. 4).

A second characteristic of all Balinese which we suggest is evidence that trance-suggestibility is universal for them is the special manner in which they employ sleep.

> The Balinese readily go to sleep during the day, and in particular, they go to sleep when they are frightened. This behavior is summarized in the common Balinese phrase, "*takoet poeles*" (literally, "afraid-sleep"). On one occasion we sent our cook boys by omnibus to our Bangli camp, carrying knives and forks and other kitchen equipment. When we arrived we found them all asleep in the Bangli kitchen and no attempt made to open the camp. They had left the knives and forks in the bus and were afraid. Similarly small children never witness child-

birth, not because they are driven away, but because they sleep through it, lying sound asleep often on the same bed as the woman in labor [p. 191].

[The authors suggest that] this handling of fear by means of sleep may be regarded as a regressive technique and is probably comparable to the relaxed regression of the child toward the father [p. 191]. [And further:] The child who is frightened by the tantrum of his child nurse falls asleep as she shrieks out her unrestrained rage right beside his closed ear. The older child who has lost or broken some valuable thing will be found, when his parents return, not run away, not waiting to confess, but in a deep sleep. . . People on the scene of an accident sit in a paralyzed semi-stupor, not talking, not looking, but nodding. . . [p. 39].

We have discussed problems of the relationship between hypnosis and sleep elsewhere. Here we want to note that the Balinese appear to use sleep as a defense against anxiety and to suggest that this technique of dealing with anxiety is related to trance.

To turn now to trance itself, the Balinese, as we mentioned, seem to encourage it only in certain specific social situations. There are two main types of trance in Bali: one is the trance in Balinese dances, of which the authors describe two: the witch play, and the trance dance, called "*sangiang*," done by young girls before the menarche. The other is the trance of the village seer, which Bateson and Mead say is the ritualized method of effecting some change in the usual rigidly determined course of events by having the gods propose such a change through the mouth of the seer while she is in trance.[5] There is some evidence that trances other than these are frowned upon. For example, Bateson and Mead describe how a man whose function it was to induce trance in a *sangiang* dancer by developing clonic contractions in his arm while holding onto a stick which the dancer in turn took hold of would himself go into trance, until he was told that if he did

---

[5] See Bateson, "An Old Temple and a New Myth" (10).

not stop he would no longer be allowed to perform the task.[6]

The authors describe the witch play, the *Tjalonarang*, in which trance plays a prominent role, as "the definitive dramatic theme of Balinese parent-child relations [which] expresses the residue in the adults of what they have experienced as children" (p. 34). These are the essential features of the plot: there are a dragon and a witch, both with disciples. The dragon apparently represents the father and the witch the mother.

Followers of the Dragon, armed with krisses [daggers], enter and approach the Witch ready to attack her. But she waves her magic cloth—the cloth baby sling [used to carry infants]—and after each attack they crouch down before her, magically cowed. Finally they rush upon her in pairs, stabbing ineffectively at the Witch who has become a half-limp bundle in their tense arms. She is uninvolved and offers no resistance, but one by one they fall on the ground in deep trance, some limp, some rigid. From this trance they are aroused by the Dragon who claps his jaws over them, or by his priest sprinkling his holy water. Now, able to move again but not returned to normal consciousness, they move about in a somnambulistic state, turning their daggers which were powerless against the Witch, against their own breasts. . . Thus symbolically they complete the cycle of childhood trauma—the approach to the mother, the rejection and the turn-in upon the self. [But note that the approach to the witch is not for affection, but to attack, an attack to which she finally offers no resistance.] The trancers of both sexes writhe and shriek in ecstasy, intermittently pausing for a blank moment, only to begin pressing their krisses against their breasts. . . In this violent scene it is rare for anyone to be injured; priests weave their way in and out, sprinkling holy water, and the Dragon, who revives them from their first deep trance, has returned to give them the support and comfort of his presence. Finally they are disarmed, carried

---

[6] As Bateson mentioned to us in a personal communication, the clonus itself is evidence of trance. A distinction then is made between trance involving only the extremity and trance with more generalized manifestations (cf. pp. 307-308).

into the temple, and brought out of trance with holy water and incense and an occasional offering of a live chick [pp. 34-35].

Bateson and Mead regard the trance as an opportunity to express intense emotion and concentration; for example:

> Trance is . . . an interval of extremely narrow concentration[7] and this is especially true of the trances of those practiced seers whose task it is to let the gods or the ancestors speak through them. . . Such a seer or priestess epitomizes . . . Balinese ceremonial; and in the trance state exhibits emotions never otherwise appropriate except on the stage—tears and intense expressions of grief and striving. All these are lived through, until again vacancy and awayness supersede [pp. 4-5].
>
> [And again:] . . . the Balinese character . . . is . . . curiously cut off from inter-personal relationships, existing in a state of dreamy-relaxed disassociation, with occasional intervals of non-personal concentration—in trance, in gambling, and in the practice of the arts [p. 47].

Balinese culture is strikingly shot through with ceremonial, ritual, and pageantry. It is but a short step to relate this to the histrionic element in hysteria and hypnosis and to ask whether there may not be more than a mere analogy between the individual phenomenon of outbursts of affect in hysterical personalities and in hypnosis, and the cultural phenomenon of ceremonial and ritual with socially prescribed affect expression in a society in which a major characteristic of child-rearing practice is to stimulate children to a peak of affect and then to turn away from them.

The trance state is not only the expression of pent-up affects, but also of the withdrawal into stupor. One is reminded of the two types of hypnotic trance, the relatively alert, and the stuporous.[8] A manifestation parallel to these two aspects of trance is the behavior of those Balinese chil-

---

[7] See our discussion of hypnosis and the concentration of attention, p. 129 ff.
[8] See p. 154.

dren who do not learn effectively or quickly enough the habit of unresponsiveness:

A few children make the adjustment very late; characteristically this means for girls a series of violent temper tantrums, while for boys it means long, almost trancelike sulks and attacks of deep physical dependency when they will lie leaning against some person or even against some inanimate object [p. 33].

We turn now from the general emotional states—hyperaffective and withdrawn—to a discussion of the Balinese body image, one which seems to us remarkably similar to the kind of body image producible in a successful hypnosis. We note first that the Balinese will allow his body to go waxy limp in another's hands and to be manipulated from without. He learns to use his body this way as a result of the direct sensorikinesthetic learning (rather than visual-acoustic or "ideational" learning) which is the major way in which a Balinese learns from infancy on.

This surrender of the body to control by another begins very early in the infant's life.

. . . the child in the sling, or supported lightly on the carrier's hip, has learned to accommodate itself passively to the carrier's movements; to sleep, with head swaying groggily from side to side, as the carrier pounds rice; or to hang limp on the hip of a small girl who is playing "crack-the-whip." Surrendering all autonomy, and passively following the words spoken in its name[9] or the rhythm of the person who carries it or the hand which snatches its hand back from a spontaneous gesture, the child's body becomes more waxy flexible as it grows older; and gestures which are all echoes of an experienced pattern

[9] "When the Balinese baby is born, the midwife, even at the moment of lifting him in her arms, will put words in his mouth, commenting 'I am just a poor little newborn baby, and I don't know how to talk properly, but I am very grateful to you, honorable people, who have entered this pig-sty of a house to see me born.' And from that moment, all through babyhood, the child is fitted into a frame of behavior, of imputed speech and imputed thought and complex gesture, far beyond his skill and maturity" (p. 13).

replace such spontaneous gestures of infancy as the pounding of the child's silver bracelets on any convenient board [p. 14].

Learning to walk, learning the first appropriate gestures of playing musical instruments, learning to eat, and to dance are all accomplished with the teacher behind the pupil, conveying directly by pressure, and almost always with a minimum of words, the gesture to be performed. Under such a system of learning, one can only learn if one is completely relaxed and *if will and consciousness as we understand those terms are almost in abeyance* [italics ours]. The flexible body of the dancing pupil is twisted and turned in the teacher's hands; teacher and pupil go through the proper gesture, then suddenly the teacher springs aside, leaving the pupil to continue the pattern to which he has surrendered himself, sometimes with the teacher continuing it so that the pupil can watch him as he dances. Learning with the eyes flows directly from learning *passively* [italics ours] while one's own body is being manipulated by another [p. 15].

We suggest that this kind of surrender of body control to another, waxy flexibility, and learning kinesthetically by movements imposed by the teacher, are kinds of body orientation which appear in good hypnotic subjects and that therefore this kind of training in the Balinese is related to their susceptibility to trance.

An interesting manifestation of surrender of voluntary control of the body is the role and importance of puppetry in Balinese life. Puppets are extensively used in Balinese theatricals and are also connected with trance phenomena:

The animated puppet, the doll which dances on a string, the leather puppets manipulated by the puppeteer, and finally the little girl trance dancers who themselves become exaggeratedly limp and soft as they dance to the commands of the audience, all dramatize this whole picture of involuntary learning, in which it is not the will of the learner, but the pattern of the situation and the manipulation of the teacher which prevail. . . In the *sangiang deling* performance, little puppets with loaded feet are suspended from a slender string supported by sticks held in the hands of two performers. The hands of the performers tremble, set up a harmonic action in the string, and the puppets are said to "be in trance, and to dance uncontrollably," thus dramatizing the confusion which is involved in all Balinese activity—the blending of the teacher and the taught, the model and the copyist [p. 17].

A second striking characteristic of the Balinese body image, and one which we will show is related to the surrender of voluntary control, is the looseness of ego boundary. It will be recalled that in our discussion of hypnosis we emphasized the fluidity and extensionability of the body-ego boundaries.

In the Balinese the body-ego boundaries can easily be extended to include something in the external environment, often something which is loosely connected to the body as on a string. This phenomenon is described by Bateson and Mead in terms of "autocosmic play," a concept which they take from the work of Erik Erikson and which they define as: ". . . some object in the outside world is identified as an extension of own body" (p. 31). Objects which are commonly used for such autocosmic play are a baby which "the Balinese treat as something between a toy and a puppet" (p. 23), fighting cocks, and "baby birds, beetles, grasshoppers, etc., which are tied and given to children as playthings" (p. 25).

> The child is taught no identifying attitudes of pity or care toward these live toys on the ends of strings and all his interest is centered on the way in which the small bird flutters and responds to the pull of the string. These living toys have a series of overtones which become part of Balinese symbolism. The children playing with them are at the same time learning to experiment with their own bodies; little girls to flick their pliant fingers as far back as possible, little boys to pull and tug at their genitals. The sense of a body part symbol[10] which is attached, but by a thread, and which has a life and willfulness of its own, becomes strongly developed [p. 25].

[10] Mead (personal communication) suggests that "play object" would convey the meaning more accurately than does "symbol."

The authors believe that most of these play objects represent the male genital (p. 131) and further that the phallus is particularly important in the "sense that own body parts . . . are very loosely attached and independently animated . . ." (pp. 25-26). These specific points, however, are less important here than the fact that this extension of the body ego is a characteristic which fits into our theoretical formulations for hypnotizability.

Our discussion of the surrender of voluntary control of the body to another emphasized how this begins with the experiences of the child in learning. But from the point of view of the adult who is teaching, we see that the child becomes an extension of the ego boundary of the adult. Surrender of voluntary control and looseness of ego boundary then are related phenomena in Balinese culture.

Bateson and Mead conceive of the use of the child's body as an extension of the adult's body ego as follows:

> . . . the child's body becomes a sort of stage and his body parts the actors on that stage. In many cultures, toys and patterns of adult play with children tend to draw the child's attention away from his own body and into the outside world, but in Bali everything combines to refocus the child's attention back upon himself. His whole body, but especially his genital, is like a toy or a small musical instrument upon which those about him play; they make him toys which tell the same tale and it is not surprising that he develops a body consciousness very different from our own [p. 26].

Or, again, we are told in Mead and MacGregor's *Growth and Culture* (166):

> The way in which Balinese children are carried, either in a cloth sling or in an arm which uses the sling as a model, sets a style in which the child can be treated safely attached to the body of the adult, like one of the adult's own limbs, and needing no continuous attention [p. 142].

The widespread nature of this kind of body image in the Balinese is indicated by the following:

> The habit of regarding external, and especially living, objects as symbolic extensions of own body recurs constantly, and can even be recognized in the behavior of the audience at a theatrical performance. The spectators are not interested in the plot and never identify with the characters portrayed in the play; but, as technicians, they are interested in the acting, and their identification is with the actors as extensions or kinaesthetic replicas of their own bodies [p. 143].

The fluidity of the boundaries of the body ego thus derives not only from the extension of the body ego onto external objects, but also from the fact that one's own body is used by others as the extension of their body ego. Leaning against the body of another is highly characteristic of Balinese interaction and further supports our view of the extensionability of the Balinese body-ego boundary.

The Balinese love of crowds, described above, appears to be a way in which the body-ego boundaries may be extended to include the entire group. In certain crowds engaged in violent action, it seems surprising that nobody gets hurt, but injury is prevented by each man putting out his hand to touch the shoulder of the man ahead of him, as though to make the tangible link which extends each individual body ego to the crowd as a whole (p. 244).

Another manifestation of the fluidity of Balinese concepts, and one which seems to us related to the fluidity of the body-ego boundaries and thus a part of the constellation which we suggest is related to the trance process and to hypnotizability, is the Balinese conception of the relationship between children and gods. Each merges into the other—the child is regarded as a god and the god as a child.

> In Bali the gods are thought of as the *children* of the people, not as august, parental figures. Speaking through the lips of those in trance, the gods address the villagers as "papa" and

"mama," and the people are said to spoil or indulge their gods, the same term being used as that which is used when spoiling or indulging a child or a monarch. Newborn babies, reincarnated and fresh from heaven, are addressed with honorific terms. . . During the early months of its life, before it is quite certain that the child will consent to stay and eat rice with it relatives, a slight aura of the sacred and uncanny surrounds the child; it may not yet put foot to the ground or enter a temple, and its willfulness and its first garbled phrases are taken as inspired. This attitude toward children is carried over and ceremonially expressed in the child trances, in which adolescent boys and grown men take great pleasure in addressing and adorning the little trance dancer, who in turn, possessed by a god, acts as a petted or petulant child. When the music begins, the little trancers begin to dance, rhythmically enacting the familiar scene in which elders attempt to dress a fractious and squirming child . . . the trancer is at once willful and compliant; she is fussy about the music . . . but at the same time she responds accurately to her cues. . . Tranced, relaxed, puppet-like, sacred and yet completely under control, compliant and yet willful, the *sangiang* dancer is the ideal object for Balinese parental attitudes, and the audience, relaxed and gay, both participates and looks on [pp. 29-30].

It seems to us that this ready exchangeability of god and child indicates the fluidity of body image or, otherwise expressed, the mutual interpenetration of identifications, and furthermore casts light on the relationship between hypnotist and subject as we have discussed it. Not only does the subject become childlike and subservient, he also participates in the omnipotence of the hypnotist; and the hypnotist is not only omnipotent and directive, he also participates in the regression and subservience of the subject. The Balinese in trance is compliant and willful, the crowd is subservient (for example, "the big boys address the little trancers with overdone politeness, 'See, your sacred ladyship, it is going to rain and you have not yet stood on my shoulders, are they not good enough for you?' " [p. 30]) but also completely in control of the subjects in trance. Furthermore, the audience both participates and looks on, again carrying out two opposite functions. The god is both god and child, powerful and weak, and the child is both child and god, petulant and sacred. It will also be remembered that in the witch play, while at first the witch magically cows the disciples of the dragon who come to attack her with their daggers, she soon becomes uninvolved, unresisting, and limp. Though it is apparently not a prescribed part of the play, the witch may go into trance herself. In this social situation in which the formalized relationship of hypnotist with subject is not set up as it is in our society, the witch, who may be said to throw the disciples of the dragon into trance, nevertheless goes into trance herself as well, while the disciples of the dragon who go into trance are evidently instrumental in putting the witch into trance. Here again it seems to us that the fluid interpenetration of hypnotist and subject, which is somewhat concealed in the hypnotic relationship usual in our culture and therefore deducible only from an analysis of the motivations of the two members of the pair, emerges more clearly in Balinese culture where the trance has become an organized part of the social ritual and not an isolated therapeutic or vaudeville device as it is in our culture. Incidentally, it should be noted that the interpenetration of the concepts of god and child is paralleled by the interpenetration of the concepts of parent and child. In the earlier presented data about autocosmic symbolism, we emphasized how the child becomes an extension of the body ego of the parent; but it must be equally true that as he moves passively and rhythmically in time with the body movements of his parent or older sibling, the child's own body ego likewise becomes extended to include that of the parent.

A third major characteristic of the Balinese body image is that the body is regarded as made up of disparate parts, each apparently autonomous.

This body, which moves only in parts and without volition, hardly seems like a unit at all, and may well be composed of a series of separate units, each with a life of its own. Such are the ideas of black magic, and of protection against black magic. Folk beliefs are filled with personified limbs, legs and arms, and heads, each animated by a mischievous will of its own, frequenting the cemetery and existing merely to torment man. And in the special set of *sangiang* performances in the District of Karangasem, there are trances in which only the hand of the performer is put in trance; it trembles independently, while he himself and the rest of his body remain uninvolved.[11]

In the hands, more intensely than in any other part of the body, this disassociation, this independence of each small unit is seen. Balinese fingers at rest rarely lie with the fingers in seriated regular flexion as our hands do, but one finger stays at one angle and another at another in a way which would prove infinitely tiring to us [p. 18].

Classic hypnotic suggestion often aims at producing just such a condition of bodily experience—e.g., "You will feel that your hand is separate from your body, that it has a will of its own, and will begin to move by itself."

In doing work the Balinese have a tendency both to split the activity into small simple units and to perform the activity while conversing on other topics as though no real attention were being given to the work.

Closely connected with the Balinese love of crowded scenes is the tendency to reduce all tasks to separate stages with a definite sequence of bodily movements necessary at each stage. The movements are then performed smoothly and fast, laughing and singing, with a minimum of conscious attention to the task. There is also a tendency to arrange matters so that a maximum number of items can be accomplished simultaneously. Thus the Balinese habit of muscular rote behavior [kinesthetic learning] combines with their love of busy and active crowds to give something which we might call "mass production" methods [p. 67].

[And again:] There is rarely any discernible relationship be-

[11] Cf. the description of our patient who used her fingers to open her "hypnotized eyes" (pp. 18-19).

tween the conversation of a group of Balinese and the activity
which they are performing. Words must be captured and repeated to have meaning for action, but there is no need at all
to translate action into words. One might listen at a spy hole
for an hour to a busy group, hearing every word spoken, and be
no wiser in the end as to whether they were making offerings,
or painting pictures, or cooking a meal. The occasional "Give
me that!" is interspersed with bits of comic opera, skits and
caricatures, songs and punning and repartee. As Americans
doodle on a piece of paper while attending to the words of a
lecture, so the Balinese doodles in words, while his body flaw-
lessly and quickly attends to the job in hand [p. 15].

This kind of dissociation between the elements of the task
and between words and actions seems to indicate a general
trend toward disunity and dissociation which can be produced in the hypnotic state, which of course, on an earlier
descriptive level, was called a state of "dissociation."

Phenomena which at first seem the obverse of the apparent
Balinese ready acceptance of the separability of body parts
and fluidity of body-ego boundaries, and which probably indicate grave anxieties concealed by this ready acceptance, are
their horror of the disintegration of the body and the many
representations and re-representations of the body which are
made in an effort finally to dispose of it after death.

The first funeral is a comparatively quiet and orderly affair
. . . This misleading simplicity, in which a death is treated
with no more ritual or fuss than a big birthday or a marriage,
belies the real feeling about death, which is expressed in the
later ceremonies in which the body is re-created—out of the
actual bones in the plains villages, or with rice in a basket in
Bajoeng Gede—only to be laboriously disposed of again; and
again re-created, and again disposed of. . . The weeks of laborious preparation culminate in three days of ceremonial. The
graves are first dressed in human clothes, then opened, and
the bones are dug up and assembled. They are dressed again
and laid out in a little town built in the cemetery. Delicate
little dolls which represent the souls of the dead are carried

home from the cemetery to the houses where they lived on earth, there to receive food and drink, to pray to the ancestors, and finally to ask leave to depart. These little "souls" are then carried back to the cemetery and placed inside the bundles of dressed-up bones. Thus the person is again re-created. On the next day, a new set of "souls" is taken to the priest's house and blessed, and the "bones" are later given a second laying-out as if they were corpses. On the third day the bones are burned in coffins shaped like animals appropriate to each caste, but the cremation fires are no sooner out than the people are poking among the ashes, gathering the small bits of specified bones and again re-creating a body upon which the little cornucopia-shaped prayer leaves are laid, so as to define again all the sacred anatomical points. Representative samples of this re-created body are then ground to dust in a mortar . . . and the dust is placed in still another human replica and finally carried to the sea. It is thrown into the sea, only to be re-created again in a new replica at stated periods thereafter. . . After each phase in the death ceremonial . . . comes the ceremony of *mepegat*, in which the souls, carried in the arms of members of the family like the babies which they will again become, ceremonially break the tie which binds them to the living—but only for a little while [pp. 46-47].

The difficulty of getting rid of the body and yet the fusions and extensions of body ego appear to be parallel to the paradox that "the sense of personal uniqueness in Bali is slight and people are shy at mentioning their own names or the names of others, but each has an impersonal individuality which is completely tough and incontrovertible" (p. 45).

Standing in sharp contrast to the fragmentation of the Balinese body image and the fluidity of its boundaries is the elaborate system of orientation in space, time, and status which the Balinese needs to feel secure and comfortable.

In a strange village, where he does not know the cardinal points [i.e., in terms of direction] or the local customs, and if he does not know what day it is in at least three of the inter-cogging weeks, nor the caste and order of birth term for the person with whom he is trying to converse, the Balinese is completely disoriented. To this state they apply the term "*paling*" which is used also for those who are drunk, delirious, or in trance. Orientation in time, space, and status are the essentials of social existence, and the Balinese, although they make very strong spirits for ceremonial occasions, with a few startling exceptions resist alcohol, because if one drinks one loses one's orientation. Orientation is felt as a protection rather than as a strait jacket and its loss provokes extreme anxiety. If one takes a Balinese, quickly, in a motor car, away from his native village, so that he loses his bearings, the result may be several hours of illness and a tendency to deep sleep [p. 11]. [This is another example of how sleep is used as a defense against anxiety.]

The many meanings of the word "*paling*" indicate not only that trance is felt to be an altered state of consciousness like intoxication and delirium, but also that it represents a disturbance in ego boundaries, like disorientation in time, space, and status, the external landmarks by which the ego recognizes its boundaries and its bearings. It seems clear that the great importance the Balinese places on orientation in time, space, and status is an effort to defend himself against and to counteract the danger of losing his bearings, his ego boundaries, and going into trance.[12]

The second major use of the trance in Balinese culture, that by the village seer, is directly related to the Balinese rigid organization of space, time, and status, as a way of breaking out of the strait jacket of this organization. As we described above, the gods speak through the mouth of the village seer in trance. Bateson and Mead state that "These trance states are an essential part of Balinese social organization, for without them life would go on forever in a fixed and rigid form, foreordained but unguessed in advance" (p. 5). And again, ". . . practiced seers whose task it is to let the gods

[12] See Erikson on the psychological significance of the space and time concepts of a culture (57, 58).

or ancestors speak through them, giving small deft turns to the course of events by suggestions spoken when in a state of trance" (p. 5).

K. R. Eissler (53) relates the Balinese conception of the future as foreordained but unknown to the nature of the Balinese body image as follows: "Since the parts of his body will move independently and not as integrated parts in a superimposed plan, the future cannot be a field of potential action. He actually does not know what the parts of the body will do, and thus he has to await what configurations will evolve out of the stream of body experiences" (p. 141).

Eissler offers an interesting explanation of how the disturbance of the Balinese body image comes about. The Balinese vigorously discourage crawling in their infants, so that the child essentially progresses from sitting to walking. Their motive in doing so is apparently to prevent the child from moving like the dogs and pigs who are the Balinese scavengers. Eissler feels that this prevention of crawling is a "kinesthetic repression" of the first total bodily movement toward a goal and therefore prevents the development of an integrated body image.[13] Interesting though this hypothesis is, it involves the obscure concept of "kinesthetic repression" and implies a number of major assumptions about the development of body image without any evidence being offered to support them.

Our discussion thus far has dealt principally with how well the Balinese body image corresponds to the subjective bodily

[13] Mead (in Mead and MacGregor, 166) attributes great importance to the low muscle tonus which she regards as characteristic of all newborn infants, but which soon disappears in our culture, and persists in the Balinese and therefore presumably plays an important role in their body image. Though she speculates that the persistence of the low tonus in the Balinese may be based upon some nutritional or genic factor, she argues that Balinese methods of child-rearing must be designed to maintain such tonus and suggests that the sling in which the Balinese infant is carried, a sling which "permits the child to be attached to the mother or child nurse without either person's making any active effort whatsoever" (p. 183), is instrumental in maintaining this low tonus.

changes characteristic of a person in our culture in hypnosis. We would now like to turn to a theory of how Balinese child-rearing practices with regard to the oral zone and its incorpo-rative mode appear to facilitate the development of trance. It will be recalled that we as well as others have emphasized oral features in hypnosis. In particular we have stressed the mechanism of identification and the underlying fantasy of oral incorporation. Food plays an enormous role in Balinese culture and its ceremonials. Bateson and Mead vividly de-scribe how the Balinese teach their infants to eat solid foods:

> The mother pre-chews a mixture of rice and banana, and then, either with her lips or her finger, she places a mound of the soft pre-chewed material on the baby's mouth, gradually manipulating more and more of it into its mouth. The infant splutters and chokes, helpless and almost always resistant to the mountain of mush which is being forced on it. Each feeding becomes a sort of attack, in which the baby . . . is forced to swallow against its will. . . All through life, the Balinese have a sensitivity in regard to open mouths . . . [pp. 19-20].

Lewin, in his illuminating review (148) of the Bateson and Mead book, emphasizes the many evidences of the Balinese struggle against unconscious cannibalism:

> The cannibal impulses are evident, not only in children, but in many fields of activity not directly connected with infant feeding. The newborn baby is a "god" till he gets big enough to trust to his own strength and no longer needs his "divinity" to protect him; for food is also a "god." So are corpses "gods." Feces, too, are apparently food, certainly to the scavenger dogs, and child training in bowel habits seems largely concerned in seeing that the feces should not be eaten. The number of times the Balinese change their minds about burying or not burying a corpse and the barbecue picnic atmosphere of the funeral suggests that they are in conflict as to whether to eat the corpse or not. . . Viewing the range of cannibal impulses in Bali, regardless of their accessibility to consciousness, it is not strange that the mouth should be "attacked" so early and that the

eating of solid food should be made painful and shameful. In cramming food into the spluttering mouths of tiny babies, the mothers appear to be vicariously attacking their own cannibal impulses [p. 384].

Lewin further relates to cannibalism the Balinese conception of the body as a tube, which he regards as a version of the body-phallus equation (147), and which latter he considers to be an oral fantasy, as well as the idea of the body as constituted of separate parts each having an independent life, which we described as part of the Balinese body image. He refers to Malcove's interpretation (162) of the dismemberment fantasy of drug deliria (36)—that the dismemberment is a reminiscence of food being cut up.

Weaning among the Balinese does not take place before at least eighteen months and even afterward "the child is permitted to steal back for an occasional sip" (p. 33). The teasing which was earlier noted as a cardinal feature of child-rearing is manifested by the mother's borrowing someone's baby "with which to tease her own, by setting the stranger, younger baby over the head of her own [higher status], or giving it the breast" (p. 32). "The intensity of the drama," say Bateson and Mead, "is centered about the mother's breast, and a Balinese baby habitually nurses at one breast and grasps firmly at the other nipple, especially when there are other children about . . ." (p. 33).

The evidence appears to abound, then, that both oral sucking and biting modes are heavily emphasized and are both stimulated and inhibited in the Balinese. We believe that trance, which is in part based on unconscious fantasies of oral incorporation,[14] is a social institution through which these accentuated oral sucking and biting modes are given sanctioned expression. We do not mean, of course, that trance is the only institution through which these modes are expressed, but that it is an important one among others, such as, for example, the burial customs.

14 See p. 86 ff.

Oral sucking and biting include of course both libidinal and aggressive impulses. Though Bateson and Mead emphasize both kinds of impulses on the pregenital level, they have little or nothing to say about the genital conflicts.[15] For example, in their interpretation of the witch play they emphasize heavily the acting out of aggression against the mother and portray the Balinese father as a friendly puppy personality. Lewin points out that nowhere do they seem to find evidence of the positive oedipus complex, defined as hostility for the father and a sexual drive for the mother, in a Balinese boy. Lewin argues, however, that the fight between witch and dragon is a representation of the primal scene. He reminds us that the Balinese child remains close to his mother for a long time and even remains in the same bed while she delivers, though, as we have mentioned, Bateson and Mead say "small children never witness childbirth, not because they are driven away but because they sleep through it" (p. 191).

It is probable then, says Lewin, that the child is present during intercourse, pretends to be asleep, and that this is the sleep feigned in the witch dance. It is worth noting that the followers of the dragon in the dance turn their daggers "against a spot which is said to itch unbearably" (p. 35). This may well represent sexual excitement evoked by witnessing the primal scene.[16] Lewin further points out that the usual method of sending the children in the *sangiang* dance into trance, which is to communicate to them through a string the rhythm of a stick which a man pounds up and down against a bowl, suggests that the ensuing trance is "an equivalent of infantile masturbation, and repetitive of the erotic sleep during the primal scene" (p. 385). He concludes his explanation of the Balinese trance thus: "We seem to have a 'conversion symptom,' 'neurotic' sleep, which is a 'genital' manifestation

[15] Eissler likewise speaks of the Balinese culture as "pregenital."

[16] The relation between itching and sexuality is obvious. Mead tells us in a personal communication that Erik Erikson suggested to her that it is the *breast* against which the dagger is turned because the child suffered its major trauma at the breast.

of the oedipus complex, a reminiscence of the primal scene"
(p. 385).[17]

Plausible though these constructions by Lewin may be, it
must be emphasized that since they are based on a theory of
universal human impulses, such constructions in individual
terms can only partially explain specific manifestations in
Balinese culture. A more complete explanation would require
a psychosocial frame of reference as well. Even in terms of
individual psychodynamics the constructions are incomplete
because they stress instinctual so much more than defensive
and adaptive considerations. In our theory of hypnosis we
have attempted to include all three aspects.

We may summarize by saying that the trance is a social
modality providing for the expression not only of oral sucking
and biting modes but phallic ones as well.

We turn now to an examination of the Balinese culture
and trance in terms of the concepts of automatization and
de-automatization and of autonomy from id and environment, which we introduced in the discussion of hypnosis.

We have described induction as coming about through the
combined effect in varying proportions of transference influence and de-automatization. How does the Balinese body
image which we have described influence this proportion? In
essence we have argued that the ease of trance induction in
the Balinese is related to the fact that their primary autonomous and attention apparatuses already possess a relative
autonomy from ordinary ego-functioning and hence can
readily be "recruited" into a subsystem. We would therefore
expect that the induction of trance in Bali would require

[17] Róheim quotes Lewin's explanation with approval (196, pp. 27-28).
Bateson informs us that Lewin has gathered several mistaken impressions
from the Bateson and Mead book. The fight between witch and dragon does
not continue after the young men go into trance, as Lewin says. Furthermore,
neither witch nor dragon is on the stage during the "attack on the self."
The man does not pound the stick up and down but, while holding the stick,
develops clonic contractions in his arm which are counterpoised against the
dancing of weighted dolls on the string. None of these corrections, we believe, invalidates Lewin's points.

less emphasis on de-automatization and more on transference influence. Actually, the induction of the three types of trance described in Bali in the Bateson and Mead book differ. In the trance of the witch dance the witch apparently induces the trance and de-automatization is not prominent; in the trance induced in the *sangiang* dancers by their holding on to the moving stick, de-automatization apparently does play a prominent role; while in such trances as the village seer's and the witch herself going into trance, some kind of self-induction appears to play the main role in the process.

The Balinese people, as generally described, seem to have a relatively restricted autonomy from the environment. Jane Belo (15) says: "I believe the Balinese exemplify by their behavior how closely the individual may be required to conform to patterns laid down by the social group, with what rhythmic and unrestrained ease he may, under such laws, accomplish the tasks exacted of him, and in what apparent contentment he may exist when no problem is without an answer in his scheme of things."

Again, since we describe the established state of hypnosis as one of diminished autonomy from the environment, we would expect that such a state could more easily be brought about in the Balinese. Indeed in the *sangiang* dancers who respond automatically to the commands of the accompanying songs, we do have a situation similar to the established state. Bateson and Mead remark further that in certain trance dances the young men dancing in trance execute various grotesque and obscene orders given them by the singers (p. 92). It is also noteworthy that the trances both of the *sangiang* dancers and of the dancers in the witch play must be terminated from without. The trance during the witch play, however, seems to be one which after induction is directed from within rather than from without, and in this sense it may be more closely allied to domination by the id after the ego has lost autonomy, to the induction phase of hypnosis and to the first phase of fugue. In this connection we may note that Belo (15) states that running amok in Bali is preceded by a period in which a man works himself up into a trancelike state.

We may ask whether trance in different cultures may vary in whether it represents chiefly domination by the id or by the environment after autonomy has been lost. In our culture, in which autonomy from the environment is fairly well maintained, trance may result in domination by the environment after the loss of autonomy, while in the Balinese culture in which autonomy from the id is fairly well maintained (as compared with autonomy from the environment), trance may result in domination by the id after autonomy has been lost. But it seems clear that such distinctions can be made only as broad generalizations. Trance in our culture may result in domination by the id as well as by the environment after autonomy has been lost, though, as we have indicated earlier, the former begins to shade into fugue, while in Bali trance may also, as in the *sangiang* dancers, be characterized by domination by the environment.

Inevitably, of course, one wonders how it came to be that the Balinese foster the particular zones, modes, and modalities which they do. Erikson has well demonstrated for the Sioux and Yurok (56) that their choice of zone, mode, and modality to foster arises from some basic relationship to the source of food. The importance of food in Balinese culture makes one suspect that the same is true, but either the original relationships have become obscured, or else they could be discerned only by someone well acquainted with the culture.

To summarize our major propositions: (a) trance in Bali is a variety of hypnosis; (b) the Balinese susceptibility to trance is an integral aspect of the kind of personality and body image fostered by Balinese culture; and (c) this kind of personality and body image in the Balinese presents in exaggerated form the kind of personality structure and body-image changes characteristic of the hypnotizable person in our own culture.

*Part III*

Part III

CHAPTER

# *11*

## EXPLORATIONS OF THE USE OF HYPNOSIS IN PSYCHOTHERAPY

### *General Considerations*

At the outset our investigation of hypnosis, begun during the war years, had as its primary focus the study of practical ways and means of using hypnosis in psychotherapy. Although our first reported highly dramatic and successful case was a female civilian (101), we made a continuous effort to transfer the principles of treatment as we saw them to patients in veterans' hospitals. In short, the prevailing exigencies at the beginning of our study were such as to encourage if not to dictate a highly empirical approach, with the implied hope, which so often flares up anew in the face of war casualties, that there might be found a way to shorten the psychotherapeutic process without rendering it utterly superficial. It is apparent from the organization of this volume that as our work proceeded, our primary focus shifted from these immediately practical concerns to problems more theoretical in nature, still using the psychotherapeutic relationship as our major source of data. Nonetheless, despite this shift in priorities of interest, we continued over the years to gather data on the use of hypnosis in various forms of psychotherapy with the aims both of evaluating the practical use of this auxiliary technique in treatment, and of understanding how it influences the therapeutic relationship. It was the pursuit of the latter aim which made it clear to us that we were at a disadvantage unless we first set up a serious study of the

321

psychotherapeutic process, in general—uncomplicated by the addition of hypnosis. Inasmuch as we had, however, contracted to pursue the study of hypnosis and not of psychotherapy, it was not feasible to commence a systematic study of the process of psychotherapy in this more general sense— a study which we now saw as a prerequisite to the even more ambitious task of seeing precisely how the hypnotic relationship alters that process. We include these apparently administrative details in the development of our investigation in order to indicate our awareness of the significant limitations of our explorations of the effect of hypnosis on various forms of psychotherapy. Despite the fact that the particular organizations which made our work possible were paragons of flexibility and tolerance, we did not feel we could embark on a four- to five-year parenthesis before proceeding to our "research proper." Accordingly, we regard the material included in this section as essentially on the level of "naturalist-clinician" observation (142). In retrospect it seems clear that we became so aware of the immense complexities of studying the psychotherapeutic process, particularly when additionally burdened by hypnosis, that we had to content ourselves with a broad survey on this level.

Even in this relatively free context, we were from the beginning keenly aware of the difficulties of evaluating our clinical data. Let us consider the most important of the problems and our (admittedly) small attempts to advance our techniques beyond that of the simple case report.

First, and of prime importance, there was the problem of finding a base line against which to measure the relative brevity (or indeed the nature) of the technique under investigation. The only procedure for comparison which seemed to us to provide a sufficiently explored and fairly standard situation was that of psychoanalysis. We were fortunate in having access to four veteran clinicians[1] who served as con-

---

[1] These were Drs. Robert P. Knight, Karl A. Menninger, Ernst Lewy, and Jan Frank, all then on the staff of the Menninger Foundation.

sultants on our cases and who, thus, provided a rough esti-
mate for us of the similarities and differences between the
sequences of an "average" psychoanalytic process and the
therapeutic processes we were studying, using hypnosis.

Another problem central to this and to all research in psychotherapy is that of setting up "controls." Where we could,
we set up a situation where the patient was his own "control." In some instances, we alternated periods of standard
psychotherapeutic procedures with periods where hypnosis
was used. In other instances where accidental circumstance
provided us with a patient who had already undergone some
form of psychotherapy, we attempted to inquire into the differences of subjective experience. This was a less telling effort
at "control" inasmuch as the therapist was now different as
well. Clearly, our attempts in this direction were rough. We
mention them only to indicate our awareness of the problem.

Finally, there was the problem of gathering objective and
reasonably accurate data. At the inception of our investigation
(now almost fifteen years ago) the notion of opening the door
to objective observation of the two participants in any psychotherapeutic process was still a highly charged and controversial issue. Nonetheless, the Menninger Foundation was one
of the first institutions in this country to set up a one-way
viewing screen for observation and facilities for the electronic
recording of interviews. These facilities were organized originally in connection with our research. Thus, we had verbatim
records of most sessions, plus notes by an observer, usually
one of us.[2]

Despite the fact that we were not in a position to set up a
systematic study of psychotherapy, our pursuit of the therapeutic use of hypnosis brought us willy-nilly face to face with
some of the major issues which we now presume may be
central to any and all psychotherapeutic relationships. It is

[2] Before this laboratory was set up, we frequently sat in on each other's
cases. Clearly, this procedure introduced yet another complication into the
situation.

our impression that while the introduction of hypnosis into the treatment complicated matters, it so caricatured certain aspects of the psychotherapeutic process as to bring into a sharp focus some of the problems. From these observations, we have developed a very general hypothesis which will require close follow-up in a careful, long-term study of the psychotherapeutic process; its particulars will become clearer in the course of this discussion and in the detailed presentation of individual cases.

The single broadest and most important hypothesis which has emerged is this: *in all psychotherapeutic relationships, there begins to develop in the patient almost at once some form of regression which includes far more than the well-known regression of transference phenomena*; it may be more or it may be less overt, more or less conscious, more or less involving of the whole personality. For the reader who has come directly to this section on clinical explorations and who has not yet read our theoretical chapters, we must repeat that by "regression" we do not mean that the patient is transported back to a specific earlier age as in a "hypnotic regression." We mean rather a state marked by a return *in some measure* to an earlier, more primitive—actually more archaic—mode of personality functioning. By saying that this regression includes *more* than transference phenomena we mean the following: regard for external reality is lessened, tolerance for delay between impulse and action is less, defenses are more primitive, feelings more intense, thinking is closer to the primary process (the prototype for which is the nature of psychic functioning in dreams), and finally, the transference as we usually think of it rests on something still more archaic, something akin to what Greenacre has called "basic transference" (108, p. 672).

In the hypnotic relationship these regressive tendencies are simply more extreme. They are usable therapeutically in some contexts, not in others.[3] When we say "psychotherapeutic contexts," we do not mean specific psychiatric syndromes. The widespread practice of listing specific applications of hypnosis to specific disease entities is, we think, a mistake. Our work has not confirmed the idea that "hypnotherapy" is useful in particular diagnostic categories and not in others. The usefulness of hypnosis as an adjuvant in *any* psychotherapy follows a set of rules (as yet unclear) which appears to be quite independent of our nosology as it now stands. Moreover, the fact that the hypnotic relationship may be used so variably in psychotherapy has led us to the conclusion that perhaps the very term "hypnotherapy" should be discarded; we say this despite the fact that we used it as a title for a previous volume. It is in fact a highly misleading expression; it implies that there is something quite specific in the use of hypnosis in therapy. It accents the hypnosis itself rather than the fact that hypnosis may be used to strengthen or underscore some aspect of an ongoing psychotherapeutic process.[4] The essence of what is happening lies in the psychotherapeutic relationship, not in the hypnotic relationship; this fact is often lost sight of in discussions of "hypnotherapy." The insistence on maintaining a separate term seems to us increasingly a matter of professional specialization politics rather than any necessary language reflection of an actual phenomenon. The danger in such specialization lies in the potentiality of further divorcing the use of hypnosis from the complex and delicate considerations which go into the immediate decisions

[3] It should be emphasized that the patient may respond to these "regressive tendencies" with a stiffening of his unconscious defenses so that he becomes essentially untreatable, or he may be unable to maintain his normal ego-functioning sufficiently that the regression remains "in the service of the ego." In the latter case we encounter a therapeutic "catastrophe," and the patient is plunged into a psychosis, a happening which is not rare in the therapy of borderline cases, whether the treatment involves hypnosis or not.

[4] Although Wolberg has on occasion discussed the use of hypnosis in various diagnostic categories, his primary emphasis is the same as ours here (230).

any responsible psychotherapist automatically makes within a given session.

Before we turn to a summing up of the various ways in which we have explored the therapeutic applications of hypnosis, we feel it necessary to make a brief excursion into the background of the hypothesis that some regression occurs in all psychotherapy: in our earlier discussion of the nature of the hypnotic state, we emphasized as one aspect of the regressive process *the heightened emotional level* so frequently found in hypnosis. This fact of emotional intensification seems to us of particular importance in any therapeutic relationship. Indeed, the history of psychotherapy abounds in discussions, if not polemics, on just how important (or not) is the fact of emotional experiencing in therapy, as against progressive intellectual understanding of the pathogenic conflicts.[5] Whereas almost all contemporary writers on this subject would probably agree that both "feeling" and "understanding" are important in psychotherapy, there is little question that history reveals a steadily shifting emphasis from the extreme of making emotional participation the solely important factor to the other extreme of giving "insight" the entire weight. The early work, for example, of Breuer and Freud held as its focal theory of cure the notion that simple affective discharge or expression was the crucial factor; hypnotic abreaction was no more nor less than the revival of intense feeling, usually associated with some real traumatic event. Presumably, the expression of such feeling issued in a kind of emotional purge for the patient. As psychoanalysis gradually developed, especially in the early years, there was a progressive turning away from the attempt to elicit such outbursts, "insight" became the leading concept, and the atmosphere of the therapeutic interview grew somewhat didactic. Unquestionably, even at this time a good therapist did not

---

[5] The famous Fenichel-Kaiser controversy is a good example of this (62, 125).

allow his clinical work to become empty by draining it of all feeling. Nonetheless, the public theoretical statements regarding psychoanalysis as a treatment were now a far cry from the original idea of experiencing deep feeling.

It seems now quite clear that some of the splinter groups which came into being during the course of the development of psychoanalysis arose at least in part as an effort to restore the emphasis to strong emotion as a vital part of all psychotherapy. Rank, for instance, to whom Alexander frankly acknowledges a debt, tried to see the entire therapeutic process as a re-enactment of the shocking experience of birth, with separation anxiety accordingly being at the center of the relationship to the therapist. Ferenczi, an even more obvious forebear of the idea of "the corrective emotional experience," attempted more broadly, and with less polemical interest in theory, to intensify the emotional level of his analyses in a variety of ways: he reports a generally active, emotionally lively participation with his patients, sometimes even acting out a role ascribed by the patient to him. It is of considerable theoretical interest that on those occasions when he felt he had succeeded in bringing about a marked heightening of the emotional level, phenomena appeared which are in many ways identical with hypnotic abreaction. He gives the following illustration:

> For example, a patient in the prime of life resolved, after overcoming strong resistances, and especially his profound mistrust, to revive in his mind incidents from his earliest childhood. Thanks to the light already thrown by analysis on his early life, I was aware that in the scene revived by him, he was identifying me with his grandfather. Suddenly, in the midst of what he was saying, he threw his arm round my neck and whispered in my ear: "I say, Grandpapa, I am afraid I am going to have a baby!" Thereupon I had what seems to me a happy inspiration: I said nothing to him for the moment about transference, etc., but retorted, in a similar whisper: "Well, but why do you think so?" [66, p. 471].

Such outbursts are a commonplace to the clinician who has used hypnosis: we have reported earlier in this volume the high frequency of intense feeling in both our group and individual sessions with veterans and civilian patients, some reporting grief over losses of friends in combat; others, vivid images of a variety of scenes of anguish—the funeral of a mother or the death of a child. We find it easy to believe that the reports of intense emotional "crises" around Mesmer's *baquet* were not exaggerated. We have concluded that this greatly heightened access to strong feeling is one of the most important aspects of the regressive process which is brought into being by the hypnotic relationship. One of us has described in detail the case of a man who the first time hypnosis was induced spontaneously commenced to relive with vivid and painful affect a crime which he had committed fifteen years before and which he was now confessing for the first time (100). We have tried to set forth in our theoretical chapter (Chapter 5) the ways in which we feel we can relate such occurrences to a general psychoanalytic theory of regression. In this discussion, however, which deals essentially with the clinical implications of this theory, we are setting forth the broad hypothesis *that every psychotherapeutic situation is to some extent an invitation to the patient to regress; that such regression usually takes place in greater or lesser amounts in all psychotherapies where the patient is reached at all; and that when hypnosis is used in psychotherapy we can observe this phenomenon more closely because it is greatly intensified.* We would go so far as to venture the speculation that it is precisely in this regression, and the way it is dealt with by the therapist—with or without the use of hypnosis—that the secret lies of maintaining an optimal affective involvement for the patient in the therapeutic process. A testing of this speculation will require a long-range investigation of the nature of psychotherapy.

Perhaps it is because the ordinary psychoanalytic setup is so recent a descendant of early hypnotic techniques that we see rather clearly in it certain important features which invite regression in the sense in which we have been using it. Macalpine (161) and Thompson (219) have commented that the analytic couch is a remnant of Freud's hypnotic era. It is our impression that this is true, not, however, in the sense of maintaining a useless piece of vestigial apparatus, but rather as an intuitive maintenance of a physical situation which does not entirely sacrifice the "props" for regression which had been so useful when Freud used hypnosis.[6]

Consider a situation in which one human being lies down supine in broad daylight in the presence of another human being who sits behind him; a situation, moreover, where reality cues and checks from the analyst are deliberately kept to a minimum, as are responses to direct questions; a situation where a person is encouraged to allow his ordinary ego-integrative and defensive processes to retreat into the background in order that he may express his every thought and feeling—including his deepest needs which for the most part must, in this situation, remain ungratified. This is surely a situation which invites some degree of regression.[7] That this invitation is often flatly rejected (particularly by compulsive and obsessional patients) cannot be doubted; it seems to us equally unquestionable that when it is accepted, we have the double-edged potentiality on the one hand for triggering a decompensation if the regressive tendencies are too strong for the ego, and on the other for effecting an emotionally meaningful reconstitution, precisely because of the regression. The clinical evidence for this is still scattered and fragmentary—made up of episodes from analyses conducted by us and by others unconnected with our research. It includes reports of body-image changes, outbursts of intense feeling, symbolic or pictorial thought and so on, reports similar in many ways

[6] All of this is aside from Freud's confession of his dislike of being stared at.

[7] There can be little doubt that Macalpine is correct in her assumption that the analytic situation is on the same continuum as the induction of hypnosis (see pp. 112-113 and p. 152).

to the data from our hypnosis research. Obviously, the existing body of literature describing transference phenomena must also be considered in this connection. A typical example from our own experience in an ordinary analysis:

"When I lie down here on the couch, something happens to me. I become weaker, more helpless. I feel younger and smaller. It's almost as if I were in my bed and you were sitting there." The patient now goes on to associations about playing sick as a child so that his mother would sit by his bed and feed him favorite dishes.

Another example taken from notes on a psychoanalytic case:[8]

The patient is talking generally about the issue of "losing control" and the fact that at certain times she finds that she gets terribly drunk on two drinks. The fact that this loss of control is unpredictable disturbs her. As the hour ends, she remarks, "I am feeling a little uncomfortable here . . . the room is getting awfully dark." The next day she says that she had felt "weird" at the end of the last hour, adding "I guess it was some sort of hysterical attack . . . I had the feeling I was slipping into another state of consciousness. It felt as if the head and foot of the couch were higher than the middle and that the couch was moving around and around." She recalls having had a similar sensation shortly after the birth of her first child. On both occasions she intuitively knew that she had to focus on something else [we would say: seek external stimulation and orienting cues] and immediately did so. This dispelled what would have turned into a "frightening experience."

Bartemeier (8), in discussing one of our early papers on the regressive alteration of ego function in hypnosis, cited instances of such occurrences during the course of psychoanalysis and remarked that these happenings had usually been dismissed by most analysts he knew as "transient hysterical manifestations" and pursued no further. It is our supposition

[8] We are indebted to Dr. Helen Gilmore for this material.

that although such clear phenomena are by no means the rule in the average psychoanalytic hour, their occasional dramatic emergence can better be conceptualized as representing a regressive change in ego function than as an erupting of hysterical symptoms.

On the basis of such anecdotal material, one can do little more than begin to formulate hypotheses which link the vast body of psychotherapeutic experience with the rather specialized data we have gathered in the course of our investigations of hypnosis. The actual demonstration of such links is a task that remains.

For the present, we will content ourselves with an account of a variety of clinical explorations we have made, using hypnosis. It will be seen that in some contexts what we have called the "regressive trends" inherent in hypnosis are psychotherapeutically serviceable; in others they are useless if not dangerous.

## Clinical Applications

In our review of the literature in 1947 (25) we listed six possible ways of using the hypnotic relationship in psychotherapy, noting at that time the necessity for a systematic exploration of these. The six uses of hypnosis we listed then were the following: (1) Prolonged hypnosis *without* either direct suggestion regarding symptom disappearance, or exploration of the problem—a kind of continuous sleep akin to extended narcosis or *Dauerschlaf*. (2) Direct suggestion of symptom disappearance: this, the oldest and most widely used technique, formed the bulk of the therapeutic reports on hypnosis during its heyday, with reported successes ranging from the removal of warts to the cure of schizophrenia. (3) Direct suggestion of the disappearance of "attitudes" underlying symptoms: in our survey we noted that originally this approach marked a historical compromise between the "emotional" appeal of hypnosis and the "rational" appeal of a naïve, common-sense psychotherapy which was flowering around the turn of the century, strikingly at about the same time that Freud was abandoning the technique of hypnotic abreaction for the more "rational" pursuit of insight. (4) The abreaction of traumatic experiences: this technique, highly dramatic when successful, has been variously credited to Janet and to Freud's famous collaborator Breuer. Its rationale, discussed in detail by Freud in his autobiography, is summed up by him as follows: "When the patient recalled a situation of this kind in a hallucinatory way under hypnosis and carried through to its conclusion, with a free expression of emotion, the mental act which she had originally suppressed, the symptom was abolished and did not return" (92, p. 35). It is noteworthy that no mention is made of the possible importance of such a reliving taking place *in the presence of the therapist*. We will return to this problem in our summary of our own experiences with this technique. (5) The use of specialized hypnotic techniques: we have previously summarized the long list of differentiated hypnotic techniques, many of them highly inventive, which have attempted to exploit the therapeutic potentialities of hypnosis; e.g., suggestion of dreams, implantation of a temporary conflict, "regression" to an earlier age, automatic writing, etc. (25, p. 75). Aside from their usefulness in certain kinds of therapeutic problems, the phenomena resulting from these specialized techniques constitute one of the richest sources we have for studying extremes of the regressive process. Archaic modes of thought are regularly called into being by most of these techniques: hallucinatory visualization, symbolic communication, revivals (at least in some measure) of ancient ego positions, as in the production of "hypnotic regressions." (6) Hypnoanalysis: we have reserved this variously used term for those approaches which combine in a variety of possible ways the techniques of hypnosis with those of psychoanalysis. In our earlier survey we commented that this method "holds the greatest promise for a shortened method of psychotherapy which, nevertheless, retains the crucially important factor of insight . . ." (25, p. 86).

Whereas it had been our original hope to explore systematically all six of these approaches, it soon became clear that so ambitious an undertaking was not possible. We decided then to concentrate our efforts on those techniques from which we could potentially learn most, regardless of the therapeutic yield. Thus, although we did include, particularly in the early phases of our work, some exploration of direct suggestion and abreaction—which we will summarize briefly—the bulk of our clinical exploration was in the use of specialized hypnotic techniques and hypnoanalysis.

Before proceeding to the account of our experiences with these various approaches, we must state one general observation regarding the therapeutic application of hypnosis which holds for all of them: *there is no correlation between the depth of hypnosis obtainable in a patient and the therapeutic result*. This observation confirms unequivocally the early work of Schilder (208). He had noticed that in some cases where the hypnosis was relatively "light" when judged by standard criteria, there were nevertheless evidences of a deep emotional participation, whereas in others where a "deep" hypnosis was producible, there seemed to exist little or no concurrent emotional involvement in the procedure. We have been unable to discover exactly what it is that makes for this "involvement" or its absence. It does seem quite clear, however, with some important exceptions to be discussed later, that it *is* the degree of such involvement and not the depth of hypnosis as such which makes for therapeutic efficacy.

For example, we worked with a fifty-four-year-old depressed woman and found her to be an excellent subject in that all the usual hypnotic responses were to be elicited from her with very little difficulty. If told while in hypnosis to hallucinate, she promptly did so; if pricked deeply with a sterilized hatpin after complete anesthesia and analgesia had been suggested, she bled without any evidence of an experience of pain, and on being questioned reported that she had felt nothing. At first, encouraged by her extreme responsiveness, we attempted to treat her depression and insomnia symptomatically by direct suggestion, but her symptoms remained unchanged. When another therapeutic effort was made, this time an attempt to explore the meaning of her illness, we were again met by the same phenomenon. She would produce richly detailed childhood memories when instructed to do so, would hallucinate long-past episodes, produce dreams: all with complete detachment. It was possible, thus, to produce a classically profound hypnosis in this patient according to the usual criteria, but she actually remained aloof from the entire experience and left the hospital in no way changed.

In striking contrast to this case stands the account of a twenty-eight-year-old soldier, discharged from the army in a state of depression and anxiety, both of which were sufficiently intense to make hospitalization necessary. When we were studying his hypnotizability, we labeled him a "poor subject" because his responses to even the mildest of suggestions in hypnosis were uniformly feeble. When told in hypnosis that, e.g., he could *not* raise his arm, he promptly did so; when instructed to have posthypnotic amnesia, he was able to recall all that had transpired. When we were on the point of concluding that, according to our standard criteria, he was a poor subject for our research on the use of hypnosis in therapy, events took a surprising turn. He came in one morning intent on telling a dream he had had the night before. After listening to his account of the dream given in the normal state, the therapist gave him the usual signal to go into hypnosis but did not attempt now to test the depth of hypnosis. The patient was simply told to relive the dream and to carry on now where it had been interrupted the night before.

In the dream he walked up a mountain path which led to a cave. He had wanted to see what was in the cave but the dream had ended. Now, in hypnosis, he was able to continue with the dream. He described a figure (which he alternately felt was "a witch" and "my mother") as though he were watching a movie. Gradually his breathing became labored and his face contorted; it was evident that he was experiencing intense feeling. He began to plead with the dream-figure, imploring her, "Tell me something—anything—is that you, Mom? —Tell me whether it's you. Just say yes or no or something. When did I ever start being afraid?" As he went on, his voice rose and in marked contrast to his usual diffidence, he clenched his fists and began to accuse his mother, who had in fact always dominated him, of having done something to him long ago to scare him; he shouted that he wasn't afraid of anything now and that he could "lick the world . . . let the chips fall where they may."

Directly following this session, the patient's symptomatic improvement was obvious to everyone who knew him. During the remainder of his stay in the hospital he was seen in waking psychotherapeutic interviews about ten times. After he had gone back to work, he came in for a few follow-up sessions and on one occasion he was asked once more to relive his dream in hypnosis. His response was startling. This time he identified the woman in the case as unquestionably his mother and climbed on her lap, seeing himself in a velvet suit and feeling young and small; then he climbed off and tried to walk away, feeling like a "grown man." He oscillated between these two roles for a while and finally decided that at last "the spell was broken" and he could leave the cave and his mother forever and assume his adult responsibilities. He reported after another six-month interval that he had never felt so completely at ease in his life. In this instance, the hypnotic relationship seemed to serve as a springboard for the partial release of apparently central conflicts in spite of the fact that this man was classified as a "poor subject" according to standard criteria. This case stands in sharp contrast to the preceding one where all of the classical signs of a "deep hypnosis" were present but where significant emotional involvement was absent.

The practical implications of this as yet little understood happening seem to us important. Frequently the literature reports of successful therapeutic ventures using hypnosis take it for granted that the patient is a good hypnotic subject. Perhaps most clinicians make the same error we initially made: they conclude that they will abandon hope of catalyzing a therapeutic process by hypnosis if their "hypnotizability interviews" reveal that a profound hypnosis by standard criteria cannot be brought about.

We have observed on occasion that the mere *attempt* to hypnotize constitutes sufficient invitation to regression (regression now in the general sense, not a hypnotic regression) for some people to permit strikingly freer access to normally hidden feeling. Our records have numerous instances where we could not say for certain that even a slight degree of hypnosis was obtainable, but where the patient's outburst of feeling during the hypnotizability interview appeared to have a quality that was quite different from anything that had gone before. We have wondered also whether the camouflage provided by the hypnotizability-interview situation is perhaps as important for the therapist as for the patient. It is quite clear that most therapists for whom we have records show a greater emotional boldness and spontaneity in their "hypnosis personalities" than otherwise. It may well be that this greater boldness—akin to Ferenczi's "active techniques"—taken together with the tacit agreement that the patient is not quite "responsible" for what he does or feels in a hypnotizability interview, accounts for those sudden and surprising upsurges of feeling in some patients who are actually not good hypnotic subjects.

It is interesting to notice on the other hand that some patients who are offered this same invitation to regression will respond by beating a defensive rapid retreat: they become far *less* communicative and *less* spontaneous than in the ordinary normal-state interview, even though they show some degree of hypnotic responsiveness by standard criteria. In two of our recorded cases, this phenomenon appeared in the extreme. One was an articulate, voluble young woman with a severe character disorder; during the initial period of history-taking she appeared quite labile emotionally and even at times inappropriately lacking in reserve; during her hypnotizability interview, she showed only fair hypnotic responses but sufficient for us to pursue our attempts; however, she was literally silent most of the time, and otherwise so blocked during the hypnotic sessions that all attempts to hypnotize her were soon abandoned. The other was a psychopathic adolescent boy who was an excellent hypnotic subject by all standard criteria. In normal-state interviews, he was somewhat accessible and rather smoothly verbal. During the hypnotic interviews, he too was almost entirely silent.[9] In both of these cases, we did not feel an absence of emotional involvement as we did in our middle-aged depressed patient. We felt rather the sudden erection of a strong defensive barrier against the sensed potential threat of the "regressive pull," the essential point here being that this threat is inherent in the hypnotic situation, regardless of the actual depth of the hypnosis.

An extreme example of the attempt to stave off the threat of being in hypnosis occurred in a young woman, a drug addict: she had been capable of producing only a very light hypnosis in the first place, and gradually began to feign deeper hypnosis. When this became clear to the therapist, the patient

[9] During the initial induction session, when motor paralyses were successfully suggested, this patient said, "If I can't move soon, I'll die." This low tolerance for the sense of helplessness in the temporary abdication of the control of motility (and probably control in general) must be related to the freezing which this boy evidenced in the subsequent hypnotic sessions. The vexing problem here is why then he would permit himself to go into hypnosis in the first place. We can only speculate that the regressive process appeared to this boy attractive only in some of its aspects, but that it soon appeared to be too threatening to him. One of the differences between him and those patients who cannot be hypnotized at all, a difference we do not understand, is in the lag between the initial good response and the mobilization of his defenses.

was directly asked why she was pretending to be in such a deep hypnosis. She replied that she wanted to please the therapist but that she intensely disliked being hypnotized because "it always makes me want to break down and cry, and that makes me feel terribly silly." If she pretended to be in a deep hypnosis, the therapist might not try to push her further and she could then remain safe.

We cannot say with any precision what it is that allows some patients to catalyze a productive emotional engagement with the therapist by way of the hypnotic relationship, whereas others are untouched by it or driven into rigidly defended positions. Certainly we can say broadly that those who can allow a "regression in the service of the ego" to take place show in other ways a certain preservation of, and resilience in, their general ego-functioning. Our best research cases—in terms of therapeutic success—were undoubtedly those whose egos to begin with showed a relative intactness. This statement, however, might safely be made also about any therapeutic success, without the adjuvant use of hypnosis.

The data in the following summary have been selected from the case reports of sixty-three patients: thirty-eight of these were treated by one or the other of us, twenty more by psychiatric residents under our supervision, and an additional five by Dr. Frederick J. Hacker in his private practice. These sixty-three cases ranged from mild hysterias of recent onset to chronic schizophrenia. The treatment methods had an equally wide range: from the simple and traditional use of hypnosis (the direct suggestion that symptoms will disappear) to complex combinations of psychoanalytic and hypnotic techniques. We will present four samples of material drawn largely from the transcribed accounts of our investigations. It is our hope that these four approaches will illustrate the widely differing ways in which the regressive process inherent in hypnosis can be used in therapy. Where the details of a given case have already been published by us, we refer to it very briefly. In other instances, we have tried to give a fuller account.

## DIRECT SUGGESTION

For the most part our limited explorations of this use of hypnosis have been restricted to what we called in an earlier paper "the magic gesture" (31). By this we mean the therapist's effort to influence a symptom rapidly by direct suggestion, without any attempt to analyze, or to discuss meanings. To be sure, direct suggestion in hypnosis is ordinarily carried out in this way. We refer now, however, to the use of direct suggestion very early in the treatment with the aim of clearing away a symptom which seems to make long-term therapy or even immediate communication impossible or impracticable; mutism, for example, or compulsive hopping militate against the quiet pursuit of expressive psychotherapy. We have had fairly good success with this use of hypnosis, and feel that at least in one instance (31) the "magic gesture" of hypnosis was a lifesaving leverage for a youngster determined to starve herself to death. In another instance, we used direct suggestion during the initial phase of treatment to relieve a severe insomnia and a bizarre set of motor symptoms (29) before entering upon the exploratory phase of the treatment, when we used hypnosis in the service of gaining insight. In disabling paralyses and severe speech disturbances, also, we have seen the initial "magic gesture" turn a bed-ridden or otherwise inaccessible patient into an ambulatory case where we have then used ordinary methods of psychotherapy. We have wondered whether a therapy which is initiated in this way is not then throughout in some way a different process from a therapy which has not included so archaic an initial appeal. Our evidence in these cases suggests that the "magic gesture" differs only quantitatively from those moves on the part of a therapist—without hypnosis—which provide some leverage for the so-called "transference cure."[10]

We shall pass quickly over the time-honored use of direct suggestion to remove symptoms. Our experience with this technique since our last published summing up of its applications (25, pp. 52-59) was largely restricted to soldiers complaining of circumscribed symptoms of recent origin, men unwilling or unable to undergo long-term expressive therapy. Our work with these men has simply confirmed our earlier view that this primitive type of psychotherapy has a real though limited value in symptom alleviation, particularly for those patients whose general life adjustment appears largely normal. Thus our records contain many examples of short periods of treatment of men in a veterans' hospital (10 to 15 hours) where by direct suggestion various psychosomatic symptoms have disappeared.

In contrast to this traditional use of direct suggestion for the circumscribed symptom, we followed early in our research a new line of inquiry which, though therapeutically unsuccessful, added a little to our understanding. In working with a severely disturbed schizophrenic girl, a girl regarded by most of the staff as hopelessly psychotic, we decided to explore the use of direct suggestion. This patient, who was, incidentally, a topnotch hypnotic subject, was becoming progressively more isolated from the other patients and from her family. Strenuous efforts to treat her by usual psychotherapeutic procedures had been made prior to those we are about to describe; these had failed completely. We include this fact only to suggest that we would not otherwise have considered *commencing* a therapy with this or any other patient in the way we are about to recount. The patient was told while in a deep hypnotic state that when she came out of hypnosis she would become interested in some other patient in the hospital; for

---

[10] We have discussed that aspect of the regressive process which is most relevant to this kind of therapeutic intervention under "The fantasy of magic power" (p. 74 ff).

several days afterward, she made active overtures to another young woman—all quite appropriate, involving invitations to bridge, walks, and the like. She seemed to enjoy these contacts and apparently had no awareness that they had been propelled by her therapist. His next direct suggestion, made in an effort to explore the limits of this kind of suggestion, was that she would become more friendly with a patient she had actively disliked. This also produced a definite result, and she began to issue similar invitations to the hitherto shunned fellow-patient. The therapist, emboldened by these "successes," now suggested that she write to her hated sister. This she did, with a fair amount of cordiality, still with no awareness that the therapist had made the suggestion. Now the therapist suggested that she write her sister to come and visit her; she wrote an appropriate and even warm invitation to which the sister eagerly responded, following her letter with the requested visit. The therapist's final suggestion—that she *feel* comfortable with her sister—failed completely; she became quite anxious and returned to her former withdrawn position.

It was difficult at the time to evaluate this episode. On the one hand, we felt this had been a naïve and tasteless therapeutic blunder, obviously bound to fail (although no one in the research group conference was sufficiently certain of this to predict it). On the other hand, there seemed then—and still seem now—both clinical and theoretical grounds on which to believe that a therapeutic turning point might be established by breaking up the rigid equilibrium of this patient in her withdrawn isolation. Indeed, until she was taxed with the unbearably heavy burden of her sister's visit, something important seemed to be shifting. Her bridge games with the other patients, though initiated by direct suggestion, did *not* have an automaton quality; her friendliness and generally improved subjective feelings extended beyond the literal suggestions given her by the therapist. It appeared almost as if she had been "set in motion," but had then continued to move by dint of her own energies.

We did not pursue this approach systematically, partly because it had felt so contrived from the outset and partly because our general research agenda left little room for this inquiry. We have included this one illustration, however, because it indicates on the one hand how a patient may obediently carry out a series of hypnotically suggested *behaviors*—and even some changes in feeling—and be unable to muster such "obedience" with regard to emotions more deeply anchored in personal history; on the other hand, it offers some hint of evidence that a therapeutic deadlock may sometimes be broken by bringing about a shift in an equilibrium which is not too rigid. This is, however, a matter for further investigation.

Before leaving this section on the use of direct suggestion, we should like to mention briefly one last variety of exploration of this approach, using a case illustration to present this variant of direct suggestion:

The patient was a forty-six-year-old successful businessman who came with the stated intention of "getting over the bad habit" of succumbing to attacks of acute anxiety which had begun nineteen years earlier but which in the three years preceding his admission had become increasingly frequent and acute. He told us the attacks were likely to occur either in a physically open situation like a golf course, or in any context where he felt confined, as in having a haircut, being in a hotel room, or often in his own car traveling. He had made one previous attempt at therapy for a period of eight months. During this, the therapist had tried to help him "understand" his problems. As he found himself getting increasingly worse, he broke off the treatment.

As he began to sketch his history, it soon became obvious that he was a man singularly lacking in psychological mindedness who had had, however, the resources to build a strong and, on the whole, quite effective system of compulsive defenses and adaptations. In spite of his phobic symptoms, he had continued to advance steadily in his firm and to maintain what he felt was a good marriage. Typical comments were, "What I need is more self-confidence. Somebody to push me into these things I am afraid of doing. If I can just do them a few times and see that nothing happens, maybe I can continue to do them." His prescription for himself was "simply getting some new habits."

The psychological tests confirmed the impression of a highly compulsive character, with no capacity for self-confrontation. They showed moreover that while he functioned remarkably well in response to specific demands, his productivity was meager when he was left on his own. There was a rigid and intense denial of dependent needs and a strong emphasis on efficiency and self-control.

Taking into account this man's nature, his recent bad experience with expressive psychotherapy, his complete incapacity to think about himself, his essentially efficient compulsive adjustment, and finally his conviction that two weeks was too long to remain in the sanitarium, the decision was made to attempt a rapid suppressive treatment of his symptoms with the aid of hypnosis. Again, the general rationale would fall under the rubric of the "fantasy of magic power," however transposed into "scientific" terms this fantasy might be.

He proved to be only a fair hypnotic subject; nevertheless, on the basis of our other experiences with light hypnoses, we proceeded as planned. He was seen for a total of ten sessions, each session commencing with a brief normal-state interview during which he would frequently restate his conviction that his illness was a "bad habit." This was not challenged by the therapist. Instead, the therapist told him that "new habits" could probably be formed in hypnosis.

During the hypnotic part of the session the therapist did almost all of the talking, elaborating and underscoring the essentially magical reassurances he had been offering in the normal state. Often the therapist couched his direct suggestions for improvement in terms of "reconditioning," an expression dear to this patient. At the same time a deliberate effort was made to support and applaud his compulsive defenses by praising his "toughness" and his reluctance to pamper himself.

Almost at once this man showed swift symptomatic improvement, making at first small and timid efforts to travel alone in his car in the face of acute anxiety. These efforts were boldly encouraged by the therapist, and after a week of treatment he drove home for a visit, a distance of over 200 miles, with no appreciable difficulty.

This case was of interest to us not only because of the striking disappearance of symptoms, but also because in spite of himself this man taught us a little of the unconscious mechanisms involved in this kind of "magic cure." He drew, for example, a strong distinction between "what goes on in my head and what goes on down here [pointing to his abdomen] and it's down here I get scared." He went on to tell the therapist, "I take in everything you say and push it down here," motioning from his mouth to his stomach. This seemed to us a good statement of the regressive incorporation of the hypnotist who is then used as an "internal ally" against his difficulties. The fact of this patient's psychological naïveté made this primitive formulation all the more persuasive.

To be sure, all therapists have had the experience without hypnosis of such rapid symptomatic improvement, particularly of circumscribed symptoms.[11] We have reported this case where hypnosis was used only to suggest that in some instances, particularly when a preliminary "mapping" of the existing equilibrium has shown the inadvisability of using expressive techniques of psychotherapy, direct suggestion in hypnosis seems to catalyze that aspect of the regressive process in hypnosis which allows for a greater freedom of the use of "magic."

[11] See Reider on brief psychotherapy (194).

Abreaction of Traumatic Experiences

Our investigations of this technique with hospitalized veterans have been fairly extensive, and have served by and large to confirm the highly optimistic conclusions of earlier workers (37, 38, 112) who reported high precentages of success *with that peculiar group of psychological disturbances which appear to issue directly from a recent traumatic combat experience.* We will omit detailed case presentations of our explorations of this approach inasmuch as excellent examples of it have frequently been given both in the older literature (33, 37, 38, 112) and in Wolberg's volume on hypnoanalysis (229). Our applications and findings differ in no significant way from the work reported by Wolberg and others.

Our efforts to employ this approach with nonveterans showed us very quickly that this technique is inappropriate for most contemporary civilian neuroses.[12] Our experience suggests that it would now be impossible to duplicate on any large scale the kinds of data supplied for example by Janet, Prince, Breuer, or Freud from their work with hysterics, except possibly with patients of a class and level of sophistication different from that of our patient population. The standard assumption to explain the difficulty in duplicating the earlier work has been that there has been an important cultural change in the "style" of neuroses, and that the "good old-fashioned hysteric" is rapidly disappearing from the psychiatric scene. While this is undoubtedly true, we must add to this idea our conviction indicated earlier in this section that the "Anna O's" of Breuer's early explorations would look very different to us now, and that we would be grossly dissatisfied with the approach to the problem and with the primitive formulations which at the time were scientific

[12] It should be noted that whereas our work with soldiers covered a wide range of socioeconomic backgrounds, our contact with civilian patients was restricted for the most part to the middle and upper classes.

milestones.[13] In short, the "abreaction" technique, while empirically effective, with limitations, for the relief of circumscribed symptoms, is in a sense an anachronism, reflecting a period in the history of psychopathology during which the search for the specific traumatic memory was the leading, and indeed at that time revolutionary, preoccupation of the therapist. It arose from a then necessarily simple theory of the mechanism of cure. The idea, for example, that the release of the strangulated affect attached to a specific repressed traumatic memory is in itself the critical process,[14] seems to us to omit, as we noted earlier,[15] the heart of the matter: namely, the fact that such release takes place in the presence of the therapist. It has been shown that when, by accident, even in the combat neuroses a traumatic memory *is* brought to awareness with its accompanying emotion—as in emergency surgery under pentothal—but without the supportive help of a psychotherapist, the emotional process is not curative. We mention this not because we believe that we—or anyone—actually understand the mechanism of cure in this or, for that matter, any of our psychotherapeutic techniques, but because this incidental observation at least calls into question the notion that the simple release of hitherto repressed feeling is in itself a curative agent. That it is possible with the aid of hypnosis to create the "field conditions" which allow for the reinstatement of such hallucinatorily vivid feelings, and often even perceptions of buried memories, is, however, one of the most important of the regressive phenomena which have contributed to our theory of hypnosis. The problem remains why such a release in the presence of a therapist—and in less dramatic ways this phenomenon is a part of all expressive psychotherapies—can *ever* be curative.

[13] In this connection see Reichard's (193) diagnostic re-evaluations of the cases in Breuer and Freud's *Studies on Hysteria*.

[14] This simple view of abreaction has been clung to by many workers in the field of hypnosis long after Freud abandoned both the technique and the theory.

[15] See pp. 276-277.

This is one of the central mysteries to be unraveled on the problem of the "mechanism of cure."

It is entirely unclear, for example, why the process of "abreaction," whether by the use of hypnosis or of pentothal, should on occasion be so strikingly effective in treating circumscribed hysterical symptoms attendant on a recent combat experience, and then utterly useless in dealing with what on the surface appears to be a duplicate case.

For example, after successfully treating a number of veterans suffering from clear-cut hysterical symptoms, we commenced to use the "abreaction" technique with a young soldier whose generalized hyperkinesis and severe astasia-abasia had, classically enough, begun directly following the explosion of a shell near his foxhole. At the outset of a series of "relivings," the patient, an excellent hypnotic subject, followed the usual routine we had come to expect in hypnotic "abreaction": he re-experienced and re-enacted in faithful detail and with obviously strong feeling the awe and terror of the combat situation which had precipitated his symptoms. After the second such reliving, his symptoms began to improve dramatically. Soon thereafter, however, not only did there come an abrupt halt to his symptomatic improvement but there occurred also a striking change in the quality of his "abreaction": it now became a pale, mechanical recital dutifully performed and obviously without real meaning for the patient. Unlike his colleagues, many of whom were ready for discharge from the hospital after several such "relivings," this man appeared to have reached a dead end and to be unable to move in any direction. It appeared that in this case there had come a point where the simple combat symptoms were merged with the extensive and complex root-system of an underlying neurosis. It seemed to us that the patient had withdrawn all genuine feeling from the "relivings" and become defensively perfunctory in his performances lest his older and more complex difficulties be drawn into the therapeutic battle arena.

Our records, written at the time of treatment, indicate our impression that the therapist in this instance had continued for too long with this tack, relying too heavily on the simple release of repressed affect as his sole therapeutic leverage, and had persisted quite mechanically in putting this patient through his hypnotic-abreactive "paces." This was a particularly clear instance of the hazard of mechanically using one or another hynotic technique without close attention to the total psychotherapeutic context and to the *current* meaning to the patient of his "abreactions."

## SPECIALIZED HYPNOTIC TECHNIQUES

In our earlier published account (25, pp. 75-79) of specialized hypnotic techniques, we characterized these techniques as the "heavy artillery" of hypnosis in psychotherapy. By this we meant that the regressive phenomena of the hypnotic relationship are exploited to their limits, and not simply used as a catalytic medium. The fact of the altered ego-functioning of the patient in hypnosis is shaped, as it were, to the immediate therapeutic necessity. The meaning of this will become clearer when we come to specific illustrations from our clinical material.

Although, during the course of our work, we have explored to some extent all of the specialized techniques including automatic writing, the implantation of experimental conflict, hypnotic "age regression," etc., our most systematic efforts have centered on the investigation of dreams in hypnosis, and on the hypnotic variants of Ferenczi's "forced fantasies" usually employing visualization or directed association.

We shall include in this section a portion of our dream studies (more will follow in the section on hypnoanalysis) and a brief comment on the "forced fantasies."

Parallel with our investigations of the use of dreams in a therapeutic setting, we organized and supervised a study[16]—

[16] The experimental sessions were actually carried out by Drs. William Finzer, Louis Kaywin, and David Hilger.

hitherto unpublished—with a nonpatient group, the original purpose of which was to recheck the well-known study by Farber and Fisher (60). They had concluded that hypnotic subjects were better able to translate dreams (even those of other people) in the hypnotic state than in the normal state. After conducting group hypnotizability tests with a total of sixty people, four men and four women were selected for this study. None of these was so far as we could determine mentally ill; none was sophisticated with regard to the psychology of dreams; all were excellent hypnotic subjects.

Each subject was seen individually and each was asked to "translate" four short dreams both in the normal and hypnotic states. In the normal state, the subject was told: "You have probably heard that dreams have meanings. I am going to tell you the dream of another person. I would like you to tell me what you think the dream means." Still in the normal state, the dream was repeated to the subject and he was asked to tell "whatever thoughts come into your mind," and finally after a third repetition the experimenter said: "I will count from 1 to 3. Tell me the first word or words that come into your mind. [Counts 1-3.] In the light of these words, how do you understand the meaning of the dream?"

Now the subject was hypnotized and precisely the same procedure was followed, with two additions: first, he was also asked to give the meaning of the dream via automatic writing (i.e., his hand would write out the meaning of the dream without his being aware of what the hand was writing); secondly, he was told he would have a dream "which will have the same meaning as the dream I just told you." We omit details of procedure included to sharpen the controls of this study.

The results of this investigation surprised us in a number of ways. First, we were surprised that the results obtained by Farber and Fisher (60) were not confirmed: we did not find as they did that 20 per cent of the subjects in hypnosis *directly* translated the dreams into the "expected" dream interpretations. In fact, none of them did. However, equally surprising was the fact that almost without exception, the hypnotic responses of all eight subjects to the four dreams had a personal flavor and color which was in marked contrast to the dull, drab, unimaginative responses given in the normal state. This is not to say that in all instances the hypnotic responses seemed to bear a discernible relationship to the objective dream stimulus, but it *is* to say that the evidence in this admittedly small sample suggests that the subjects in hypnosis were in closer touch *with their own unconscious conflicts and unsolved problems* than in the normal state. In only a few instances did we know enough about the subject to trace what often seemed surrealist responses to the dreams. It was clear, however, from the *quality* of the hypnotic response together with the degree of emotionality shown (rapid breathing, expressions of fear, horror, etc.) that normally unconscious material was being brought to the surface by the dream stimuli when these were given to the hypnotized subject.

We have included this brief summary of a nontherapeutic investigation in this section because it seems to us to offer one additional bit of evidence for an assumption on which we have proceeded clinically: although we cannot expect a hypnotic subject to be a seer (and to translate *directly* the dreams of other people), we can expect that in hypnosis he *will* be in some ways better able to feel and sometimes to state, however indirectly, unconscious conflicts of which he is normally unaware. We say "in some ways" because the precise manner in which a hypnotic subject may be in touch with his own unconscious processes is an exceedingly complex and delicate affair. It is never in our experience simply a matter of "stripping" the subject of his defenses so that the underlying unconscious content of a conflict is revealed. It is rather a highly individual establishing of new balances between the ego functions—which are continuously changing in character—and a host of unconscious impulses which are pressing for expression. This is true whether the stimulus is provided as in our experiments by offering a ready-made dream or whether the subject (or patient) is asked to provide his own "dream."

In a previously published paper (20) one of us has discussed this problem at length. We found, for instance, that when a patient in hypnosis is asked to dream—as part of the therapeutic attempt to explore his unconscious conflicts—he will respond with a production which may fall anywhere within an extremely wide range, the average production having a structure which seems intermediate between the daydream and the spontaneous night dream. The regressive nature of the hypnotic state seems to dictate a greater use of the primary process than is common in waking thought, though less than in the night dream.[17]

We have distinguished at least four kinds of production which may issue from the instruction to "dream":

*The embellished reminiscence.* An example of this occurred in a woman diagnosed as a hysterical character who was being treated for symptoms of anxiety, depression, and multiple somatic complaints. She complained, while in hypnosis, of a pervasive sense of failure and deficiency in the ability to make people like her. She was given the suggestion to dream about this problem and reported: "I saw two of my girl friends on the porch of my home. I was there too. I seemed to be about fifteen years old. They told me they were not going to come back that evening as they had planned, but would come another time." This dull and rather banal response was not typical for this patient, who frequently reported highly condensed hypnotic dreams.

*The static pictorial image.* The following examples are from the records of a middle-aged man with a well-compensated, compulsive character, who was being treated for torticollis. He was not deeply hypnotizable, but at the suggestion to dream in hypnosis he sometimes produced static pictorial images which he found startling. A surprising number of them dealt with his being gazed at intently. In one of the most

17 See pp. 57-59.

striking he saw a vivid picture of a figure of indeterminate sex nailed to a cross, with head turned to the right and down, the same position into which the torticollis had twisted his own head. As he watched the figure, the head slowly lifted and the eyes fused into one which gazed at him intently and with great sorrow. The patient had not had, since early childhood, any interest in religion. This image, while it has a dreamlike quality, is relatively static and brief. In another such image he saw an owl watching him intently with great, wide eyes—"as though telling me not to be a fool."

*The quasi allegory.* This kind of production is a hybrid form resembling the conscious daydream but including in a rather obvious and primitive fashion some elements of unconscious symbolism. An example of this variety of hypnotic dream is taken from a case, reported by McDowell (165), of a veteran with the presenting symptoms of severe anxiety and ejaculatio praecox. This man was an unsophisticated person who, as far as we know, had no knowledge of the unconscious meaning of symbols. The production we will now describe occurred shortly after the disappearance of his ejaculatio praecox. He was told by the therapist that he would have a dream in hypnosis which would explain the meaning of his previous symptom of "being like a jack rabbit," as he called it. The therapist left the room and when he returned the patient reported the following.

"There were long white stairs going up into the sky, as far as I could see. There were women lined up on both sides of the stairs. They were all reaching out for me as I was running up the stairs as fast as I could run, always running. At the top of the stairs is a beautiful girl with no clothes on, lying on a big, white, soft bed. I reached her, got into bed with her, 'came' in a hurry, and started running up the stairs again just like before. I looked back and she was still lying there with her arms raised toward me, looking disappointed, but I kept running." This sequence is repeated several times, and he concludes: "I got off the bed the last time and started walking."

Now all the other girls were gone, the beautiful woman was waiting, and after he had "calmly climbed the stairs, began intercourse calmly—no hurry. We were still doing it when the dream ended."

There is a shallowness and transparency in this response which gives it a rather contrived flavor. At the same time, the presence of the classic symbol of ascending the staircase in this naïve man links this production to the regressive, archaic night dream.

*The quasi dream.* This form is closest to the usual night dream, and taken out of context is sometimes indistinguishable from a night dream. The following example is taken from the analysis of a young hysterical woman where hypnosis was used from time to time as an adjuvant. This young woman was possessed of an intense ambition to become a famous writer, having written many elaborate novels while working as a saleswoman. She came for treatment of "spells" during which she became rigid and talked wildly. During the initial interviews she had been told by a young and inexperienced resident physician that if she wanted to be cured of her "spells," she might have to give up her writing. Though dismayed by this prospect, she agreed to come for therapy. She was hypnotized occasionally during the course of the analysis, in periods of great resistance. In one such period, when it seemed that her unconscious competitiveness with the analyst as a defense against her strong passive wishes was fairly close to consciousness, she was hypnotized and told simply, "You're going to have a dream." Her response (in part) follows.

I'm in a hospital bed . . . I like the room . . . it's not an ordinary hospital . . . it's way up high with a beautiful view . . . the walls are tinted pale green . . . I see the nurse's face or something . . . and it ought to startle me because her finger tips are gone . . . on the first two fingers, down to the second joint . . . and I was going to interrupt and tell the nurse . . . if it is a nurse . . . that part of her fingers are gone . . . but I hate to interrupt when they're talking ["they" unidentified at this point] . . . so I don't say anything . . . they're talking pleasantly and I'm comfortable.

She was asked directly, still in hypnosis, what she thought the dream meant; she could make nothing of it. Accordingly, she associated in the usual way, and it then appeared to the analyst that she was expressing both her wish for and her fear of the analyst's power over her, the specific threat to her own power being expressed in the symbol of the missing fingers, which on one level meant she could no longer type her novels, and would thus be deprived of her most important weapon. The dream was not interpreted, and she was given the posthypnotic suggestion to have a night dream which would embody the same meaning as this hypnotic dream. The next day she reported a night dream which seemed to state more clearly her intense defensive strivings for power. This was also not interpreted and again, on successive days, she was told to "dream" in hypnosis, with the instruction that these "dreams" would state even more clearly the same conflict (still not interpreted to her). Finally, she produced the following in hypnosis.

I am sitting at a desk . . . a big desk . . . outdoors, looking down . . . I'm high up . . . looking down over beautiful scenery . . . there's a lake, a lot of trees . . . but no other person . . . just me . . . my desk is smooth and polished and large . . . I don't know how it got there.

This seemed a simpler dream than the one about the missing fingers. Her associations in hypnosis made it clear that she was attempting to usurp the analyst's position. Her wish to be lofty and godlike, the *defense* against her passive needs and against her fears of helplessness, now obliterated the wishes to be taken care of.

We have offered here this small sampling of the variegated kinds of "dream" production which occur in hypnosis to highlight the potential clinical usefulness of this specialized technique, and to suggest its complexity. At the same time, it has been our purpose to present data drawn from clinical sources which further substantiate our general hypothesis regarding the regressive character of the hypnotic state. The possible theoretical significance of these data has been elaborated to some extent in the paper previously mentioned (20).

We are not at all certain that the so-called "forced fantasy" in hypnosis involves a different *kind* of process from the "dream" productions we have just described. It is likely that the only difference lies in the instruction to the patient. As a matter of fact, when we have told patients, "You will now see a scene which will in some ways help us to understand . . . etc.," we have again obtained a similarly wide range of response—some more, some less symbolic, some more, some less regressive in nature. The constants appear to lie in the fact of the altered ego-functioning, and in the explicit encouragement or stimulation to permitting access to unconscious content by the special instruction to "dream," to visualize, or to fantasy. Examples of all of these will be given in our presentations of case material.

## HYPNOANALYSIS

The hyphenated term "hypno-analysis" was coined by Hadfield (112) to refer to a combination of cathartic hypnosis and a somewhat didactic process of "re-education." Since that time, the word "hypnoanalysis" has been used to denote a multitude of hybrid varieties of psychotherapy, some employing psychoanalytic theory and practice, some explicitly opposed to both. We have reviewed these varieties in some detail in our earlier survey (25).

When we have used this term, we have tried to restrict its use to a form of psychotherapy which attempts to deal systematically with resistance and transference, and which continuously or intermittently uses some form of hypnotic technique as an adjunct. Just as we have come to the conclusion that the term "hypnotherapy" is misleading and should be

abandoned, so do we feel the term "hypnoanalysis" is sufficiently lacking in specificity as to be useless. Hypnosis may be
enlisted minimally as an adjuvant in a psychoanalytic therapy
by simply inducing a hypnotic state from time to time,[18] or
it may be used more actively by employing one or another of
the specialized hypnotic techniques, described by us (25, 101)
and by Wolberg (229).

Assuming that hypnosis is a particular kind of circumscribed regressive process, we conclude that its function at any
given moment in an analytic therapy is to accomplish one of
two things: either to bring into focus a current transference
issue, or by dint of its alteration of ego function to so change
the operation of defensive (and adaptive) mechanisms as to
allow for the clearer emergence of the nature of an unconscious conflict. The assumption here of course is that transference phenomena as well as unconscious conflicts are to a
great extent regressive in nature. Corollary to the heightened
emotional level may be the recovery of memories hitherto
kept unconscious by the work of the ego.[19]

Optimally, the auxiliary use of hypnosis in this therapeutic
process brings about at least temporarily that balance which
allows for an upsurge of feeling with identifiable content
*without* so obliterating other ego functions as to make the
material useless for the building of progressive insight. We
presume that such an optimal balance occurs frequently in a
psychoanalysis which is proceeding well without the use of
hypnosis. The relationship to the analyst, plus the physical
conditions of the analysis, provide in an attenuated form
what the hypnotic relationship provides in a more extreme
form. Just as we have no way as yet of predicting—nor of
precisely controlling—the factors which make up this optimal

[18] We must assume that the introduction of hypnosis so alters the total
relationship with the therapist that the process is significantly different from
ordinary analytic therapy.

[19] We have not induced posthypnotic amnesia except in a few experimental instances. This is in contrast to the routine "hypnoanalytic" technique used by Lindner (157).

balance in psychoanalysis, so are we unable to achieve exact predictions or controls in a therapeutic process made further complex by the addition of hypnosis. As we have indicated earlier, our investigations have made it quite clear that the standard "indications and contraindications for hypnotherapy" in terms of nosological entities do not stand up under scrutiny. It has become equally clear that the same difficulties which preclude rule-of-thumb handbooks on any psychoanalytic psychotherapy operate here; and that the therapist must rely on moment-to-moment as well as day-to-day clinical judgments of *what is currently going on between him and his patient* if he is to have any way of knowing whether to attempt to alter the therapeutic equilibrium by introducing hypnosis.

In the one published paper (30) where we discussed specifically this issue, we said that "hypnosis is not and should not be considered an independent 'kind' of psychotherapy nor a procedure which should be 'engrafted' to any therapeutic relationship mechanically. Rather it should be regarded as a special sort of inter-personal relationship which may be used in countless ways and with utmost flexibility as a tool in the course of a psychotherapy, the precise time and mode of application to depend on the nature of the problem, the current psychodynamic balance and the therapeutic aims being pursued" (p. 49). The bulk of this paper is a case report on a borderline psychotic patient whose central conflict lay in her struggle to maintain compulsive defenses against an intense wish to be dependent. It was shown that, whereas at the outset of therapy, when the patient was overwhelmed with acute anxiety, hypnosis could be used as a valuable adjuvant to provide the necessary sense of protection and security, its continued use was contraindicated when after a certain point it appeared to be a deterrent to the rebuilding of the patient's defenses.

It is no accident that that paper was largely case material. This is inevitable when one is trying to report experience which it is not yet possible to subsume under clear theoretical constructs. This will continue until the psychotherapeutic process generally is better understood. In the meantime we content ourselves with the reporting of clinical experience (already highly sifted, to be sure), hoping to abstract from this experience items sufficiently general to fill out existing theory and provide sharper hypotheses for the next exploration. Thus, we have numerous recorded instances where the adjuvant use of hypnosis seemed at a given time to facilitate the analytic process and many where it seemed to make no difference. We have some where it seemed clearly to be a deterrent and had to be discontinued.

Whereas in some of our earlier cases we had tried to arrive as quickly as possible at the content of the unconscious conflict by attempting to "cut through" the defenses, we later explored the possibility of commencing with standard psychoanalytic technique in the normal state, analyzing defenses, introducing hypnosis from time to time to see whether the period of "working through" could not be cut down. It seemed to us that—inasmuch as in all therapy we do not deal simply with an abstract time factor but in part with the problem of helping the patient progressively to absorb and use insight in an emotionally meaningful way—it might be possible to reduce the periods of repetitive stalemate if an optimal balance could be maintained between the regressive trends in therapy and the normal defensive and adaptive functions of the ego. We thought it a reasonable hypothesis that if the regressive character of the hypnotic state could keep the emotional level fairly high *without* obliterating ego functions, then learning in the broadest sense would occur more rapidly. By now it is axiomatic that *all* learning progresses more quickly when deep feelings are involved. It is perhaps less axiomatic that "working through" is in fact a learning process.

The actual attempt to maintain the optimal balance proved no small undertaking. It is our assumption that this major problem is present and central in all psychotherapy, but that the difficulties are less dramatically evident than in a therapy which tries to tip the scale with hypnosis.

For example, in one variant of our numerous "clinical experiments" we decided—in the case of a hysterical young woman, whom we knew to be a good hypnotic subject—to commence a standard psychoanalysis *without hypnosis,* and to continue with this procedure uutil both the therapist and the research consultant (a highly experienced psychoanalyst)[20] felt they had a fairly clear picture of this patient: her character structure, her major defensive operations, her pace of therapeutic advance, in short, her personal flavor both as a person and as a person in treatment.

It was further decided that subsequently, when it seemed clear that her special techniques of resistance (in the technical sense) were being used with particular strength, the therapist would introduce hypnosis in an effort to tip the scales. The immediate result of this first experiment taught us quickly some of the positive strengths as well as the major hazards of using hypnosis in an analytic therapy.

During the initial four months of psychoanalysis, it became evident that this girl was engaged in a relentless campaign to deny all of her genuine feelings, to be a model of what she called "studied calm" and sophistication, and to "shrug off such petty emotions as envy, jealousy, and loneliness." She aspired to be a great novelist, and at first pretended that she had already had a book published. All of her talk up to this point carried a Pollyanna, vulgarly romantic flavor. She described herself as an extremely "dramatic" person and wondered at times whether her presenting symptom ("spells"— in which she would "go out of my head and talk nonsense") might not be some kind of unconscious play-acting. In spite of this dim awareness of herself, she managed throughout this period to maintain her defenses, to produce a steady stream of pseudosophisticated associations during her analytic hours, the only indication of personal involvement in these associa-

[20] Dr. Robert P. Knight.

tions being that at the conclusion of each session, she was beet red. She denied any connection between her extreme flushing and what she had been talking about, and certainly denied any feeling toward the therapist.

Finally, when her productions became repetitive and their quality, in a sense, predictable, she was hypnotized. During the hour itself, the most striking change that was noted was a reduction in her glibness and many long pauses in her flow of talk. The next day she came to her hour severely scratched and bruised, her arm in a sling. The therapist did not hypnotize her, but simply listened to her story. With an unprecedented display of feeling, she now gave a nightmarish account of having been raped by a man whom she had "picked up" not long after the hypnotic session, of having fought with him and slashed his face with her compact mirror during the struggle. For the next several hours, she spoke of nothing else; it was evident from her animated manner that while this experience had been a frightening one, it had also been tremendously exciting, and was now in a sense a pleasure to tell. It was also evident that there was something phoney in the account; it became clear only much later what this was. The only thing that was clear *at this time* was that the introduction of hypnosis had indeed altered the balance of forces and had triggered a major piece of acting out. The patient herself did not connect the hypnosis with this "rape episode," and commented several days later that she had not had time to mention any of her reactions to the hypnosis because she had been so preoccupied with her "terrible experience." When she now talked briefly about her feelings regarding the introduction of hypnosis, she said only that she had felt vaguely resistant to it until she had been told she could remember whatever she wanted to; that it had been actually more pleasant than she had thought it would be, "like taking ether"; but that it had made her want to cry, which was not pleasant. She said nothing of her feelings toward the therapist.

Now for approximately three weeks hypnosis was not used, and her productions became especially superficial and empty. The therapist hypothesized that the essential motive in all of this at this time was her desperate effort to maintain a complete detachment from the therapist. A systematic effort was made without hypnosis to interpret this to the patient. It met with no success. Finally, when it seemed quite apparent to the therapist from a variety of cues that indeed her resistance had as its major function her defensive need to keep distance, she was once again hypnotized. Her voice-quality and manner changed at once: she spoke softly, haltingly, and seemed troubled. Her associations led directly back to the "rape" episode. During this hour, she told the therapist she had not been raped but had invited the attack, and had then physically struggled with the man and cut him "hoping to leave a scar." The next day, again in hypnosis, she reported a night dream that she was a homosexual.

Without any pushing, she began to discuss her feelings toward the (female) therapist, concluding with her longing for and terror of attachment to anyone. She cannot stand "losses of people" and is therefore afraid to get involved with anyone: "I don't have any will power about them . . . they're always in power over me."

Only now was it possible to reconstruct the meaning of the entire sequence from the first attempt to hypnotize her. This had meant to her an opening move on the part of the therapist toward both emotional intimacy and domination. She had asserted her own power and fear of emotional intimacy by vanquishing a man (as in her novels the heroine routinely brought to his knees "the strong, cold man with nerves of steel"), hoping simultaneously to increase thereby her distance from the therapist by alienating her and by "changing the subject" in the analytic hours. Obviously, this is a highly simplified fragment of all that was analyzed in this sequence. We have pared it down to those aspects relevant to the use of hypnosis.

On the one hand, it became clear that the initial disturbance of the therapeutic equilibrium had indeed set off an extreme piece of blindly defensive and potentially dangerous behavior; on the other hand, it appeared also that the second attempt broke a deadlock and focused the transference issues in a way unprecedented in this therapy.

We have presented these two reactions to the introduction of hypnosis (in the same patient) because they show rather clearly both the potential hazard and the potential gain in catalyzing the therapeutic process by introducing hypnosis into an analytic therapy. It is not clear why the first hypnosis set off the blind flight into action and the second the productive engagement with analytic material. We have speculated that the series of interpretations made in the normal state—between the two hypnotic sessions—may have had more effect than was immediately apparent. Such hypotheses, however, by the very nature of clinical research are not provable. However, when empirical experience reveals the various alternatives which *may* issue from a radical intervention by the therapist, clinical judgment is sharpened. One of our purposes in giving this detailed account was to show the crucial necessity for making day-to-day judgments as to when hypnosis should be used and when it should be withdrawn.

In most of our cases, as in this one, the effect of introducing hypnosis into the treatment was highly variable. Thus, we cannot say simply that the introduction of hypnosis does or does not facilitate the focusing of transference problems or cut down the "working through" process. In a very few instances, there was a clearly consistent effect, or absence of effect, throughout the period of treatment.

In one case of severe depression in an obsessive-compulsive woman, periods of analysis with hypnosis were alternated with periods of analysis alone. Although she protested bitterly when hypnosis was not used, and in fact would frequently go into spontaneous hypnotic states in defiance, the research group could discern no real difference in the material, the pace, nor the emotional engagement during the hypnotic as against the nonhypnotic periods. Her treatment seemed quite typical of the plodding, "constipated" variety so familiar to all psychoanalysts in their severely obsessional and compulsive patients. We have studied too few such patients in the course of our work to know whether this consistent absence of observable effect of hypnosis is characteristic for this group.

In striking contrast to this is the case reported by one of us in collaboration with Dr. Karl Menninger (102), where it seemed that transference issues were regularly made more accessible by the use of hypnosis, and where periods of "working through" were cut down. The patient, diagnosed as an anxiety hysteric, was a twenty-nine-year-old teacher with functional somatic symptoms and anxiety attacks. The patient was hypnotized at the beginning of each hour while lying on a couch and asked to associate freely. The essential difference between the method used and psychoanalysis lay in the fact that the therapist very actively pursued the critical issues by the use of specialized hypnotic techniques (such as suggesting the reliving of earlier experiences) in order to expedite the appearance in consciousness of unconscious conflicts and actual memories.

The following example illustrates the consistent rapidity with which significant material appeared. In one hour a dream was interpreted to her by the therapist as indicating a sexual interest in her father. She was shocked and said she did not see how such a thing could possibly be true. During the next hour she reported that she had had a nightmare but was completely unable in her waking state to recall it. After much insistence under hypnosis the dream returned to her. She had dreamed that she was thirteen years old, at home in bed asleep and having a nightmare: a dream within a dream. It seemed to her in the nightmare that she had done something so terrible that her family would have nothing to do with her but she could not remember what it was. Within the course of the next three interviews she had recovered the memory that at the age of thirteen she had once pressed herself against her father's body in an affectionate embrace. This she now knew was the "terrible thing" she had done. Her father had pushed her away and warned her never to do that again. She realized now that this serious rebuff had marked a turning point in her attitudes toward men and sex.

Although it is of course very difficult to demonstrate that this precise series of events would not have occurred in a standard psychoanalysis, it was the opinion of our research consultant[21]—again a psychoanalyst of wide experience—who followed the case from day to day, that the hypnotic forcing of the recovery of the nightmare had brought back the significant memory more quickly than would otherwise have been possible, and had been therapeutically important.

After 130 hours the patient was entirely asymptomatic and had achieved good insight into her illness, but the positive transference had not been fully resolved. Six months after her discharge, she wrote to the therapist to tell him that she had had several dreams which she had been able to unravel by lying down, imagining herself in hypnosis, and then proceeding to associate to them. She gave the dreams and their interpretations in detail, showing that she clearly understood her previously unconscious desires for sexual contact with the therapist. She felt that she had now really finished the treatment. Two years later, she continued well and happy. In addition to carrying out her usual domestic duties, she had achieved national recognition for her work in a women's organization. This was the only case we studied where the effect of the hypnotic relationship appeared *consistently* to support and advance the patient's progress in therapy. It should be added that this is the only case in *all* of our therapeutic experience, hypnotic or nonhypnotic, where such a steadily upward course was pursued in an expressive psychotherapy. In fact, the very (apparent) simplicity of the course

---

[21] Dr. Karl Menninger.

of events has led us to question how well we have understood this case.

In another case, the effort to establish the "optimal" regression level was for the most part successful, though without the consistency of the treatment of the teacher described above. This was a compulsive young woman, given to depression, though not so severely ill as the obsessive patient described earlier in this section, where the use of hypnosis made no discernible difference in the therapy. In this instance, during the course of treatment the temporary primitivization of function was such as to issue in an abundance of dreamlike imagery, unusually strong emotional involvement both with the therapist and with her own material, a transference course in which the infantile fantasies and fears emerged with an unusual clarity, and during one short period a spontaneous emergence of archaic behaviors ranging from thumb-sucking through playing with toes to open masturbation during the treatment hour.[22] In this nonpsychotic girl, it can be supposed that such phenomena were, to say the least, surprising, and at times alarming. Withal, however, she managed to continue to work at her job as a nursery school teacher and to battle through to a successful termination of treatment. She was able to take sufficient distance from these regressive happenings to use them productively in the analysis.

We have seen, however, the double-edged character of trying to weight with hypnosis the regressive aspects of the therapeutic process in the case of another young woman with a severe character disorder. She was an excellent hypnotic subject both by standard criteria and by her capacity to reach down into her unconscious, as it were, and come up with emotionally meaningful material. From the very beginning, her productions in the therapy hours (when hypnosis was used) were profuse. Frequently she would report her experiences in the hour of vivid, highly symbolic and arresting pic-

22 See pp. 53-55.

torial imagery. When the therapist would try, however, to help her to reach a "translation" of these symbols—to bring the material to a level where secondary processes of thought could be brought into play—she regularly responded with a new primary-process statement, at least as symbolic as the first. More important even than this tenacious sticking to a dreamlike character of thought process was her complete abdication of emotional controls *during her hours* (though she continued to work with reasonable efficiency as a dental technician throughout her treatment). When, early in treatment, she burst into childlike sobbing during her hypnotic treatment sessions, this seemed to us potentially a source of therapeutic leverage in this normally reserved, rather stiff young person. However, when this pattern continued with very little variation and small clinical improvement, it became obvious that the opportunity for regression had been unconsciously seized upon by this patient as an avenue for the attempt to maintain the *status quo* in her illness. She behaved as if she had done all that anyone could expect when she had "delivered' to the therapist a barrage of tangled feelings, visual images, and fragmentary thoughts. She appeared to be incapable of taking any responsibility for trying to understand or in any way to deal with her own productions. Clearly here we had utterly failed to achieve that optimal balance between regressive trends and normal ego-functioning. Sometimes she would state directly that this uncontrollable flood of chaotic material was a direct outcome of her being in hypnosis (which was after all the therapist's responsibility). The attempt was made to analyze this problem in the normal state; the patient saw intellectually what she was doing, but was unable to change her established pattern. There were periods in which it seemed broken, but again it would return. Finally, the attempt to use hypnosis was abandoned, and nonhypnotic psychotherapy was instituted. For a time she would go into spontaneous hypnotic states and attempt to revive the old stalemate. Although she finally gave up this effort, she now mobilized other more standard techniques of resistance and made slow progress. It was evident in this case that to have continued to use hypnosis would have been antitherapeutic. The invitation to regression which we believe to be inherent in all psychotherapy, and most extremely in the hypnotic relationship, was for this patient overwhelming. It is our belief that the danger described in this case is the most serious of all in the use of hypnosis in psychotherapy.[23]

In another case, much the same technical difficulty arose, the form being somewhat different: a man in his middle forties came for treatment, complaining only of feelings of inadequacy and some difficulty in concentration on his work. Careful clinical study and a battery of psychological tests revealed little which would give us pause in accepting him for the hypnosis research project. He had proved a good hypnotic subject in the group hypnotizability test, at this time a routine procedure for most new patients at the Menninger Clinic. The story he told, toward the end of the evaluation period, of the peculiarly strong influence on him of a chiropractor who had treated both him and his wife alerted us, but we proceeded nonetheless to use hypnosis with this patient. Inasmuch as this patient was seen before our described research facilities were set up, an observer as well as the therapist was present at all interviews; both were men. The patient began to produce meaningful material readily but very soon reported that he was becoming acutely anxious. Then he reported a frightening experience which "could have been a dream, but might have happened while I was awake" that he saw a man peering at him through the window. Shortly thereafter he had a night dream in which two men were holding him down on a toilet, one on each side (the physical arrangement closely resembling the treatment setup). He was not certain what

---

[23] It is our impression that this particular kind of impasse, in attenuated and less obvious forms, is one of the most frequent rocks on which nonhypnotic psychotherapeutic attempts founder.

their intentions might be and did not himself associate either of them with the therapist. Careful questioning now elicited the information that he was not at all certain that the "influence" of the hypnotist terminated at the end of the treatment session. His dream of being held down was untouched and hypnosis was abandoned. After a period of psychotherapy, he was discharged apparently none the worse for his experience. It was clear here also that the regressive character of the hypnotic relationship had stimulated his latent paranoid trends in an explosive way which might have led to a florid psychotic outbreak. The existence of strong paranoid trends, close to the surface, is the only contraindication for the use of hypnosis in an expressive psychotherapy which we have found statable in nosological terms.

It has been abundantly clear in all of these clinical examples that the intensity of transference phenomena is decidedly increased in an analysis which employs hypnosis (at least in those cases where the hypnosis makes a perceptible difference in the course of events). In line with our general hypothesis we regard this heightened intensity of transference phenomena as one aspect of the generally regressive character of hypnosis. Before closing this section we should like to elaborate briefly on some of the transference and countertransference problems.

It is generally conceded for nonhypnotic psychotherapy that the transference development and the way in which it is handled is a matter of crucial importance, even when the therapy is only supportive, and certainly when it has more ambitious, exploratory goals. Most analytic therapists would agree, other things being equal, that when the patient sees something characteristic of himself in the transference situation, it has the best chance of making a real and therapeutic impression. Although no one yet knows precisely why this should be so, there is a hint of the underlying reason in Freud's classic comment that "an enemy cannot be slain in effigy." He was referring to the fact that the last hiding place of a resistance is to be found in the transference; it is in the immediate, emotionally real *and present* relationship to the therapist that the patient usually experiences the greatest difficulty in expressing strong feeling.

It is our hypothesis that the rapidity and intensity with which such strong transference feeling develops in consciousness in all psychotherapy are directly related to the degree of regression which is brought about by the total situation. For example, with the exception of certain kinds of obsessional patients who manage to remain "reasonable" no matter what, it has been our observation in the treatment of the neuroses that a sitting-up, face-to-face psychotherapy usually puts brakes on the development of *transference* phenomena.[24] This is in contrast to the relatively faster pace in the analytic patient who is not able to gather as many reality cues from the therapist's expression, responsiveness, etc. Frequently, on clinical grounds, face-to-face psychotherapy is regarded as the treatment of choice in a given case precisely because of an intuitive recognition that a particular patient has not the ego resources at his disposal to cope with a rapid flood of infantile transference material which has too high an affective charge for him to deal with successfully. Here again the clinician empirically seeks to find the optimal balance between releasing strong feeling in the transference and preserving ego activity. As we have shown in our case illustrations, this general problem is brought into relief where hypnosis is used, and where the effect of the hypnosis on some patients seems to be to leave the patient with no emotional "brakes" at all.

There is yet another complication which on the surface appears to be unique to a therapy using hypnosis, but which again appears to us to be only a relative matter. We know in general that when a "transference interpretation" is made, it should in fact be an interpretation which shows the patient

[24] There are various exceptions to this general statement, the most frequent being the patient whose anxiety is sufficiently allayed (by sitting up) to allow for freer expression.

that his response is not appropriately geared to the actual behavior of the therapist, but is in fact an expression of something ancient in himself which he has brought to the situation. We must now ask ourselves what is our position in this connection if we introduce a technique (hypnosis) which implicitly states, "By dint of what I am doing you will find yourself able to do things you otherwise cannot and unable to do things you otherwise can." In short, if we take a position which implies superior power, how can we ask the patient to analyze the *irrational, transference* aspect of his being hypnotizable at all? Yet we have done just this, usually in the face of bitter resistance from our patients, some of whom, as we have seen, said they would prefer to give up the use of hypnosis entirely rather than analyze its meaning for them. As one might expect, despite what one might call the "reality provocation" of inducing hypnosis, it has been possible to tease out the specifically personal projections of each individual and, on the basis of what the hypnotic relationship seemed to mean to him, to make use of these in the treatment.

Yet is this *qualitatively* different from the nonhypnotic standard psychoanalysis where we ask the patient to lie down while we sit up, where we arrogate to ourselves the privilege of responding or not as we see fit, where we ask the patient to let us see him completely though he cannot see us, and finally where from time to time we tell him what is "really" going on? Does not all of this too imply that we regard ourselves as "in charge" of the situation in a uniquely powerful way? Indeed, how commonly this is the lament of the analysand. Yet, the fact remains that each analysand reacts in his own way to this "provocation" too, and reveals his archaic and established patterns of feeling and behavior as transference phenomena.

As a kind of mirror image of the intensity of the transference relationship in an analytic therapy where hypnosis is used, the countertransference tends to be somewhat stronger than in standard psychoanalysis.[25] To be sure, different kinds of psychotherapy present different hazards to each therapist. It is well known, for example, that many experienced psychoanalysts who are able to deal competently with intense transference manifestations in the usual psychoanalytic situation become anxious and overwhelmed by strong feelings in a face-to-face psychotherapy where the physical arrangement precludes the formation of the protective barrier which the couch-chair arrangement usually provides. Conversely, we have often seen in supervising the work of analytic candidates that the absence of the direct interchange of face-to-face psychotherapy leaves them rudderless, in a peculiar way lonely, and thus given to academic, empty comments which bear no relevance to the emotional situation at hand.

A therapy which uses hypnosis carries with it its own special hazards which stem directly from the nature of what we have called "the hypnotic relationship." It will be recalled from our earlier discussion, where we presented partial data on the "structure of the hypnotist," that there is some evidence that the therapist who elects to use hypnosis is frequently a person who is in part eager to assume the role of an omnipotent parent, a parent who will encourage the regressive longings of his child (patient). We have seen moreover that he is frequently also a person who has the more deeply defended impulse to satisfy such longings in himself via an identification with his patient. Again, as before, we must emphasize that we do not feel this constellation qualitatively sets the hypnotist-therapist apart from other therapists (whether in physical medicine or in psychiatry). We do feel, however, that these dynamics emerge more sharply in the hypnotic relationship partly because the procedures of hypnosis are so overt and, in a sense, lacking in subtlety. It is our impression also that precisely because of this overt character, the hypnotic relationship is potentially a source of greater con-

[25] See our earlier discussion of the "nature of the hypnotist," p. 91 ff.

scious anxiety (at least to analytically trained therapists) than the more accepted techniques of psychotherapy. In fact, it is quite usual that a therapist will give up hypnosis entirely as he progresses with his analytic training. It is our impression that often this is because he begins to feel more conscious anxiety about the infantile aspects of his wish to hypnotize, but that equally often it represents his growing wish to cease being a deviant rebel and to join the respectable ranks of his analyst and his teachers.

When we consider the particular countertransference problems arising from the use of hypnosis we are led only to the same practical conclusion which holds for all other countertransference problems: to a certain extent they are ineradicable (all talk of the "thoroughly analyzed analyst" notwithstanding), but to a certain extent also they are controllable by self-scrutiny and need not be crippling.

### General Conclusions

1. The role of hypnosis in psychotherapy will not be understood until we have a clearer framework for the nature of the psychotherapeutic process in general.

2. Despite this limitation, one can formulate *hypotheses* regarding the process of psychotherapy by the study of phenomena emerging from the adjuvant use of hypnosis. (a) The most general such hypothesis we have developed is this: in all psychotherapeutic relationships, some form of regression (including but not restricted to transference phenomena) develops. (b) We hypothesize further that perhaps the essential practical task of all psychotherapy is to maintain an optimal balance between these developing regressive trends and normal ego-functioning.

3. The nature of the regressive process is more sharply focused by the use of hypnosis in psychotherapy because of the relatively greater tendency to develop regressive trends

in a hypnotic relationship. We refer now to the phenomena of induction and of the established state described in Chapters 1 and 2, for example, the changes in bodily experience, the heightened emotionality, and the general alterations of ego function which lead in a psychotherapeutic context to such phenomena as an increased access to unconscious material, a more rapid development of the transference, etc. Although in some instances this sharpening of the transference (and lowering of resistance) remains in the service of the therapeutic aim, in others it becomes a hazard.

4. Indications and contraindications for the use of hypnosis in psychotherapy cannot be stated in terms of nosological entities.

5. There is no correlation between the depth of hypnosis judged by standard criteria and the therapeutic result.

6. Our explorations of the use of hypnosis for direct suggestion and for the abreaction of traumatic experiences show that there is still a real though limited use for both of these techniques. Our experience with the latter technique confirms the work of others who have found it particularly effective for the treatment of neuroses issuing from a recent traumatic experience.

7. Of all of the specialized hypnotic techniques, our work suggests that the use of dreams in hypnosis is probably the most fruitful. Although we were unable to confirm the work of Farber and Fisher (60), we do conclude that a person is usually better able to state *his own* unconscious conflicts more sharply via the hypnotic exploration of dreams than by such an exploration in the normal state.

8. The same complexities which preclude rule-of-thumb handbooks on any psychotherapy operate here. It can only be said that we do not regard the adjuvant use of hypnosis as a separate *kind* of therapy; in fact we have concluded that the term "hypnotherapy" should be dropped from scientific nomenclature. We do believe, however, that this peculiar rela-

tionship between two people called "hypnosis" can be used in many ways as a tool in the course of psychotherapy, the timing and type of use to depend on the current therapeutic aims being pursued. We have offered a variety of clinical situations to illustrate.

# BIBLIOGRAPHY

(1) Abeles, M., and Schilder, P., Psychogenetic Loss of Personal Identity: Amnesia. *Arch. Neurol. Psychiat.*, 34:587-604, 1935.

(2) Ackner, B., Depersonalization. *J. Ment. Sci.*, 100:838-872, 1954.

(3) Adrian, E. D., Berger Rhythm in the Monkey's Brain. *J. Physiol.*, 87:83-85, 1936.

(4) Aserinsky, E., and Kleitman, N., Regularly Occurring Periods of Eye Motility, and Concomitant Phenomena, During Sleep. *Science*, 118:273-274, 1953.

(5) Barber, T. X., Experiments in Hypnosis. *Sci. Amer.*, 196:54-61, 1957.

(6) Barber, T. X., "Sleep" and "Hypnosis": a Reappraisal. *J. Clin. Exp. Hyp.*, 4:144-159, 1956.

(7) Barker, W., and Burgwin, S., Brain Wave Patterns During Hypnosis, Hypnotic Sleep and Normal Sleep. *Arch. Neurol. Psychiat.*, 62:412-420, 1949.

(8) Bartemeier, L., Discussion of "Alterations in the State of the Ego in Hypnosis." *Bull. Menninger Clin.*, 11:66, 1947.

(9) Bartlett, J. E. A., A Case of Organized Visual Hallucinations in an Old Man with Cataract, and Their Relation to the Phenomena of the Phantom Limb. *Brain*, 74:363-373, 1951.

(10) Bateson, G., An Old Temple and a New Myth. *Djaiva*, 17, 1937.

(11) Bateson, G., and Mead, M., *Balinese Character: A Photographic Analysis*. Special Publications of the New York Academy of Sciences, Vol. II, 1942.

(12) Bauer, J., and Schilder, P., Über einige psychophysiologische Mechanismen funktioneller Neurosen. *Dtsch. Z. Nervenhk.*, 64:279-299, 1919.

(13) Beck, A., and Guthrie, T., Psychological Significance of Visual Auras. *Psychosomat. Med.*, 18:133-142, 1956.

(14) Bellak, L., An Ego Psychological Theory of Hypnosis. *Int. J. Psa.*, 36:375-379, 1955.

(15) Belo, J., The Balinese Temper. *Character and Pers.*, 4:120-146, 1935.

(16) Bernstein, M., *The Search for Bridey Murphy*. New York: Doubleday, 1956.

(17) Bexton, W. H., Heron, W., and Scott, T. H., Effects of Decreased Variation in the Sensory Environment. *Canad. J. Psychol.*, 8:70-76, 1954.

(18) Blake, H., and Gerard, R., Brain Potentials During Sleep. *Amer. J. Physiol.*, 119:692-703, 1937.

(19) Bonnard, A., The Metapsychology of the Russian Trials Confessions. *Int. J. Psa.*, 35:208-213, 1954.

(20) Brenman, M., Dreams and Hypnosis. *Psa. Quart.*, 18:455-465, 1949.

(21) Brenman, M., Experiments in the Hypnotic Production of Anti-Social and Self-Injurious Behavior. *Psychiatry*, 5:49-61, 1942.

(22) Brenman, M., Chairman, Problems in Clinical Research: Round Table, 1946. *Amer. J. Orthopsychiat.*, 17:196-230, 1947.

(23) Brenman, M., Chairman, Research in Psychotherapy: Round Table, 1947. *Amer. J. Orthopsychiat.*, 18:92-118, 1948.

(24) Brenman, M., On Teasing and Being Teased: And the Problem of "Moral Masochism." *The Psychoanalytic Study of the Child*, 7:264-285. New York: International Universities Press, 1952.

(25) Brenman, M., and Gill, M. M., *Hypnotherapy*. New York: International Universities Press, 1947.

(26) Brenman, M., and Gill, M. M., Some Recent Observations on the Use of Hypnosis in Psychotherapy. *Bull. Menninger Clin.*, 10:104-109, 1946.

(27) Brenman, M., Gill, M. M., and Hacker, F., Alterations in the State of the Ego in Hypnosis. *Bull. Menninger Clin.*, 11:60-66, 1947.

(28) Brenman, M., Gill, M. M., and Knight, R. P., Spontaneous Fluctuations in the Depth of Hypnosis and Their Implications for Ego-Function. *Int. J. Psa.*, 33:22-33, 1952.

(29) Brenman, M., and Knight, R. P., Hypnotherapy for Mental Illness in the Aged. *Bull. Menninger Clin.*, 7:188-198, 1943.

(30) Brenman, M., and Knight, R. P., A Note on the Indications for the Use of Hypnosis in Psychotherapy: an Illustrative Case Report. *Bull. Menninger Clin.*, 12:49-56, 1948.

(31) Brenman, M., and Knight, R. P., Self-starvation and Compulsive Hopping with Paradoxical Reaction to Hypnosis. *Amer. J. Orthopsychiat.*, 15:65-75, 1945.

(32) Brenman, M., and Reichard, S., Use of the Rorschach Test in the Prediction of Hypnotizability. *Bull. Menninger Clin.*, 7:183-187, 1943.

(33) Breuer, J., and Freud, S. (1895), Studies on Hysteria. *Standard Edition*, 2:1-335. London: Hogarth, 1955.

(34) Brickner, R. M., and Kubie, L. S., A Miniature Psychotic Storm Produced by Super-ego Conflict over Simple Post-hypnotic Suggestion. *Psa. Quart*, 5:467-487, 1936.

(35) Brill, A. A., *Freud's Contribution to Psychiatry*. New York: Norton, 1944.

(36) Bromberg, W., and Schilder, P., Psychologic Considerations in Alcoholic Hallucinosis—Castration and Dismemberment Motives. *Int. J. Psa.*, 14:206-224, 1933.

(37) Brown, W., Hypnosis in Hysteria. Letter to the editor of *Lancet*, 15:505, 1918.

(38) Brown, W., Hypnosis, Suggestibility and Progressive Relaxation. *Brit. J. Psychol.*, 28:396-411, 1938.

(39) Campbell, J. W., Jr., Design Flaw. *Astounding Science Fiction*, October, 85-94, 1955.

(40) Charcot, J. M., *Metallothérapie et Hypnotisme*. Oeuvres Complètes, Tome IX. Paris: Bourneville et E. Brissaud, 1890.

(41) Claparède, E., Recognition and "Me-ness." In (184), pp. 58-75.

(42) Critchley, M., *Shipwreck-Survivors; a Medical Study*. London: Churchill, 1943.

(43) Darrow, C. W., Changes in Inter-area Parallelism of EEG in Hypnosis. Unpublished ms.

(44) Darrow, C. W., Henry, C. E., Brenman, M., and Gill, M. M., Inter-area Electroencephalographic Relationships Affected by Hypnosis: Preliminary Report. *EEG Clin. Neurophysiol.*, 2:231, 1950.

(45) Darrow, C. W., Henry, C. E., Gill, M. M., Brenman, M., and Converse, M., Frontal-motor Parallelism and Motor-occipital In-phase Activity in Hypnosis, Drowsiness and Sleep. *EEG Clin. Neurophysiol.*, 2:355, 1950.

(46) Darrow, C. W., Henry, C. E., Gill, M. M., and Converse, M., Electroencephalographic Phase-relationships in Hypnosis: a Preliminary Report. Unpublished ms.

(47) David-Neel, A., *Magic and Mystery in Tibet*. New York: Crown, 1932.

(48) Davis, L. W., and Husband, R. W., A Study of Hypnotic Susceptibility in Relation to Personality Traits. *J. Abn. Soc. Psychol.*, 26:175-182, 1931.

(49) Dement, W., Contribution to the Physiology of Dreaming. *Med. Alumni Bull. Univ. Chicago*. June, 1955.

(49a) Dement, W., Dream Recall and Eye Movements During Sleep in Schizophrenics and Normals. *J. Nerv. Ment. Dis.*, 122:263-269, 1955.

(50) Dement, W., and Kleitman, N., Incidence of Eye Motility During Sleep in Relation to Varying EEG Pattern. *Fed. Proc.*, 14:216, 1955.

(51) Ehrenreich, G. A., The Influence of Unconscious Factors on Hypnotizability: a Case Report. *Bull. Menninger Clin.*, 15:45-57, 1951.

(52) Ehrenreich, G. A., The Relationship of Certain Descriptive Factors to Hypnotizability. *Trans. Kansas Acad. Sci.*, 52:24-27, 1949.

(53) Eissler, K. R., Balinese Character. *Psychiatry*, 7:139-144, 1944.

(54) Erickson, M. H., and Erickson, E. M., Concerning the Nature and Character of Post-hypnotic Behavior. *J. General Psychol.*, 24:95-133, 1941.

(55) Erickson, M. H., and Kubie, L. S., The Successful Treatment of a Case of Acute Hysterical Depression by a Return Under Hypnosis to a Critical Phase of Childhood. *Psa. Quart.*, 10: 583-609, 1941.

(56) Erikson, E. H., *Childhood and Society*. New York: Norton, 1950.

(57) Erikson, E. H., Childhood and Tradition in Two American Indian Tribes. *The Psychoanalytic Study of the Child*, 1:319-350. New York: International Universities Press, 1945.

(58) Erikson, E. H., The Dream Specimen of Psychoanalysis. *J. Amer. Psa. Assoc.*, 2:5-56, 1954.

(59) Erikson, E. H., The Problem of Ego Identity. *J. Amer. Psa. Assoc.*, 4:56-121, 1956.

(60) Farber, L. H., and Fisher, C., An Experimental Approach to Dream Psychology Through the Use of Hypnosis. *Psa. Quart.*, 12:202-216, 1943.

(61) Federn, P., *Ego Psychology and the Psychoses*. New York: Basic Books, 1952.

(62) Fenichel, O., Concerning the Theory of Psychoanalytic Technique. *The Collected Papers of Otto Fenichel*, 1:332-348. New York: Norton, 1953.

(63) Fenichel, O., On the Psychology of Boredom. *The Collected Papers of Otto Fenichel*, 1:292-303. New York: Norton, 1953.

(64) Fenichel, O., *The Psychoanalytic Theory of Neurosis*. New York: Norton, 1945.

(65) Fenichel, O., Trophy and Triumph. *The Collected Papers of Otto Fenichel*, 2:141-162. New York: Norton, 1954.

(66) Ferenczi, S., Child-Analysis in the Analysis of Adults. *Int. J. Psa.*, 12:468-482, 1931.

(67) Ferenczi, S., Introjection and Transference. *Sex in Psychoanalysis*. New York: Brunner, 1950, pp. 35-93.

(68) Ferenczi, S., Sensations of Giddiness at the End of the Psychoanalytic Session. *Further Contributions to the Theory and*

*Technique of Psychoanalysis.* London: Hogarth, 1950, pp. 239-241.

(69) Fisher, C., Amnesic States in War Neuroses: the Psychogenesis of Fugues. *Psa. Quart.,* 14:437-468, 1945.

(70) Fisher, C., Fugue with Awareness of Loss of Personal Identity. *Psa. Quart.,* 18:480-493, 1949.

(71) Fisher, C., Studies on the Nature of Suggestion. Part I: Experimental Induction of Dreams by Direct Suggestion. *J. Amer. Psa. Assoc.,* 1:222-255, 1953.

(72) Fisher, C., Studies on the Nature of Suggestion. Part II: The Transference Meaning of Giving Suggestions. *J. Amer. Psa. Assoc.,* 1:406-437, 1953.

(73) Fliess, R., The Hypnotic Evasion: a Clinical Observation. *Psa. Quart.,* 22:497-511, 1953.

(74) French, T., Psychogenic Material Related to the Function of the Semicircular Canals. *Int. J. Psa.,* 10:398-410, 1929.

(75) Freud, A. (1936), *The Ego and the Mechanisms of Defence.* New York: International Universities Press, 1946.

(76) Freud, S. (1900), The Interpretation of Dreams. *Standard Edition,* Vols. 4 & 5. London: Hogarth, 1953.

(77) Freud, S. (1905), Three Essays on the Theory of Sexuality. *Standard Edition,* 7:125-245. London: Hogarth, 1953.

(78) Freud, S. (1905), Wit and Its Relation to the Unconscious. *The Basic Writings.* New York: Modern Library, 1938, pp. 633-803.

(79) Freud, S. (1912), The Dynamics of the Transference. *Collected Papers,* 2:312-322. London: Hogarth, 1948.

(80) Freud, S. (1914), On Narcissism: an Introduction. *Standard Edition,* 14:67-102. London: Hogarth, 1957.

(81) Freud, S. (1915), Instincts and Their Vicissitudes. *Standard Edition,* 14:109-140. London: Hogarth, 1957.

(82) Freud, S. (1915), Repression. *Standard Edition,* 14:141-158. London: Hogarth, 1957.

(83) Freud, S. (1915), The Unconscious. *Standard Edition,* 14: 166-215. London: Hogarth, 1957.

(84) Freud, S. (1916), A Metapsychological Supplement to the Theory of Dreams. *Standard Edition,* 14:217-235. London: Hogarth, 1957.

(85) Freud, S. (1919), Introduction to *Psycho-Analysis and the War Neuroses. Standard Edition,* 17:205-210. London: Hogarth, 1955.

(86) Freud, S. (1919), The "Uncanny." *Standard Edition,* 17:217-252. London: Hogarth, 1955.

(87) Freud, S. (1920), Beyond the Pleasure Principle. *Standard Edition,* 18:7-64. London: Hogarth, 1955.

(88) Freud, S. (1921), Group Psychology and the Analysis of the Ego. *Standard Edition*, 18:67-143. London: Hogarth, 1955.

(89) Freud, S. (1921), Psychoanalysis and Telepathy. *Standard Edition*, 18:177-193. London: Hogarth, 1955.

(90) Freud, S. (1923), *The Ego and the Id*. London: Hogarth, 1927.

(91) Freud, S. (1923), Remarks on the Theory and Practice of Dream-Interpretation. *Collected Papers*, 5:136-149. London: Hogarth, 1950.

(92) Freud, S. (1925), *An Autobiographical Study*. London: Hogarth, 1946.

(93) Freud, S. (1925), Negation. *Collected Papers*, 5:181-185. London: Hogarth, 1950.

(94) Freud, S. (1926), *The Problem of Anxiety*. New York: Norton, 1936.

(95) Freud, S. (1930), *Civilization and Its Discontents*. London: Hogarth, 1946.

(96) Freud, S. (1936), A Disturbance of Memory on the Acropolis. *Collected Papers*, 5:302-312. London: Hogarth, 1950.

(97) Freud, S. (1937), Analysis Terminable and Interminable. *Collected Papers*, 5:316-357. London: Hogarth, 1950.

(98) Freud, S. (1938), *An Outline of Psychoanalysis*. New York: Norton, 1949.

(99) Geleerd, E., Hacker, F., and Rapaport, D., Contribution to the Study of Amnesia and Allied Conditions. *Psa. Quart.*, 14:199-220, 1945.

(100) Gill, M. M., Spontaneous Regression on the Induction of Hypnosis. *Bull. Menninger Clin.*, 12:41-48, 1948.

(101) Gill, M. M., and Brenman, M., Treatment of a Case of Anxiety Hysteria by an Hypnotic Technique Employing Psychoanalytic Principles. *Bull. Menninger Clin.*, 7:163-171, 1943.

(102) Gill, M. M., and Menninger, K. A., Techniques of Hypnoanalysis Illustrated in a Case Report. *Bull. Menninger Clin.*, 10:110-126, 1946.

(103) Gill, M. M., and Rapaport, D., A Case of Amnesia and Its Bearing on the Theory of Memory. *Character and Pers.*, 11:166-172, 1942.

(104) Glover, E., The Screening Function of Traumatic Neurosis. *Int. J. Psa.*, 10:90-93, 1929.

(105) Gorton, B. E., The Physiology of Hypnosis. *Psychiat. Quart.*, 23:317-343, 457-485, 1949.

(106) Greenacre, P., Certain Relationships Between Fetishism and the Faulty Development of the Body Image. *The Psychoanalytic Study of the Child*, 8:79-98. New York: International Universities Press, 1953.

(107) Greenacre, P., Further Considerations Regarding Fetishism.

*The Psychoanalytic Study of the Child*, 10:187-194. New York: International Universities Press, 1955.

(108) Greenacre, P., The Role of Transference: Practical Considerations in Relation to Psychoanalytic Therapy. *J. Amer. Psa. Assoc.*, 2:671-684, 1954.

(109) Greenacre, P., *Swift and Carroll: a Psychoanalytic Study of Two Lives*. New York: International Universities Press, 1955.

(110) Greenson, R., On Screen Defenses, Screen Hunger, and Screen Identity. *J. Amer. Psa. Assoc.*, 6:242-262, 1958.

(111) Grinker, R. R., and Spiegel, J. P., *Men Under Stress*. Philadelphia: Blakiston, 1945.

(112) Hadfield, J. A., Treatment by Suggestion and Hypnoanalysis. In *The Neuroses in War*, ed. E. Miller. New York: Macmillan, 1940, pp. 128-149.

(113) Hartmann, H., Comments on the Psychoanalytic Theory of the Ego. *The Psychoanalytic Study of the Child*, 5:74-96. New York: International Universities Press, 1950.

(114) Hartmann, H. (1939), *Ego Psychology and the Problem of Adaptation*. New York: International Universities Press, 1958.

(115) Hartmann, H., Notes on the Reality Principle. *The Psychoanalytic Study of the Child*, 11:31-53. New York: International Universities Press, 1956.

(116) Hartmann, H., and Schilder, P., Hypnoseversuche an Paralytikern. *Jahrb. Psychiat. Neurol.*, 44:194-202, 1925.

(117) Hoffer, W., Mouth, Hand and Ego-Integration. *The Psychoanalytic Study of the Child*, 3/4:49-56. New York: International Universities Press, 1949.

(118) Horsley, J. S., Narcotic Hypnosis. In *Experimental Hypnosis*, ed. L. M. LeCron. New York: Macmillan, 1952, pp. 141-149.

(119) Hull, C. L., *Hypnosis and Suggestibility: an Experimental Approach*. New York: Appleton-Century, 1933.

(120) Isakower, O., A Contribution to the Patho-psychology of Phenomena Associated with Falling Asleep. *Int. J. Psa.*, 19:331-345, 1938.

(120a) Jackson, D., An Episode of Sleepwalking. *J. Amer. Psa. Assoc.*, 2:503-508, 1954.

(121) Jacobson, E., The Self and the Object World: Vicissitudes of Their Infantile Cathexes and Their Influence on Ideational and Affective Development. *The Psychoanalytic Study of the Child*, 9:75-127. New York: International Universities Press, 1954.

(122) Janet, P., *The Major Symptoms of Hysteria*, 2nd ed. New York: Macmillan, 1920.

(123) Jones, E., The Nature of Auto-Suggestion. *Papers on Psychoanalysis*, 5th ed. Baltimore: Williams & Wilkins, 1948, pp. 273-293.

(124) Jones, E., *On the Nightmare*. London: Hogarth, 1949.
(125) Kaiser, H., Probleme der Technik. *Int. Z. Psa.*, 20:490-522, 1934.
(126) Kanzer, M., The Metapsychology of the Hypnotic Dream. *Int. J. Psa.*, 34:228-231, 1953.
(127) Kardiner, A., *The Traumatic Neuroses of War*. New York: Hoeber, 1941.
(128) Kartchner, F. D., and Korner, I. N., Use of Hypnosis in Treatment of Acute Combat Reactions. *Amer. J. Psychiat.*, 103:630-636, 1947.
(129) Kaufman, M. R., and Beaton, L. E., A Psychiatric Treatment Program in Combat. *Bull. Menninger Clin.*, 11:1-14, 1947.
(130) Kennedy, A., and Neville, J., Sudden Loss of Memory. *Brit. Med. J.*, August 24, 1957.
(131) Kinkead, E., A Reporter at Large. The Study of Something New in History. *New Yorker*, October 26, 102-153, 1957.
(132) Knight, R. P., Determinism, "Freedom," and Psychotherapy. *Psychiatry*, 9:251-262, 1946. Also in *Psychoanalytic Psychiatry and Psychology, Clinical and Theoretical Papers*, Austen Riggs Center, Vol. I, ed. R. P. Knight and C. R. Friedman. New York: International Universities Press, 1954, pp. 365-381.
(133) Knight, R. P., Introjection, Projection and Identification. *Psa. Quart.*, 9:334-341, 1940.
(134) Koestler, A., *Darkness at Noon*. New York: Macmillan, 1941.
(135) Kris, E., On Inspiration. *Psychoanalytic Explorations in Art*. New York: International Universities Press, 1952, pp. 291-302.
(136) Kris, E., On Preconscious Mental Mechanisms. In (184), pp. 474-493. Also in *Psychoanalytic Explorations in Art*. New York: International Universities Press, 1952, pp. 303-318.
(137) Kris, E., The Psychology of Caricature. *Psychoanalytic Explorations in Art*. New York. International Universities Press, 1952, pp. 173-188.
(138) Kubie, L. S., The Distortion of the Symbolic Process in Neurosis and Psychosis. *J. Amer. Psa. Assoc.*, 1:59-86, 1953.
(139) Kubie, L. S., Influence of Symbolic Processes on the Role of Instincts in Human Behavior. *Psychosom. Med.*, 18:189-208, 1956.
(140) Kubie, L. S., Instincts and Homeostasis. *Psychosom. Med.*, 10:15-30, 1948.
(141) Kubie, L. S., Manual of Emergency Treatment for Acute War Neuroses. *War Med.*, 4:582-598, 1943.
(142) Kubie, L. S., Discussion in (22), pp. 196-203.
(143) Kubie, L. S., The Use of Induced Hypnagogic Reveries in the Recovery of Repressed Amnesic Data. *Bull. Menninger Clin.*, 7:172-182, 1943.
(144) Kubie, L. S., and Margolin, S., A Physiological Method for the

Induction of States of Partial Sleep, and Securing Free Association and Early Memories in Such States. *Trans. Amer. Neurol. Assoc.*, 68:136-139, 1942.

(145) Kubie, L. S., and Margolin, S., The Process of Hypnotism and the Nature of the Hypnotic State. *Amer. J. Psychiat.*, 100:611-622, 1944.

(146) LeCron, L. M., A Study of Age Regression Under Hypnosis. In *Experimental Hypnosis*, ed. L. M. LeCron. New York: Macmillan, 1952, pp. 155-174.

(147) Lewin, B. D., The Body as Phallus. *Psa. Quart.*, 2:24-47, 1933.

(148) Lewin, B. D., Book review of *Balinese Character*. *The Psychoanalytic Study of the Child*, 1:379-387. New York: International Universities Press, 1945.

(149) Lewin, B. D., Dream Psychology and the Analytic Situation. *Psa. Quart.*, 24:169-199, 1955.

(150) Lewin, B. D., Inferences from the Dream Screen. *Int. J. Psa.*, 29:224-231, 1948.

(151) Lewin, B. D., *The Psychoanalysis of Elation*. New York: Norton, 1950.

(152) Lewin, B. D., Reconsideration of the Dream Screen. *Psa. Quart.*, 22:174-199, 1953.

(153) Lewin, B. D., Sleep, the Mouth, and the Dream Screen. *Psa. Quart.*, 15:419-434, 1946.

(154) Lifton, R. J., Thought Reform of Western Civilians in Chinese Communist Prisons. *Psychiatry*, 19:173-195, 1956.

(155) Lilly, J. C., Mental Effects of Reduction of Ordinary Levels of Physical Stimuli on Intact, Healthy Persons. *Psychiat. Res. Reports*, 5:1-9, 1956.

(156) Lindner, R., Hypnoanalysis in a Case of Hysterical Somnambulism. *Psa. Rev.*, 32:325-339, 1945.

(157) Lindner, R., *Rebel Without a Cause*. New York: Grune & Stratton, 1944.

(158) Lindsley, D. B., Bowden, J., and Magoun, H. W., Effect Upon the EEG of Acute Injury to the Brain Stem Activating System. *EEG Clin. Neurophysiol.*, 1:475-486, 1949.

(159) Loomis, A. L., Harvey, E. N., and Hobart, C., Electrical Potentials of the Human Brain. *J. Exp. Psychol.*, 19:249-279, 1936.

(160) Lundholm, H., and Löwenbach, H., Hypnosis and the Alpha Activity of the Electroencephalogram. *Character and Pers.*, 11:145-149, 1942.

(161) Macalpine, I., The Development of the Transference. *Psa. Quart.*, 19:501-539, 1950.

(162) Malcove, L., Bodily Mutilation and Learning to Eat. *Psa. Quart.*, 2:557-561, 1933.

(163) Mann, T., Mario and the Magician. *Stories of Three Decades.* New York: Knopf, 1936.

(164) Mayer-Gross, W., On Depersonalization. *Brit. J. Med. Psychol.,* 15:103-126, 1935.

(165) McDowell, M., An Abrupt Cessation of Major Neurotic Symptoms Following an Hypnotically Induced Artificial Conflict. *Bull. Menninger Clin.,* 12:168-177, 1948.

(166) Mead, M., and MacGregor, F. C., *Growth and Culture: a Photographic Study of Balinese Childhood.* New York: Putnam, 1951.

(167) Menninger, K. A., Cyclothymic Fugues. Fugues Associated with Manic Depressive Psychosis: a Case Report. *J. Abn. Soc. Psychol.,* 14:54-63, 1919.

(168) Moloney, J. C., Psychic Self-Abandon and Extortion of Confessions. *Int. J. Psa.,* 36:53-60, 1955.

(169) Moruzzi, G., and Magoun, H. W., Brain Stem Reticular Formation and Activation of the EEG. *EEG Clin. Neurophysiol.,* 1:455-473, 1949.

(170) Murray, H. A., *Explorations in Personality.* London: Oxford University Press, 1938.

(171) Newman, R., Katz, J., and Rubenstein, C. R., An Aspect of Hypnotic Dreams. Unpublished ms.

(172) Nunberg, H., States of Depersonalization in the Light of the Libido Theory. *Practice and Theory of Psychoanalysis.* New York: International Universities Press, 1955, pp. 60-74.

(173) Pardell, S. S., Psychology of the Hypnotist. *Psychiat. Quart.,* 24:483-491, 1950.

(174) Poer, D. H., Newer Concepts in Treatment of Paralyzed Patients Due to War-time Injuries of Spinal Cord. *Ann. Surg.,* 123:510-515, 1946.

(175) Prince, M., *The Dissociation of a Personality.* New York: Longmans, Green, (1905) 1957.

(176) Rado, S., The Economic Principle in Psycho-Analytic Technique. *Int. J. Psa.,* 6:35-44, 1925.

(177) Rapaport, D., The Autonomy of the Ego. *Bull. Menninger Clin.,* 15:113-123, 1951.

(178) Rapaport, D., Book Review: J. Dollard and N. F. Miller, *Personality and Psychotherapy, an Analysis in Terms of Learning, Thinking and Culture,* New York, McGraw-Hill, 1950. *Amer. J. Orthopsychiat.,* 23:204-208, 1953.

(179) Rapaport, D., Cognitive Structures. In *Contemporary Approaches to Cognition.* Cambridge: Harvard University Press, 1957, pp. 157-200.

(180) Rapaport, D., The Conceptual Model of Psychoanalysis. *J. Pers.,* 20:56-81, 1951. Also in *Psychoanalytic Psychiatry and Psychology, Clinical and Theoretical Papers,* Austen Riggs

Center, Vol. I, ed. R. P. Knight and C. R. Friedman. New York: International Universities Press, 1954, pp. 221-247.

(181) Rapaport, D., Consciousness: a Psychopathological and Psychodynamic View. In *Problems of Consciousness*, Transactions of the Second Conference. New York: Josiah Macy, Jr. Foundation, 1951, pp. 18-57.

(182) Rapaport, D., *The Development and the Concepts of Psychoanalytic Ego-Psychology*. Twelve Seminars given at the Western New England Institute for Psychoanalysis, 1955, ed. S. C. Miller. Mimeographed ms.

(183) Rapaport, D., *Emotions and Memory*, 2nd ed. New York: International Universities Press, 1950.

(184) Rapaport, D., ed., *Organization and Pathology of Thought*. New York: Columbia University Press, 1951.

(185) Rapaport, D., The Psychoanalytic Theory of Consciousness and a Study of Dreams. Unpublished ms.

(186) Rapaport, D., *Seminars on Advanced Metapsychology*. Six Seminars given at the Western New England Institute for Psychoanalysis, 1957, ed. S. C. Miller. Mimeographed ms.

(187) Rapaport, D., Some Metapsychological Considerations Concerning Activity and Passivity. Two lectures given at the staff seminar of the Austen Riggs Center, 1953. Unpublished ms.

(188) Rapaport, D., The Structure of Psychoanalytic Theory: A Systematizing Attempt. In *Psychology: a Study of a Science*, Vol. 3, ed. S. Koch. New York: McGraw-Hill, in press.

(189) Rapaport, D., The Theory of Ego Autonomy: a Generalization. *Bull. Menninger Clin.*, 22:13-35, 1958.

(190) Rapaport, D., and Gill, M., The Points of View and Assumptions of Metapsychology. *Int. J. Psa.*, in press.

(191) Reich, A., Early Identifications as Archaic Elements in the Superego. *J. Amer. Psa. Assoc.*, 2:218-238, 1954.

(192) Reich, A., Narcissistic Object Choice in Women. *J. Amer. Psa. Assoc.*, 1:22-44, 1953.

(193) Reichard, S., A Re-examination of "Studies in Hysteria." *Psa. Quart.*, 25:155-177, 1956.

(194) Reider, N., Psychotherapy Based on Psychoanalytic Principles. In *Six Approaches to Psychotherapy*, ed. J. L. McCary. New York: Dryden, 1955.

(195) Renneker, R., Presleep Mechanisms of Dream Control. *Psa. Quart.*, 21:528-536, 1952.

(196) Róheim, G., Psychoanalysis and Anthropology. *Psychoanalysis and the Social Sciences*, 1:9-33. New York: International Universities Press, 1947.

(197) Rosen, H., *Hypnotherapy in Clinical Psychiatry*. New York: Julian, 1953.

(198) Rosen, H., and Myers, H. J., Abreaction in the Military Setting. *Arch. Neurol. Psychiat.*, 57:161-172, 1947.

(199) Rosenberg, M. J., and Gardner, C. W., Some Dynamic Aspects of Posthypnotic Compliance. *J. Abn. Soc. Psychol.*, 57:351-366, 1958.

(200) Rosenzweig, S., and Sarason, S., An Experimental Study of the Triadic Hypothesis: Reaction to Frustration, Ego-Defense and Hypnotizability. *Character and Pers.*, 11:1-19, 1942.

(201) Sarbin, T. R., Contributions to Role-Taking Theory: I. Hypnotic Behavior. *Psychol. Rev.*, 57:255-270, 1950.

(202) Schafer, R., Regression in the Service of the Ego: The Relevance of a Psychoanalytic Concept for Personality Assessment. In *Assessment of Human Motives*, ed. G. Lindzey. New York: Rinehart, 1958, pp. 119-148.

(203) Schafer, R., A Study of Personality Characteristics Related to Hypnotizability. Masters thesis, 1947. Unpublished ms.

(204) Schilder, P., *Goals and Desires of Man.* New York: Columbia University Press, 1942.

(205) Schilder, P., *The Image and Appearance of the Human Body.* New York: International Universities Press, 1950.

(206) Schilder, P., *Medical Psychology.* New York: International Universities Press, 1953.

(207) Schilder, P., The Relations Between Clinging and Equilibrium. *Int. J. Psa.*, 20:58-63, 1939.

(208) Schilder, P., and Kauders, O., A Textbook of Hypnosis. In *The Nature of Hypnosis*, P. Schilder. New York: International Universities Press, 1956, pp. 43-184.

(209) Schneck, J., The Elucidation of Spontaneous Sensory and Motor Phenomena During Hypnoanalysis. *Psa. Rev.*, 39:79-89, 1952. Also in *Studies in Scientific Hypnosis.* New York: Nervous and Mental Disease Monographs, 1954, pp. 64-77.

(210) Schwarz, B. E., Bickford, R. G., and Rasmussen, W. C., Hypnotic Phenomena, Including Hypnotically Activated Seizures, Studied with the Electroencephalogram. *J. Nerv. Ment. Dis.*, 122:564-574, 1955.

(211) Silberer, H., Report on a Method of Eliciting and Observing Certain Symbolic Hallucination-Phenomena. In (184), pp. 195-207.

(212) Sperling, O. E., A Psychoanalytic Study of Hypnagogic Hallucinations. *J. Amer. Psa. Assoc.*, 5:115-123, 1957.

(213) Sperling, S. J., On Denial and the Essential Nature of Defence. *Int. J. Psa.*, 39:25-38, 1958.

(214) Stengel, E., On the Aetiology of the Fugue States. *J. Ment. Sci.*, 87:572-599, 1941.

(215) Sterba, R., The Fate of the Ego in Analytic Therapy. *Int. J. Psa.*, 15:117-126, 1934.

(216) Sumner, J. W., Jr., Cameron, R., and Peterson, D. B., Hypnosis in Differentiation of Epileptic from Convulsive-like Seizures. *Neurology*, 2:395-402, 1952.

(217) Tarachow, S., A Somnambulistic Act, with its Probable Meaning. *Psychiat. Quart.*, 19:195-197, 1945.

(218) Thigpen, C. H., and Cleckley, H. M., *The Three Faces of Eve*. New York: McGraw-Hill, 1957.

(219) Thompson, C., *Psychoanalysis: Evolution and Development*. New York: Hermitage House, 1950.

(220) True, R. M., and Stephenson, C. W., Controlled Experiments Correlating Electroencephalogram, Pulse, and Plantar Reflexes with Hypnotic Age Regression and Induced Emotional States. *Pers.*, 1:252-263, 1951.

(221) Watterson, D. J., Visual Imagery and Inaction. Unpublished ms.

(222) Weitzenhoffer, A. M., *Hypnotism*. New York: Wiley, 1953.

(223) Wells, W. R., Experiments in Waking Hypnosis for Instructional Purposes. *J. Abn. Soc. Psychol.*, 18:389-404, 1924.

(224) Wheelis, A. B., The Vocational Hazards of Psycho-Analysis. *Int. J. Psa.*, 37:171-184, 1956.

(225) Wheelis, A. B., Will and Psychoanalysis. *J. Amer. Psa. Assoc.*, 4:285-303, 1956.

(226) White, R. W., A Preface to the Theory of Hypnotism. *J. Abn. Soc. Psychol.*, 36:477-505, 1941.

(227) White, R. W., The Types of Hypnotic Trance and Their Personality Correlates. *J. Psychol.*, 3:279-289, 1937.

(228) Whittaker, J. C., *We Thought We Heard the Angels Sing*. New York: Dutton, 1943.

(229) Wolberg, L. R., *Hypnoanalysis*. New York: Grune & Stratton, 1945.

(230) Wolberg, L. R., *Medical Hypnosis*. New York: Grune & Stratton, 1948.

(231) Young, P. C., Antisocial Uses of Hypnosis. In *Experimental Hypnosis*, ed. L. LeCron. New York: Macmillan, 1948, pp. 376-415.

# NAME AND SUBJECT INDEX

# NAME INDEX

391

# SUBJECT INDEX

Nosology
and hypnotic therapy, 325, 357, 368, 373
and hypnotizability, xiv-xv, 74, 77-79, 162, 217-218, 233, 236, 245-247, 251, 276-278, 280

Obliviousness, 174-176, 181, 183, 190, 290
Obsessionality, 80, 287
Orality, 14, 84, 152, 244, 313-315; see also Hypnosis and orality
Oral triad, 14, 244
Organ language, 108
Organism-environment matrix, 179, 184
Organ zone, 295, 318
oral, 313

Paresis, 155
Passivity, see Hypnosis and passivity
Perception, xxii, 44, 101, 111, 118, 169, 174, 175, 186, 188, 213, 283
Personal identity
and fugue, 235, 252-257, 261, 264, 266, 268, 278
and traumatic neurosis, 274
Posthypnotic state, 103-104, 116, 276
Posthypnotic suggestion, 104, 227, 263
Presleep states, xix, xx, 5, 30, 110, 224, 226, 232, 233; see also Hypnagogic phenomena; Hypnosis and related states
Press, 176-191, 195, 290
social and nonsocial, 177
see also Environment
Primal horde, 115, 118, 139
Primal scene, 315-316
Primary process, 188, 206, 237-238, 254, 255, 267; see also Thinking
Projection, 42, 80, 210
Psychoanalysis, xi, xii, xxi-xxii, 97, 108, 162, 167, 179, 322-323, 327, 338, 356
and brain-washing, 281
and environment, 117
and regression, 118, 144, 152, 328-331
as a regression in the service of the ego, 159

theory of autonomy and, 169
theory of dreams of, 237-243
theory of instincts of, 106-107, 141
see also Hypnosis and related states; Hypnosis, theories of
Psychoses, 161, 163, 254, 325
motility and unconscious wish in, 56-57, 147
Psychotherapy, 285, 286, 321-374
and regression, 324-331, 367, 369, 372
feeling and insight in, 326-327
hypnosis as a tool in, 357, 373-374
mechanism of cure in, 346-347
see also Hypnosis and therapy

Rapport, 229-231
Reality
and autonomy, 170, 179
maintenance of sense of, 4, 7-8
obliviousness to, 172
see also Environment; Press; Synthetic function of the ego
Reality-testing, 150, 211, 213-214
and motility, 127
Re-automatization, 191, 194, 204
Regression, xix-xx, 54, 59, 87, 100-101, 106-117, 144, 151-152, 157-167, 168, 176, 182, 184-187, 195-196, 198, 202-218, 233, 246, 270-271, 291-292, 324, 328-329, 336, 344
age, 59, 102, 106, 108, 157-158, 253, 269, 332, 348
and adaptation, 161, 208-209
and affect, 324, 326-328
and attention, 129-134
and defense, 325
and environment, 163-164, 167
and loss of autonomy, 184-195
and motility, 126-129
and primary-process thinking, 147, 206-207
and psychotherapy, 324-331, 367, 369, 372
and revivification, 158, 212
and sensory intake, 101, 122, 123-126
and transference, 112, 117, 324, 356, 369, 372